PREFACE TO ECONOMETRICS

An Introduction to Quantitative
Methods in Economics
Second Edition

MICHAEL J. BRENNAN

Professor of Economics
Brown University

Published by

SOUTH-WESTERN PUBLISHING COMPANY
Cincinnati / Chicago / Dallas
Burlingame, Calif. / New Rochelle, N. Y.

H21

Preface

Econometrics is the application of modern statistical methods to economic theory that has been formulated in mathematical terms. It is a tool of analysis now widely used in economic research. Though still in an experimental stage, it develops and grows in importance each day. For the past thirty years econometricians have pushed ahead with scientific developments: existing procedures have been improved, new ones forged, and the implications of economic theory explored and tested. The net result is a body of literature that is highly significant for private business decisions and public economic policy. For example, problems of business management are treated as optimum-decision problems under conditions of uncertainty. Rules of action are formulated in such a way as to achieve given goals most efficiently under specified conditions. Likewise, relationships that influence national income, employment, and the general price level have been subjected to statistical measurement, and these have great significance for government economic policy. In this effort to systematize and measure, econometric studies have touched areas that are of interest to others as well as econometricians.

Most of the results of earlier investigations appeared in journal articles or monographs with restricted appeal. The journal *Econometrica* and the Cowles Commission for Research in Economics were founded for the specific purpose of publishing econometric research. With the growing interest in quantitative analysis, econometric studies gradually appeared more frequently in the professional journals and books that are directed toward economists generally. Until recently, however, students had been left with the task of collecting materials from diverse sources in order to get a comprehensive view of the subject. Even then, the presentation was often too complex for the interested student with limited training. Of the few textbooks that exist, most of them presuppose a knowledge of mathematics and statistics which is, in most cases, too advanced for the undergraduate student of economics (and for many graduate students who are not specializing in econometrics).

Econometrics, which was once considered an esoteric and highly specialized appendage to economics proper, has now come to be incorporated as a generally accepted and a widely used method of research. Yet little of it has penetrated to the reaches of the undergraduate students, who often conceive of economics as consisting of theory only. The common practice of excluding measurement and testing leaves a serious gap in the presentation of economics as an empirical science. The applications of abstract economic theory to practical situations are usually reduced to institutional descriptions or vague references to statistical data.

This book is an introduction to econometrics. Just as an elementary textbook on the principles of economics will not make an economist of the student, so this text will not make an econometrician of him. To become an econometrician, there is no good substitute for a sequence of courses in mathematics and statistical inference. The book is designed primarily to give the student enough familiarity with the subject and enough "feel" for it to enable him to understand the nature of econometric research and to judge quantitative policy recommendations intelligently. For the student who will pursue further work, it is a starting point. Even if he has no intention of specializing in econometrics, he should be able with the aid of this text to discover the relevance of mathematics and statistics to the subject matter of economics. In addition, this book supplies him with methods of computation that can be used to solve elementary problems. The last pages in the book contain suggestions for more advanced readings in econometrics.

The author has attempted to be correct, yet as nontechnical as possible. Since the book presupposes that the student has knowledge of economic theory, no attempt is made to teach economic theory proper. Price theory drawn from any intermediate text and national income theory from an introductory text are sufficient for understanding the economic theory contained in the book. No mathematical knowledge beyond elementary algebra is assumed. Neither does the book require any previous statistical knowledge beyond a course in elementary statistics at the undergraduate level.

Since the main objective of this book is the presentation of a comprehensive and understandable body of knowledge, certain difficulties arise. Many facets of econometrics cannot be given precise meaning without the use of techniques that are assumed to be beyond the grasp of the student. Where a choice was required, it was decided to sacrifice rigor and precision for the sake of simplicity. Consequently, many of the ideas are intuitive, and proofs have been omitted to allow more space for applications. For pedagogical reasons, only the simpler mathematical and statistical materials and their economic applications have been treated in detail. To round out the discussion, certain of the more advanced principles and problems of econometrics are touched upon, but these are given only cursory consideration. For the individual's first exposure to the subject, appreciation and a broad horizon are important. Let depth come with familiarity!

Preface to Econometrics is divided into five parts. Part I deals with the elementary mathematical formulation of economic theory. Part II treats elements of calculus. In Part III the preceding two parts are drawn together in the discussion of econometric models. Part IV surveys statistical inference and applications to econometric models. Finally, Part V discusses some of the less obvious aspects and some of the recent developments in econometrics.

I wish to express my gratitude to Professor Everett H. Johnson, who read the manuscript in detail and made several valuable suggestions. Of course, the responsibility for any errors or ambiguities which remain is totally mine. I am also indebted to Professor Sir Ronald A. Fisher, Cambridge, and to Messrs. Oliver and Boyd Ltd., Edinburgh, for permission to reprint Table No. IV from their book *Statistical Methods for Research Workers*. Dover Publications, Inc., New York, has generously given permission to reproduce two tables from *Mathematical Tables* by Herbert Bristol Dwight. Finally, my thanks are due to my wife Tommi for editorial and typing assistance and to Miss Mary Dionne who typed the major portion of the manuscript.

M. J. B.

Brown University,
Providence, Rhode Island.

Preface to the Second Edition

Aside from corrections and modifications throughout the volume, the major changes in the revised edition center upon three chapters and problem assignments.

Chapter 6 has been expanded and generalized, with a view toward the treatment of material in Chapters 23 and 24. More attention has been given to generalized determinants of order n. Whereas the first edition limited discussion of matrices to notation only, solutions to equations in matrix form have been covered briefly here—keeping in mind the main purpose and theme of the book.

Chapter 23 on identification has been substantially revised and expanded. And a new Chapter 24, building upon Chapter 23, presents a survey of estimation procedures for exactly identified and overidentified models. Much more space has been allotted to the reduced form parameters and their relationship to the structural parameters of econometric models.

The problems have been reorganized in terms of two groups wherever applicable. The first, labeled Group I, are sufficient to demonstrate the basic concepts presented in the chapter without detailed mathematical manipulation. The second, Group II, are designed for greater "involvement" in the mathematics. For those instructors who feel that the facility required for Group II problems is unnecessary for the purposes of the course, the Group I problems provide ample opportunity for the student to demonstrate his grasp of the text material.

I am grateful to the many instructors who have been good enough to offer their comments and criticisms. No doubt the book has been improved by their suggestions.

M. J. B.

Brown University
Providence, Rhode Island

Contents

CONTENTS

PART IV

Statistical Inference

PART V

Econometric Models Reconsidered

Introduction

The analysis of an economic problem can be approached in various ways. Description of the problem and presentation of the solution are sometimes expressed verbally. Quite often, however, the verbal expression is supplemented with charts or graphs. Graphical methods are appropriate in economics, as well as in some other fields, because the concepts under investigation are quantitative magnitudes. In the study of price theory one is introduced to demand curves, cost curves, and so forth. National income analysis usually includes the aggregate consumption curve, the investment curve, and the liquidity preference curve. In all these areas of economic theory geometric diagrams can be used to illustrate the relationships assumed to hold between concepts that are quantitative in nature. For instance, a demand curve relates the quantities demanded of a commodity by consumers to various market prices of the commodity; an average cost curve of a firm shows the behavior of the cost per unit produced when the output of the firm is varied; an aggregate consumption curve for the entire economy illustrates the way in which total consumption is related to national income. A curve depicted in a diagram is a convenient device for expressing some definite behavioral pattern between magnitudes that bear upon any economic problem.

Since most economic concepts (such as price, production, and income) are quantitative, other techniques of analysis have stimulated progress in economics, especially in the past thirty years. Economic theory is sometimes formulated in mathematical language. Statistical methods are employed to measure the relationships stated mathematically and to test the validity of economic theory. The combined use of mathematics and statistics to solve economic problems is called econometrics.

This introduction is intended to provide a bird's-eye view of the entire field of econometrics. The integration of economics, mathematics, and statistics will be described in broad outline. This back-

1

ground is useful in relating the following chapters to one another, since each chapter treats one segment of the subject matter. With a general outline at hand, the various parts of econometrics can be approached with some knowledge of how each part fits into the total picture. Still, a warning is in place! Summary descriptions are necessarily general and abstract. Therefore, it is unlikely that the reader will fully grasp all of the implications contained in this introduction except by becoming thoroughly familiar with the entire book. After the complete structure has been studied in detail, a survey of the field will acquire more practical meaning and concrete significance.

A. THE METHODS OF SCIENCE

Economics, as a scientific inquiry, utilizes the so-called scientific method of investigation. Econometrics is concerned with the quantitative side of economics; so it is actually a special case in which the general methods of science are adapted to quantitative data in economics.

There is no such thing as *the* scientific method. The methods of science vary from one field to another. They vary from one research worker to another within a field, and even from investigation to investigation by a single worker. It is possible, however, to find a pattern common to virtually all scientific research. This pattern consists essentially of four elements or steps: (1) the assembly of facts or existing information; (2) the formation of a hypothesis or hypotheses, that is, the formation of a system of general propositions to explain the behavior of the facts; (3) the prediction, which is an explanation obtained by deducing from the hypothesis certain specific conclusions not already known from the mere collection of facts; and (4) the testing of the prediction by reference again to observed facts. Let us consider each of these four elements in more detail.

1. The Assembly of Facts

A research worker chooses a problem in which he is interested. In biology the problem may be the discovery of the rate at which infected cells multiply under given conditions. In psychology the problem may involve an explanation of how animals react to given stimuli. In economics the problem may be the determination of the demand for cigarettes. Whatever the field and whatever the problem, the worker's first step is the accumulation of known facts which bear upon that problem. The results of some previous research or the orderly array of some observed events will usually be taken into account. In the economic problem presented above, these facts may be such items as recorded prices of cigarettes, quantities of cigarettes consumed, prices of pipe tobacco and cigars, and income figures. The data may also include institutional information about the market. This compilation of existing information is guided by the investigator's judgment and the nature of the problem.

2. The Formation of Hypotheses

When one looks at the real world, he cannot help being awed by its great complexity. In order to understand some phenomenon, it is necessary to make certain simplifying assumptions and to proceed from there. The mere accumulation of data will not provide an explanation of the behavior of items in the data. One must discover the general relationships that exist among the observed events. For example, if one item in the data shows a change, the researcher attempts to discover what caused this change. Another item in the data may have produced the change. Hence, the researcher's next step is to formulate a hypothesis or tentative explanation of the phenomenon under investigation. He systematizes and rationalizes the known facts. In order to do this he makes assumptions, such as the existence of a perfect vacuum or the fact that consumers maximize utility. This is the process of abstraction and generalization. Some facts are selected as important determinants of the phenomenon under consideration; some are ignored as irrelevant. Since it is humanly impossible to treat all complicated and interrelated events simultaneously, some simplification is demanded if any progress is to be made. For example, the price of ice cream may be considered as irrelevant to the price of cigarettes. In reality it may have some influence, but this influence is so small that it can be ignored in order to make the problem manageable.

Not only are some simplifying assumptions inevitable in all fields of inquiry, but they are extremely valuable in permitting the scientist to generalize. Explanatory statements can be made to refer to all events of a given kind, not just to this or that particular instance. The generalized statement of relations among the facts, the scientific hypothesis, must, of course, be logical; furthermore, it must be subject to empirical verification or disproof. Hypotheses with which any conceivable occurrence would be compatible (for example, that the phenomenon is due to fate) cannot advance our ability to predict or control events. Hence, they are not regarded as scientific hypotheses.

3. The Deduction of Predictions

By prediction we do not necessarily mean explanations of events that will occur in the future. That is a special kind of prediction called forecasting. Scholars often attempt to predict events that have occurred but which have not yet been observed. In other words, they make explanatory statements about events not already known and used in the formation of the hypothesis. In the field of history the historian's prediction might consist of a statement to the effect that the death of a king must have happened in 803 A.D., given some other known circumstances. If a search of the records (the facts) reveals that his death did occur in that year, the prediction is confirmed. If, on the other hand, the records show that his death occurred in 603 A.D., the prediction is refuted and rejected. Again, from the general heliocentric hypothesis of planetary motion, an astronomer may predict the existence of an undiscovered planet which will be in a given location at a given time. The training of powerful telescopes on the site may reveal the planet. In economics, certain general hypotheses about the factors that determine national income and employment may be applied to a specific situation, for example, the recession of 1957–1958. Predictions about the causes of the recession are drawn from the hypotheses. The specific predictions are derived from the general hypothesis by logical deductive reasoning. Certain assumptions contained in the hypothesis prove fruitful in the sense that important logical inferences follow from them. These inferences or deductions are the predictions.

In order to make our discussion more concrete, let us consider an economic example in greater detail. In economics we assume that consumers maximize total utility, subject to certain constraints. This abstract assumption implies the demand hypothesis: the quantity demanded of any good or service is inversely related to the price of that good or service, other things remaining constant. Note that this is a general statement applicable to any commodity, not simply to wheat or watches only. To take a trivial but simple case, we may know that the supply of cigarettes in New York City has increased and that the prices of related commodities and consumer income are unchanged; hence, the demand has not changed. We would predict that the price of cigarettes in New York has fallen or will fall. Note that this is a specific testable statement referring to a concrete situation. It refers to a particular place at a particular time, and one can judge if it is correct by observation. Similar procedures of formulating general hypotheses and deriving concrete predictions are followed in the natural sciences and other social sciences.

4. Statistical Inference

Finally, the predictions must be tested. If observed facts contradict the predictions, the hypothesis is proved false and we reject it. If the predictions correspond to what is actually observed, the predictions are confirmed by the facts, and we say that the hypothesis has been verified. It has not been proved; rather we have failed to disprove it. We accept a general hypothesis only so long as its specific predictions are not contradicted by the facts. The test of a hypothesis may take the form of a laboratory experiment in some fields, such as physics or chemistry. In other fields, astronomy and the social sciences for example, experimentation in the strict sense is not possible. That is, it is not possible to control the environment by actually removing the influence of all other items in the data and thereby to measure the influence of one item on another. In these fields other tests, in particular certain statistical tests, have been developed.

Sometimes many hypotheses are equally valid—they are compatible with the same observed events. If this is the case, we must find other principles for choosing among the alternative hypotheses. One such principle is to choose the simplest, where the simplest is defined as that hypothesis which requires the least number of assumptions to predict the observed events.

In summary, then, we can say that any scientific investigation consists of four steps: (1) the collection of facts, (2) the formation of an abstract hypothesis or the general explanation of the behavior of the facts, (3) the predictions yielded by the hypothesis to determine the behavior of the facts in specific cases, and (4) the tests of the predictions by reference to a new set of facts in order to determine whether or not the predictions are correct. The hypothesis and the predictions it yields comprise an explanation which must be tested against empirical evidence. Of course, when actually engaged in research, one does not always follow a neat four-step pattern. There is continual interaction among the four steps. Hypotheses help to explain facts. But additional facts or new interpretations of existing facts may cause scientists to revise their hypotheses.

In general, steps two and three are called theory. It follows that economic theory is a set of hypotheses and predictions about economic phenomena. The theorist's main concern is deductive logic. He asks himself if there is any logical error in the reasoning process by which the predictions are deduced from the assumptions. The theorist may also be engaged in exploring new inferences from given assumptions. But in the final stage the theory must be tested against the facts. Granted that the logic is correct, the criterion of a good scientific theory is that it be successful as a predictor.

B. THE MEANING OF ECONOMETRICS

In the eighteenth and nineteenth centuries a so-called armchair economist might have speculated about the forces that determine prices, production, employment, etc., without concern for the ability of his theories to stand up under rigorous empirical tests. That day is gone. In the beginning this speculation was necessary; organized data were scarce, and a body of hypotheses was helpful for theoretical progress. Even today, however, the terms "economics" and "economic theory" are often used synonymously. But we have seen that theory is only one part of the total research process. Regardless of its elegance and logical consistency, a theory cannot stand on its own merits without some empirical testing.

Most of the concepts with which economists deal are quantitative. Prices, income, savings, amounts of commodities produced and consumed, wage rates, etc., are magnitudes that in principle are subject to measurement. The employment of mathematical symbols is, therefore, perfectly natural when the relationships among magnitudes are under discussion. In this sense econometrics is the natural outgrowth of the historical development of economic science. It completes the circuit by utilizing both theory (stated in mathematical terms) and tests of the validity of theory. *Econometrics* consists of (1) the mathematical formulation of economic theories, and (2) the use of statistical procedures to measure the theoretical relationships and to verify or reject the theories. It is primarily concerned with quantitative predictions, measurement, and statistical test of the predictions.

This is not to say that econometrics is the only, or even the best, approach to all economic problems. Study of the legal framework of economic institutions, purely historical research on underdeveloped areas, verbal statements of relationships among qualitative concepts, etc., are very useful methods of economic research. There are cases in which the scarcity of data or difficulty of measurement prevent econometrics from shedding much light on a problem. Nevertheless, most verbal propositions in economic theory imply mathematical relationships. Consider the theoretical proposition, "in equilibrium for a firm marginal cost equals marginal revenue," or "the quantity demanded of a commodity is inversely related to its price." Even when mathematical relationships are not absolutely necessary, it is hardly reasonable to ignore them if they are able to facilitate the explanation of a problem or to render it more concise.

Econometrics must be distinguished from mathematical economics on the one hand and from statistical economics on the other. It is, however, closely related to both, for it applies modern statistical procedures to theoretical systems that have been formulated in mathematical terms.

1. Econometrics and Mathematical Economics

There is no fundamental difference between mathematical economic theory and economic theory that does not use mathematics. Many economic theories have been stated in a literary way and later restated mathematically. Mathematical economic theory states the axioms or basic assumptions of economic theory in terms of mathematical symbols. It then uses the methods of mathematics to derive theoretical conclusions from the assumptions. For example, one basic assumption of economic theory is that firms maximize net profit. It can be inferred from this assumption by verbal demonstration that a firm will produce that quantity at which marginal cost of production equals marginal revenue. Mathematical economics defines the same axiom mathematically and derives the inferred proposition by means of mathematical tools. The same conclusions are reached whether the theory is stated verbally or mathematically, but certain advantages are obtained from the mathematical formulation: (1) It introduces rigor into the definitions and relationships; (2) it makes the assumptions explicit at each stage of the reasoning process, and thereby avoids hidden assumptions not easily discovered in a verbal presentation; (3) it brings out clearly the limitations of the theory; (4) and it avoids the digressions of vague argumentation.

Econometrics differs somewhat from mathematical economics, however. It differs in that its mathematical formulations are designed with a view to statistical measurement and testing. Since mathematical economics is a language for expressing pure theoretical statements, it takes no heed of the problems encountered in dealing with the empirical (statistical) part of economic research. For one thing, mathematical economics denotes that all theoretical relationships are exactly fulfilled. For example, in the market for a given commodity, it states that the quantity demanded exactly equals the quantity supplied in equilibrium. Such exactitude exists only in the world of theory. In econometrics this conclusion would be modified. An allowance is made for so-called random disturbances that show up in all empirical data. The equilibrium statement would be that the quantity demanded equals the quantity supplied plus or minus some random deviation, which emerges from the limitations of the data to which the theory will be applied. These random deviations from the patterns suggested by mathematical economics are essential features of the econometric scheme. By combining mathematical formulations of theory with empirical data, the econometrician is able to pass from the abstract theoretical scheme to numerical results in concrete cases.

2. Econometrics and Statistical Economics

Statistics is also an important aspect of econometrics. Yet we must distinguish econometrics from what we may call statistical economics.[1] This is a form of quantitative economics that avoids economic theory and claims to provide a statistical summary of the economic data themselves. The recording and charting of waves (periodic fluctuations) of total United States production over a number of years is an example of statistical economics. Another example is the tabulation of the price and the quantity consumed of a commodity and comparison of their relative movements. As we have seen in the first part of this chapter, the mere accumulation and ordering of data seldom provide solutions to important problems. Some theory is required to explain the behavior of items in the data; explanations do not come ready-made. Furthermore, there is probably some "hidden theorizing" in the selection, organization, and interpretation of the data. Since some theory is unavoidable, it is best that it be made explicit. Econometrics, unlike statistical economics, combines data with theory to obtain quantitative results.

---

[1] G. Tintner, *Econometrics* (New York: John Wiley & Sons, Inc., 1952), p. 12.

3. Importance of Econometrics

We have shown that mathematical formulations of theory possess rigor and precision. Statistics can be used to organize and interpret data. But what are the practical implications of mathematics and statistics as applied to economics? Economists have suspected for some time that the demand for agricultural products in the United States is relatively inelastic. In practice, this means that to a 1 per cent change in price corresponds, other things being equal, a change in the quantity demanded of less than 1 per cent. It is extremely valuable for government policy makers to know that, within a specified probability limit defined by statistical analysis, this elasticity of demand is between, say, $-.1$ and $-.2$. Econometrics can supply such estimates of elasticities, and in a wide variety of other cases it can provide equally valuable numerical results. The monetary authority would welcome knowledge about the quantitative effect of a given increase in the money supply on the general price level. In the absence of econometric analysis an economist may be able to conclude that, given knowledge about other relevant forces, the general price level will rise as a result of a given increase in the money supply. But he can say little with respect to how much the price level will rise. Neither can his analysis provide a check on the reliability of his conclusions. When similar examples are drawn from tax policy, wage legislation, and other areas, it is easy to see how valuable econometrics can be for sound economic policies.

We shall discuss the procedures of econometrics from the viewpoint of its two major aspects; mathematical theory and statistical analysis. Each is treated as if it were a separate procedure. It is well to keep in mind, however, that one influences the other. The specific type of mathematical formulation presupposes a type of statistical investigation, and the statistical investigation may suggest revisions in the mathematical formulation.

C. MATHEMATICAL THEORY

In econometrics a theory is called a model. Economic theory, like any other theory, is not merely descriptive; and it certainly does not aspire to the impossible task of presenting a complete, detailed description of economic phenomena. In order to discover and relate the important causes and effects operating in the economy, it is necessary that the theorist be selective. From a complex of interrelated events, some are neglected and others are chosen for investigation. These events are chosen because it is believed that they are the important determinants of other events. The theorist, therefore, constructs abstract representations or models of the "real world" based upon certain simplifications.

1. Model Construction

In econometrics one views economic life as explainable by a set of simultaneous mathematical equations. These equations express the relationships among economic magnitudes which guide economic behavior. A *model*, then, is a complete system of mathematical equations, and the system may be as broad or as narrow as the problem being studied. One model may be designed to predict national income in the United States, for which purpose it assumes that aggregate United States investment and the average United States wage rate are given. Another model may be broader; it may attempt to explain national income and at the same time investment and the wage rate. It will introduce equations to explain these magnitudes also. The ultimate choice among several such models will, in part at least, depend upon the predictive success of each.

a. Definitional and Behavioral Equations.

A model is a system of structural equations. They are called structural because they show the basic structure of the economic system being studied. There may be only one structural equation, or there may be many. In general, the structural equations (relationships) are classified into two types: definitional and behavioral equations. *Definitional equations* are identities or truisms that must hold in all instances by definition of the terms. They contain neither causal statements nor descriptions of decision processes. "Total expenditures on a commodity equals its price times the quantity bought" and "income equals consumption plus savings" are examples of definitional equations. *Behavioral equations*, as the name implies, describe the behavior of individuals or groups in the economy, such as households, entrepreneurs, or speculators. The equations are means of describing their reactions to price, income, cost, or whatever the case may be. Such familiar economic relationships as supply functions, demand functions, and production functions are examples of behavioral equations.

Our next step is to consider the structural equations in more detail. We have seen that they are statements of relationships among variables. In economics the variables are economic magnitudes that may assume different values, such as prices, output, interest, profit, or income. All the variables contained in a model are either systematic or random.

b. Systematic Variables. For our purposes we may define the *systematic variables* as those to which definite values can be assigned with certainty and which are related to each other in an orderly and predictable way. To illustrate, suppose that there is a known relationship of the price of shoes to the quantity of shoes supplied on the market. Suppose further that this supply function states that the quantity supplied is always ten times the price. Then for any change in the price, the quantity supplied will change by an amount equal to ten times the change in price. Price and quantity supplied are systematic variables—the behavior of one is related to behavior of the other in an assignable or predictable way. *Random variables*, on the other hand, do not follow any specified pattern or show any predictable relationship to other variables. We shall discuss them a little later. First, we must distinguish between endogenous and exogenous systematic variables.

The *endogenous variables* are those which are explained by the model. They both determine other variables in the model and are, in turn, determined by other variables. The *exogenous variables* are not explained by the model, but rather are determined by forces outside the model. They determine the endogenous variables but are not influenced by those endogenous variables. Another way of saying this is that the values of the exogenous variables are assumed to be known and taken as given for the purposes of the model. In a simple national income model we may assume that investment is exogenous and that consumption and income are endogenous. Then the model will enable us to determine consumption and income, but it will not in itself enable us to determine investment. In order to explain investment—to express investment as dependent on some other variable—we would need a different model with additional variables. All the systematic variables must be either exogenous or endogenous. If a theory seeks to explain a particular variable, other variables must be chosen as determinants of the variable in question. Yet some variables will remain unexplained; they are assumed to be determined by some systematic processes which the model does not attempt to take into account.

c. Random Variables. Let us return now to the random variables and illustrate their role by an example. One of the structural equations in the model may be a demand function; the quantity of a commodity demanded depends in some assignable way upon the price of that commodity. Here both the quantity demanded and the price are systematic variables. We know, however, that generally the quantity demanded depends also upon the prices of other commodities, income, tastes, etc. We might, therefore, write the equation as: quantity depends upon price and a random variable. The random variable will include all those forces which are not included explicitly in the equation. Even if we were to include price, income, and an index of tastes in the equation, the quantity demanded would still be subject to variation from some causes that we do not know about. After all of the assignable causes have been specified, the variable to be explained is still subject to variation from these unknown causes. It is these unassignable causes, or as they are often called, random "errors," which create the need for the concept of probability.

In ordinary speech "random" suggests "hit or miss." We come closer to its statistical meaning by defining a *random variable* as one such that any value it may assume is as likely as any other. By the introduction of random variables the model is prepared for statistical analysis based upon a probability calculus; in this way the model differs from mathematical economics. We have seen that the random variables are sometimes called random "errors." They are errors in the sense that when we come to apply the model to empirical data, we find that our systematic relationships do not hold exactly because there are errors in measurement. Using statistical procedures, we can say something more about these errors.

d. *Errors of Observation and Omission.* The preceding example of the demand function may have implied that all errors in the equations are the result of excluding certain variables. Actually the errors in the model spring from two sources: errors of observation and errors of omission. Errors of observation arise because our data are never exactly correct. Published tables on production, for example, may involve mistakes in collecting or in recording the figures. Sometimes adequate information is not available to the collector of data, and estimates have to be made; or the respondent to a questionnaire may make a calculated guess at certain figures requested. These and like circumstances lead to errors of observation.

Errors of omission arise because we cannot possibly take into consideration separately all of the forces that determine a particular variable. They would exist even if our data were perfect. Errors in the equations will result from both sources, but our statistical tools are not yet capable of handling both simultaneously. Consequently, we assume that all of the error in an equation is due to either one or the other. If our judgment suggests that we have included all of the important determining variables, we attribute the error to observation. If we have a high degree of confidence in the reliability of our data, we attribute all of the error to omission of variables.

Any disturbances in the variable that we seek to explain which cannot be explained by changes in the systematic variables are assumed to be random. The errors or disturbances may actually contain systematic rather than random components, but it is permissible to regard them as random if the components are many, individually small, and independent of each other. Their sum will then behave as if it were random.

e. A Schematic Summary. These classifications can be summarized by presenting them in the following schematic way:

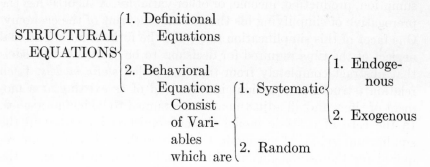

MODEL

A Complete System of:

STRUCTURAL EQUATIONS
1. Definitional Equations
2. Behavioral Equations Consist of Variables which are
    1. Systematic
        1. Endogenous
        2. Exogenous
    2. Random

The system of equations (the model) is complete when the number of equations in the entire set of structural equations is just enough to determine all the endogenous variables, given the exogenous variables. We must develop at least as many structural equations as we have endogenous variables. If we know the quantitative characteristics of the model, we can predict the course of certain economic magnitudes for known values of other economic magnitudes.

2. Types of Models

We have discussed model construction from the viewpoint of the components that make up an econometric model. When engaged in a quantitative investigation, the economist regards economic magnitudes such as prices, incomes, outputs, etc., as variables. Some of these variables the theory seeks to explain, whereas others are taken as given in order to provide the explanation. The way in which one variable influences another is viewed in the form of an equation, and the entire set of structural equations comprises the complete model. We shall now turn to another aspect of theory which hinges upon the assumptions made by the economist with respect to (1) time and (2) the perfection of knowledge.

a. *The Time Factor.* There is continual change and adjustment to change occurring in the economy. Consumers and firms react to price changes, and laborers make adjustments in hours worked in response to alterations in wage rates. Obviously, the changes and adjustments take some time to work themselves out. For example, a change in the purchasing habits of consumers does not occur instantaneously with a change in income or price. Yet the economist may ignore the time durations necessary for adjustments in consumption, production, income, or other variables. A theorist has the prerogative of simplifying his theoretical blueprint of the economy. One facet of this simplification may take the form of an intentional neglect of the time required for decisions to be carried out. Models that abstract completely from time are called *static models.* Each relation (structural equation) is conceived of as existing at a moment of time, and all adjustments are assumed to be instantaneous. In the case of a static model the economist is interested in the equilibrium values of economic variables rather than the time required for the establishment of the equilibrium. In this sense the model is "timeless."

If the economist wishes to take account of the time period involved in a movement to equilibrium, of time lags in adjustments to change, or of the course of a variable through time, he introduces time explicitly into the model. Then he is working with a *dynamic model.* The exogenous and endogenous variables are defined at specific time points which need not be the same for every variable. For instance, a structural equation may contain as variables the price in the current month and the price in a previous month. Dynamic models include time as an integral part of the model and permit the economist to trace the path of a variable through time.

b. *Degree of Knowledge.* The second aspect of model types has to do with the degree of knowledge imputed to decision makers in the economy. One convenient assumption is that entrepreneurs, consumers, and owners of factors of production have perfect knowledge of market and technological conditions. They know with complete certainty prices, wage rates, costs, and so on. On the other hand, it may be assumed that decision makers do not have perfect knowledge. They do not know the market and technological conditions with exact certainty, but they have some idea of the prevailing or expected conditions. In this case their knowledge of economic variables is only probable. Decisions with respect to how much will be purchased, produced, or sold must be made on the basis of information which is probable rather than certain.

c. *Four Model Types.* When these aspects of time and degree of knowledge are combined, econometric models fall into four types:

	STATIC	DYNAMIC
CERTAINTY	I	II
UNCERTAINTY	III	IV

Depending upon the assumptions made, every model will be one of the four types. But sometimes the model will be comprised of a mixture, containing elements of the four types in its structural equations. The distinctions among the four types are clearly illustrated by the theory of the individual firm. In Case I, static theory under conditions of certainty, we have the usual case presented in elementary textbooks on economics. The entrepreneur is assumed to make his decision about production at a point in time. Another way of saying this is that we abstract from time as a factor entering the decision of the entrepreneur. Furthermore, we assume that he does this with full knowledge of his costs and the demand for his product at that instant of time.

In the dynamic model under certainty, Case II, time enters the decision of the entrepreneur. Here we are involved in planning over time with full knowledge of all conditions on the part of the entrepreneur. For example, a sequence of future levels of production, sales, and inventories are planned, and we suppose that the technological and market conditions change according to a pattern known to the decision maker.

In Case III uncertainty exists at a single time point; the information about cost or market conditions prevailing at that time is incomplete. In Case IV, the dynamic model under conditions of uncertainty, we have a more realistic and complete problem. The future is, in general, uncertain. Therefore, planning over time cannot be isolated from uncertainty except as a provisional device. This uncertainty on the part of the entrepreneur reduces his decision to an "if" type rather than an absolute type. He will produce X quantity of the product six months hence if the price then is Y and costs are Z. This concept of uncertainty suggests the notion of probability; the basic procedure that has been adopted for handling theories involving uncertainty is statistical probability.

Similar distinctions can be made for other single units in the economy, such as individual consumers or owners of factors of production. Economics is a social science, however. Economists are interested in the behavior of individual firms and households primarily as a stepping stone for analyzing group behavior in the market. From the behavior of individual units, the economist attempts to say something significant about the social effects of all units combined. Here the assumption of uncertainty may require the substitution of expected values for known values. Take the case of the supply of agricultural products. Farmers as a group may be assumed to respond to expected (uncertain) prices rather than to known prices. Aggregate storage levels of a commodity may be assumed to depend upon expected price spreads between two periods and the expected costs of storage, or aggregate United States consumption may depend upon expected future income as well as present and past income.

All these characteristics of uncertainty refer to the "actors" in the economy. There is another interpretation of uncertainty, though, which is ever-present and which pervades all econometric models of group behavior—the uncertainty of the researcher about the relationships in the model. As a consequence, the structural equations describing group behavior have a random component; they are not known with certainty by the econometrician. For example, in a static exact (certain) model we may write the market-clearing condition as quantity demanded exactly equals quantity supplied. A random element can be introduced in the static model by writing the market-clearing condition as quantity demanded equals quantity supplied plus a random term. The market is cleared except for random deviations which arise from the imperfections of empirical data. As we shall see later, statistical probability theory will prove useful in coping with this uncertainty.

D. STATISTICAL INFERENCE

After the formal relationships among variables have been specified, the econometrician leaves the area of theoretical model construction and turns to the problems of empirical measurement and testing of the theory. To judge the validity of the theory, the model must ultimately be subjected to statistical investigation.

Statistics is of two kinds: descriptive statistics and analytical statistics. The organization and presentation of empirical data in the form of tables or charts constitute what is known as *descriptive statistics*. It summarizes the facts, and it may replace data that are too complex or voluminous by a few simple measures, such as averages or standard deviations. In econometrics one is only incidentally concerned with descriptive statistics. More important is *analytical statistics*, which is used to draw general conclusions about the model from observed data. Since the reasoning is inductive—from the particular to the general—another name for analytical statistics is *statistical inference*. From the characteristics of a limited number of observations called a *sample*, one attempts to infer the characteristics of a much larger body called the *universe* or *population*. For example, statistical inference enables us to learn something about the spending patterns of all people from the spending patterns of some people.

Econometric models consist of general equations or statements of economic laws. These theoretical equations refer to the entire economic body being studied. If a behavioral equation states that consumers increase their total consumption whenever their incomes increase, the equation implies that this relationship holds for all consumers. Not only this or that household taken in isolation is presumed to satisfy the relationship but all households on the average are claimed to follow this pattern of behavior. In other words, the theoretical statements refer to the population—in this case to the population comprised of all possible observations on consumption and income, not just a select few. The population is an abstract term and refers to all conceivable observations of some stated kind. Note that it is not the Americans themselves, but all possible observations on their consumption and income, which make up the population.

One obvious way to find out whether a theory is correct or not is to actually examine every individual to which the theoretical statements refer. In the case of the consumption equation, one could in principle observe the consumption and income of every American family. If the relationship is approximately satisfied in an acceptable number of cases, we could then conclude that the theory is verified. Conversely, if we find that consumption and income do not obey the predicted pattern of behavior, we can conclude that the theory is false.

In most cases, however, it is not practical to examine every conceivable, observable item in the population. In almost all cases such complete enumerations of the population are impossible or impractical because of the cost, problems of social custom, or inadequacies in the methods of covering the entire population. Imagine the cost and practical difficulties of trying to examine the way in which consumption and income vary for every American family. As a consequence, a sample of observations must suffice. The sample might consist of observations on the incomes and consumption of one thousand families chosen at random from a list of all American families. The problem then is to infer from the characteristics of the sample the characteristics of the population.

The theory of random sampling describes the relationships between samples and the population (we shall discuss it in more detail in a later chapter). It is sufficient to point out here that there will not be exact correspondence between the population and any one sample drawn at random from the population. What we get in the sample depends on chance, and we cannot draw any conclusions about the population unless we take into consideration this dependence. Such errors of random sampling make it impossible for inferences to be made about the population with certainty; they can be made only in terms of probabilities. Modern statistical inference is based upon the idea of the random variable. This is a variable which can assume certain values with definite probabilities. Since random variables enter into the construction of econometric models, statistical inference enables the econometrician to relate the abstract model to concrete empirical data.

1. Statistical Estimation

The first problem in statistical inference is measurement or estimation. The population has certain characteristics called *parameters*, for example, the average height of adult males in the United States. The corresponding characteristics in the sample are called statistics, for example, the average height of, say, one hundred adult males in the sample. The problem is to estimate the unknown population parameter from knowledge of the sample statistic. Of course, we cannot hope to determine the value of the parameter exactly. The most we can expect is to obtain a notion of the limits within which the value of the parameter lies.

In practice one almost always works with one sample. From the sample a statistic is computed, and by use of this statistic the unknown population parameter is to be estimated. The estimate takes the form of a range—an upper and a lower boundary. The interval between the two boundaries is called the *confidence interval*. One asserts that the true value of the population parameter is between the upper and lower confidence limits so computed from the sample. For instance, the unknown average height of American males might be estimated to lie between 5 feet 9 inches and 5 feet 10 inches.

This inference about the population is based upon a specified probability. Hence, one cannot know whether the assertion is true in this specific instance. The most one can do is to say that it is probably true and to specify the degree of probability. If the level of probability chosen in advance of the estimate was 95 per cent, one can conclude that if a great many confidence limits were computed on the 95 per cent probability basis, then in the long run, these limits would enclose the true population value in 95 per cent of the cases. In 5 per cent of the cases the true population value would fall outside the limits. That is, we cannot know whether the assertion about the population parameter is true in this specific instance; but we do know that if a great many such confidence limits were computed on the 95 per cent probability basis, in the long run these limits would enclose the true population parameter.

Let us consider an example drawn from econometrics. The unknown parameter to be estimated is the price elasticity of demand for food products in the United States. Note that this is a population parameter. The probability level for the estimate is set at 95 per cent. A sample of observations on the demand for food products is collected. The upper and lower limits are computed from the sample and turn out to be $-.12$ and $-.25$. The estimate of elasticity should be interpreted in the following way. We can say that a change of 1 per cent in the price of food products will, other things being equal, be accompanied by an opposite change in the quantity demanded that is not less than $\frac{1}{8}$ of 1 per cent and not more than $\frac{1}{4}$ of 1 per cent. This statement has a chance of being right in about 95 out of 100 cases in the long run because it is based on the 95 per cent probability level.

Another method of estimation is called *point estimation*. By this method one obtains a single figure (rather than limits) for an estimate of the unknown population parameter. The statistician uses a number of methods, the two most important of which are the method of maximum likelihood and the method of least squares. Under certain conditions the two methods are equivalent in the sense that they lead to the same estimate.

Statistical estimation procedures can be used to measure the unknown coefficients in the structural equations from a sample of empirical observations. In principle, estimations can be obtained for the elasticities of demand and supply, the coefficients in the production function, the marginal propensity to consume, and other parameters of econometric models. This statistical aspect of econometrics enables the econometrician to replace symbolic coefficients of the equations in the theoretical model by actual numerical estimates of their values.

2. Tests of Hypotheses

The second function of statistical inference is to provide tests of hypotheses. We have a general theoretical statement or hypothesis and a sample of observations. The problem then is: should we accept or reject the hypothesis on the basis of the sample? Again, probability analysis is utilized. The acceptance or rejection of a hypothesis turns on the probability of securing this particular sample in a random selection of samples from the population. We have seen that errors of random sampling permit us to make only probable statements about the population, that is, about the hypothesis. In some cases these probable statements will refer to the unknown population parameters, and the sample statistics are used to make the inference.

The general scientific method that is applied in situations of this kind is that of framing a hypothesis and testing it statistically. The hypothesis is formulated from considerations of theory and is independent of the statistical investigation. Economic theory may postulate that the demand for wheat in the United States is relatively price inelastic, or even more specifically that it has an elasticity of $-.5$. We then want to test the reliability of such a statement. More generally, a test, based on probability analysis, is constructed to determine whether a sample actually observed could have reasonably come from a specified population (or from a population with specified values of its parameters). If the sample is such that it could reasonably have come from that population, the hypothesis is accepted. Owing to sampling errors there is no sharp dividing line between samples that could and could not have come from the population. It is only possible to give a probability that a sample like the one observed could have come from the population under consideration. If the probability is low, the hypothesis is rejected; if it is high, the hypothesis is accepted and the deviation between the sample and the postulated population is regarded as being reasonably attributable to errors of sampling.

The econometrician in his role as statistician may make two crucial errors when testing hypotheses: (1) he may wrongly reject a true hypothesis; (2) he may wrongly accept a false hypothesis. Situation (1) gives rise to what are commonly called *errors of the first kind*, and situation (2) to *errors of the second kind*.

The test of a hypothesis is usually designed in the following way. For a given probability of type (1) error (called the level of significance) we use the test which at the same time minimizes the type (2) error. The reason for specifying the level of significance in advance is that the two kinds of errors are in a sense competitive. The smaller the chance we take of making an error of the first kind, the greater is the likelihood that we shall make an error of the second kind. So if we try to make the probability of one error as small as possible, we may find that we have increased the probability of making an error of the second kind. To avoid this, we fix the size of the probability of one kind of error in advance and then minimize the probability of making the other kind. Usually the probability of type (1) error is set in advance. What size level of significance to use is largely arbitrary and depends on the relative importance of the two kinds of errors in the problem under investigation.

One level of significance commonly chosen is 5 per cent. Suppose we were to choose this level and execute a test of a hypothesis that we have formulated. We will reject (disprove) the hypothesis if the probability of type (1) error turns out to be less than 5 per cent. This means that we reject the hypothesis as untrue if the probability of wrongly rejecting it is less than 5 per cent. The probability of being correct in our rejection of the hypothesis is then at least 95 per cent. Had this probability of type (1) error turned out to be greater than 5 per cent, we would accept (fail to disprove) the hypothesis. The test should also be constructed, if possible, in such a way that it rejects more false hypotheses than any other test with the same level of significance. Such tests may not always exist in econometrics. If such a test does not exist, we must apply other criteria for the best among all tests with the same level of significance.

Suppose we wish to test the hypothesis that the unknown "true" elasticity of demand for capital goods with respect to the interest rate is approximately -1. This hypothesis may be based upon theoretical considerations drawn from economics. We take a sample of observations on total investment and the relevant interest rate. From this sample we intend to accept or reject the hypothesis at the 5 per cent level of significance. Our sample will lead to an empirical value for the elasticity and, in general, it will differ from the theoretical value. Is the difference enough to reject the hypothesis? That is, can it be attributed to errors of sampling, or is the true elasticity significantly different from -1? Our test may indicate that it is extremely unlikely that such a large deviation is due to chance alone. Hence, our hypothesis will be rejected since the probability of wrongly rejecting it is less than 5 per cent, the level of significance.

2. Relationship Between Estimation and Tests of Hypotheses

The relationship between estimation and tests of hypotheses is no doubt already apparent. The error of excluding the correct value of the population parameter from the confidence interval is the same as the error of rejecting a true hypothesis. Likewise, the error of including an erroneous value in the confidence interval corresponds to an error of the second kind in testing hypotheses. Testing the hypothesis that a certain parameter has a particular value is usually equivalent to calculating the confidence interval for that parameter. If the value designated by the hypothesis is within the confidence interval, the hypothesis is accepted; if not, it is rejected. As we shall see later when we come to deal with actual problems, the two operations may collapse into one. The procedure of estimation yields, at the same time, a test of the hypothesis, that is, the estimated value itself now regarded as a hypothesis. We treat the two problems separately because estimation deals solely with parameters of the population, while tests of hypotheses do not. Also, alternative hypotheses (those which may be true if the one under test is not) play a more crucial role in testing hypotheses.

E. SUMMARY

The methods of econometrics are but a special case of general scientific methods. The use of econometrics as a technique of analysis requires knowledge of mathematics and statistics as well as economic theory. The reason for this lies in the quantitative nature of economic data. Nevertheless, rather than a highly specialized and isolated branch of the science of economics, econometrics ought to be regarded as an integral part of economics and a normal research procedure. At least the general principles that guide econometric research (if not the mathematical and statistical techniques themselves) must be taken into account if nonsense or ambiguous conclusions are to be avoided.

The four steps common to all scientific research can be restated as they apply specifically to the field of economics:

(1) The assembly of facts. After the problem to be studied has been chosen, the next step is the collection and review of existing information that bears upon the problem. One source of information consists of previous studies related to the area of investigation. Another consists of published empirical data on the economic magnitudes involved, such as published figures on prices, wage rates, production, and savings. If published data do not exist, they may have to be collected from diverse sources by the economist through questionnaires, personal interviews, or some other similar means.

(2) The formation of hypotheses. Recorded changes in the data do not in themselves explain those changes. Hence, a general theoretical explanation is needed. There exists a body of accepted general economic theory with which the student is already familiar. The econometrician states this theory in the language of mathematics.

(3) The deduction of predictions. Within the framework of the general theory appropriate restrictions are introduced to accord with the institutional setting of the problem. Then by logical (mathematical) analysis, specific predictions are deduced from the general hypothesis.

(4) Statistical inference. From a sample of economic data the econometrician attempts to estimate the quantitative characteristics of the theory. He also attempts to test its validity by comparing the quantitative predictions with the facts.

Steps (2) and (3) comprise the procedure called model construction, which is nothing more than economic theory formulated in mathematical terms. Step (4) consists of statistical estimation of the parameters of the model and tests of hypotheses.

PART I

Elementary Mathematical Formulation

CHAPTER 1

Variables and Functions

One idea was uppermost in the preceding introductory sketch of the field of econometrics; namely, that economics as an empirical science has two aspects: (1) Theoretical explanations of events in the economy are phrased in terms of mathematics; and (2) the mathematical equations that describe economic behavior are subjected to statistical analysis. It is the former of these two aspects with which we are concerned in the first chapters. We shall want to see how the familiar notions of economic theory can be phrased in mathematical terms. In a sense, these terms are a language for the expression of theoretical propositions. This means that no new or different economic theory will be introduced, but some elementary mathematical terms will be defined. As we shall see, these terms, once understood, permit us to state the usual economic theory in a convenient symbolic fashion.

A. VARIABLES

As a first step in the mathematical formulation of economic theory, it is necessary to understand the mathematical elements that make up that formulation. The most basic of these is the variable. A *variable* may be defined as an unspecified number. It is a variable number in that it is any number whatever from a given set of real numbers and it is always symbolized by a letter such as x, y, or z. Suppose that the variable under consideration is called x and that x can take on any positive value from zero to one million. Then, we say that such arbitrary numbers as 0, $\frac{1}{2}$, 1, 2, $15\frac{1}{8}$, 27, and 1000 are values of x. x is an unspecified number—it may assume any value from zero to one million. Particular numbers for which the variable can stand are called the *values* of the variable; the whole set of possible values makes up the *range* of the variable.

A variable is said to be a *continuous variable* if its range is either the whole set of real numbers or any interval of the set. By this we mean that the values of a continuous variable can be ordered so that they are indefinitely dense and without gaps. Assuming x to be continuous and again with a range from zero to one million, x can assume any real number from zero to one million. For example, it can assume the following values: 0; $\frac{1}{1,000,000}$; 1; $1\frac{9}{13}$; 2; $2\frac{1}{111}$; $100,001$; $750,000 \frac{1}{342}$; $999,999$; $\frac{999}{10,000}$; etc. The variable x can assume the value of any integer from zero to one million inclusive. Furthermore, taking any two adjoining integers in an ordering, say 3 and 4, there is an indefinitely large number of values that it can assume between the two integers.

On the other hand, a *discontinuous variable*, often called a discrete variable, has a range that is neither the whole set of real numbers nor any interval of the set. The values of the discrete variable cannot be arranged in order of magnitude without gaps. The set of positive integers $(1, 2, 3, 4, \ldots)$ or of multiples of $\frac{1}{2}$ $(\frac{1}{2}, \frac{1}{4}, \frac{1}{8}, \ldots)$ will provide a range that is discontinuous. For instance, in the set of integers any number lying between 1 and 2, such as $1\frac{1}{2}$ or $1\frac{7}{8}$, is not included as a value that the variable may assume—there are gaps in the ordering.

Scientists have found that empirical magnitudes can be considered as variables (continuous or discrete) and symbolized by letters. Weight, height, time, distance, energy, etc. are denoted by symbols in the physical sciences. The letter w might be used to denote the weight of some object. Under varying pressures its weight will vary. Hence, its weight is a variable: it can assume different values. Variables in economics are such magnitudes as price, income, profit, labor hours, production, and cost. They can assume many values. The price of a commodity might be designated by the letter p, where p may assume, among others, such values as \$.00, \$.05, \$1.15, and \$90.00. The other economic magnitudes mentioned can be symbolized conveniently in the same way. As a matter of fact, practically all of the concepts with which economists deal can be treated as variables.

B. FUNCTIONS

Not even the pure mathematician is interested in variables for their own sake. He attempts to relate one or more variables to others. In economics, too, we have seen that theory tries to determine the relationships among concepts (variables). If we have two variables

x and y, we can let the letter R denote some relationship between x and y. Then the symbolic statement $R(x, y)$ indicates that the numbers x and y satisfy that relation. If a pair of values for x and y are given, we can tell whether they satisfy the relation or not.

The notion of a *function* follows upon the idea of a relationship. It is a special kind of relationship with the property: for any arbitrary x, y is determined such that $R\ (x, y)$ is satisfied. The function concept is very important. The variable y is a function of the variable x if y depends upon x in the sense that by fixing the value of x, one or more corresponding values of y are determined. The variable x, whose numerical value may be arbitrarily assigned, is called the *independent variable*. The variable y, whose numerical value is determined after a value has been assigned to x, is the *dependent variable*.

When we want to indicate that y is a function of x, without fixing the form of the function, we use the notation $y = f(x)$. This means that y depends upon x in some (unspecified) way; in general, whenever the value of x changes, the value of y will change in some way. Instead of f we could use other letters, such as $y = g(x)$, $y = h(x)$ or $y = \alpha(x)$. We also often write $y = y(x)$. The mode of expression is mostly a matter of convenience. Indeed, as a shorthand expression, we sometimes speak of the function y, implying that y is a function of x. We need not even refer to y at all; we can say $f(x)$ is a function of x and talk about the function f. In our discussion, however, we will write out the complete notation using $y = f(x)$ or some letter other than f to designate the functional relation.

To point out the usefulness of this mathematical symbolism, let us take an example from economics. Suppose we want to express the demand for a commodity in symbolic form. Let p denote the price of the commodity and q the quantity of that commodity demanded by consumers. Then, the demand function can be conveniently written $q = f(p)$. That is, the quantity demanded depends in some way, as yet unspecified, upon the price of the commodity. Likewise, we might write the consumption function as $C = h(I)$, where C designates aggregate United States consumption and I designates United States national income. In this case C signifies the dependent variable and I the independent variable. The symbolic expression $C = h(I)$ is taken to mean that consumption is a function of income. Whenever national income changes, it will produce some change in aggregate consumption. Other examples taken from economics can readily be brought to mind. The market supply function for a good or service, the production function for a single firm or company, and cost as a function of the output of a firm can all be expressed symbolically.

Having grasped the idea of a function, we can now proceed to specify functions. When we specify a function, we not only state that y depends upon x, but we state the exact way in which it depends upon x. This is done by means of an equation. An *equation* is a statement of equality between two quantities. For instance, $2a = 19 - 4b$ is an equation. Our function f, that is, $y = f(x)$, might be specified as:

$$y = 6 + 3x$$

An equation tells us what the value of y is for any given value of x. It also tells us by how much y changes (if at all) when x changes by a given amount. In the equation above, if $x = 0$, then $y = 6$; if $x = 2$, then $y = 12$; if $x = -3$, then $y = -3$; etc. Note that for this equation any change in the value of x produces a change in the value of y.

Two technical terms can now be introduced. An *implicit function* is a mutual relation between two or more variables, and either variable determines the other. An *explicit function* is one in which the value of one variable, say y, is made to depend in some definite way upon the value arbitrarily assigned to one or more other variables, say x. The following is an implicit function:

$$f(x, y) = 6x + 3y - 12 = 0 \qquad (1.1)$$

We can solve the equation for y as an explicit function of x:

$$y = g(x) = 4 - 2x \qquad (1.2)$$

On the other hand, we can solve the equation for x as an explicit function of y:

$$x = h(y) = 2 - \tfrac{1}{2}y \qquad (1.3)$$

The function f as originally stated implicitly in (1.1) does not specify that either x or y is the dependent variable. They are mutually dependent. Consequently, either may be written as an explicit function of the other, as in (1.2) and (1.3). Each of the two functions g and h is called the *inverse* of the other. The function g in (1.2) emphasizes that y is the dependent variable and x is the independent variable. It is possible in many cases to invert this relationship (as it is in this case) so that x is the dependent variable and y is the independent variable, as in the function h in (1.3).

Other cases of inverse functions are: if $y = x^2$, then $x = \sqrt{y}$; or if $y = \log_{10} x$, then $x = 10^y$. It may be difficult but it is frequently possible to change from an implicit formulation to an explicit formulation in which the inverse functions can be specified without ambiguity.

We shall also define a *single-valued explicit function*. This is a function such that one and only one value of the dependent variable corresponds to each given value of the independent variable. The functions g and h in (1.2) and (1.3) are both single valued. In (1.2) for any given value of x there is one and only one value of y. In (1.3) for any given value of y there is one and only one value of x. There are functions, however, in which for each value of the independent variable there is more than one value for the dependent variable. Consider the function $y = \sqrt{x}$. If $x = 16$, then the square root of x can be $+4$ or -4, for $(+4)^2 = 16$ and $(-4)^2 = 16$. Hence for $x = 16$, $y = +4$ or $y = -4$. These are called *multivalued functions*, but we shall not be directly concerned with them in this book. If y is a single-valued function of a continuous variable x and if y increases as x increases, then y is called an *increasing function* of x. Similarly, if the value of y decreases as x increases, y is said to be a *decreasing function* of x.

Let us now return to the demand function mentioned earlier: $q = f(p)$, where p is the price of the commodity and q is the quantity demanded. We might write this demand function explicitly as:

$$q = 100 - 2p \tag{1.4}$$

We could also write it implicitly as:

$$q + 2p - 100 = 0 \tag{1.5}$$

By expressing the demand function explicitly as in (1.4) we not only state that q depends upon p, but we go further and state the exact way in which q depends upon p. q is a decreasing function of p such that for any given value of p we can uniquely determine the value of q. The student has probably already gathered that this is a specific statement of the general "law of demand."

1. Functions of One Variable

The notation $y = f(x)$ signifies no more than the proposition that we are taking y as some explicit function of x. More specifically, it states that y is a function of one variable only, x. Both y and x

enter the equation, but there is only one independent variable. Hence, we say that this is a function of one variable. There are several types of explicit functions of one variable, and we shall discuss some types that are commonly used in econometrics.

a. **Linear Function.** A *linear function* is one in which only the first power of the independent variable appears in the equation. (The reason for the name "linear" will become clear when we discuss graphs of functions.) The equation for this function is sometimes called a first-degree equation. The following equations all represent linear functions:

$$(1)\ y = x \qquad (3)\ y = 4 + 3x$$
$$(2)\ y = 2 - x \qquad (4)\ y = a + bx$$

Equation (4) is a general statement of a linear function. The letters a and b refer to any arbitrary *constants*. This general statement may take the form (1) if the constant a is set equal to zero and b is set equal to 1; it will take the form (2) if a is set equal to 2 and b is set equal to -1; and so forth. It is called the general form of a linear function because a and b represent any constant numbers rather than some particular constant numbers.

b. **Quadratic Function.** Another common type is the *quadratic function*. Such a function is said to be of second degree, that is, it involves at most the second power of the independent variable in the equation. The following set of equations all represent quadratic functions:

$$(1)\ y = x^2 \qquad (3)\ y = 2 - 3x + 4x^2$$
$$(2)\ y = 10 + 3x^2 \qquad (4)\ y = a + bx + cx^2$$

Equation (4) is again the general quadratic form with a, b, and c as arbitrary constants.

c. **Cubic and Higher Power Functions.** Higher powers of the independent variable may also be included. The *cubic function* includes at most the third power of the independent variable: $y = a + bx + cx^2 + dx^3$. Fourth powers or higher might well be used to describe the function $y = f(x)$.

d. **Other Types of Functions.** Several other types of functions often appear in econometric work. We shall mention but three of them at this point.

Type of Function	*Examples*

(1) Logarithmic Functions.........$\begin{cases} y = 6 + 4 \log x \\ y = \log (x^2 - 3) \\ y = \log 2x \end{cases}$

(2) Exponential Functions.........$\begin{cases} y = 2^x \\ y = 10^x - 1 \\ y = 3 - 4^x \end{cases}$

(3) Hyperbolic Functions..........$\begin{cases} y = \dfrac{2}{x} \\ y = 3 - \dfrac{86}{x} \\ y = \sqrt{2x^2 - 9} \end{cases}$

It can easily be seen from these few examples that when we write $y = f(x)$, we mean that y depends upon x in any one of an indefinite number of ways. Any one of the above equations, or any other equation involving y and x, could be the equation that specifies this function.

2. Functions of Two or More Variables

Not all explicit functions are functions of a single variable, but there is little difficulty in extending the function concept and notation to include explicit functions of two or more variables. We have seen that an implicit function in two variables, such as $f(x, y)$, can be written as either of two explicit functions of one variable, that is, $y = g(x)$ or $x = h(y)$. Likewise, an implicit function relating three variables, $f(x, y, z)$, can be written as any one of three explicit functions: $z = g(x, y)$, $y = h(x, z)$, or $x = j(y, z)$.

Suppose that the implicit function takes the form:

$$3x + 2y - 4z + 12 = 0 \tag{1.6}$$

This equation implies that any one of the three variables can be written as a function of the remaining two. In particular, it implies the three following explicit functions follow from (1.6):

$$z = 3 + .75x + .50y \tag{1.7}$$
$$y = -6 - 1.50x + 2z \tag{1.8}$$
$$x = -4 - .67y + 1.33z \tag{1.9}$$

We merely solve for each of the three variables in terms of the other two. In this particular instance we have chosen to write the coefficients as decimals rather than fractions.

More generally we can write a functional relationship among any number of variables, say n variables. We would denote this by the implicit function $f(x_1, x_2, x_3, x_4, \ldots, x_n)$. Instead of using different letters to stand for different variables, different subscripts on x refer to different variables. Again this is simply a matter of convenience in expression; it does not alter the meaning. Given certain conditions, the function f implies that any one of the n variables can be written as an explicit function of the other $n - 1$ variables. For example, suppose we choose x_3 as the dependent variable. Then, we can denote the explicit function by the following notation:

$$x_3 = g(x_1, x_2, x_4, x_5, \ldots, x_n)$$

This is merely an extension of the notation we used in the case of a function of one variable.

If we wish to use the letter y, then a dependent variable y can be given as an explicit function of n independent variables $x_1, x_2, x_3, \ldots, x_n$. This function would be expressed as

$$y = f(x_1, x_2, x_3, \ldots, x_n)$$

Assume that we have an implicit function consisting of four variables: $x, y, z,$ and u. Let us express u as an explicit function of the remaining three. Just as in the case of a function of one variable, there are many types of functions of more than one variable. For instance, the explicit function might take one of the following forms:

(1)	$u = 2 + x - 3y + 24z$	Linear Equation
(2)	$u = (xyz)^2 + 4$	Quadratic Equation
(3)	$u = 7 - y^2 - 9xz$	Quadratic Equation
(4)	$u = 1 + \log (xyz)$	Logarithmic Equation
(5)	$u = 5 + x^3 - y^2 + z$	Cubic Equation
(6)	$u = 2^x + 6^y - 8^z$	Exponential Equation

These are but a few of the equations by which a function of three variables might be specified.

Returning to the subject matter of economics, let us turn once more to our demand function. In general, we know that the quantity of a commodity demanded depends upon variables other than the price of that commodity. The prices of substitutes and/or complements in consumption, consumer income, and tastes are especially important. Therefore, when we state that quantity demanded depends upon the price of the commodity only, we actually assume that these other forces are constant. There is a certain mathematical relationship between price and quantity demanded for given (constant) other prices, incomes, tastes, etc. Variations in the quantity demanded are attributed to variations in the price of the commodity only.

A more general statement of the demand function would explicitly include these other forces as variables rather than constants; so we may write the quantity demanded as a function of more than one variable. Suppose that in the demand for commodity X we decide to include the prices of the substitute commodities Y and Z, income, and tastes. Let q_x denote the quantity of commodity X demanded, p_x the price of commodity X, p_y the price of commodity Y, p_z the price of commodity Z, I income, and T tastes. The demand function is then written:

$$q_x = f(p_x,\ p_y,\ p_z,\ I,\ T)$$

If this demand function is linear in all of the independent variables, it might take the form of the following equation (as an illustration):

$$q_x = 78 - 16p_x + 2p_y + .07p_z + .6I + .03T$$

Then, if we know the values of all the independent variables, we could predict the amount of the commodity that would be demanded. Of course, the equation that corresponds to the demand function need not be a linear one. It could be quadratic, cubic, logarithmic, or any one of a large number of types.

C. SUMMARY

Several definitions have been introduced in this chapter. Since the concepts will be used in later work, it is necessary that they be understood fully at the outset. It will help to establish these concepts if the most important ones are presented schematically.

A. Variables: Magnitudes that may assume any permissible value.
  1. Continuous Variables: May assume any value within a defined range.
  2. Discrete Variables: May assume only certain stipulated values within a defined range.

B. Functions: Relationships among variables such that any given values assigned to certain variables determine the values of other variables.
  1. Implicit Functions: The variables are mutually dependent.
  2. Explicit Functions: One variable (the dependent variable) is assumed to depend upon one or more others (the independent variables).

a. Single-valued Explicit Functions: Fixing the values of the independent variables determines one and only one value of the dependent variable.

(A) Functions of One Variable: one dependent and one independent variable.

(B) Functions of Two or More Variables: one dependent and two or more independent variables.

C. Equations: Specify the forms of functions.
    1. Equations Corresponding to Implicit Functions.
    2. Equations Corresponding to Single-valued Explicit Functions.
       a. Explicit Functions of One Variable.
          (A) Linear: The first power of the independent variable appears in the equation.
          (B) Quadratic: Includes at most the second power of the independent variable.
          (C) Cubic: Includes at most the third power of the independent variable.
          (D) Other Types of Equations.
       b. Explicit Functions of More than One Variable.
          (A) Linear: The first power of the independent variables appear in the equation.
          (B) Quadratic: Includes at most the second power of at least one of the independent variables.
          (C) Cubic: Includes at most the third power of at least one of the independent variables.
          (D) Other Types of Equations.

PROBLEMS

GROUP I:

1. Let $y = f(x) = x$.
   Find $f(1), f(4), f(16), f(64)$.
2. Let $y = f(x) = 10$.
   Find $f(0), f(3), f(1,000), f(-100)$.

3. Let $y = f(x) = 8 + 2x$.
   Find $f(0), f(1), f(10), f(-3), f(-6)$.

4. Let $y = f(x) = .5x$.
   Find $f(0), f(1), f(10), f(-3), f(-6)$.

5. Let $y = f(x) = 1 + 2x + 3x^2$.
   Find $f(0), f(1), f(4), f(-1), f(-2)$.

GROUP II:

6. Let $y = f(x) = -4 + x - .5x^2$.
   Find $f(0), f(1), f(3), f(100), f(-10)$.

7. Let $y = f(x) = 2^x$.
   Find $f(0), f(1), f(2), f(3), f(-1), f(-2)$.

8. Let $y = f(x) = 4^x$.
   Find $f(0), f(1), f(2), f(-1), f(-2)$.

9. Let $y = f(x) = \dfrac{2 - x^2}{3x}$.
   Find $f(0), f(1), f(5), f(-2)$.

10. Let $y = f(x) = 1 - 2x^3$.
    Find $f(2), 3f(1), 2f(4), -4f(3)$.

11. Let $y = f(x, z) = 10x^2 - 3z$.
    Find $f(1, 2), f(2, 1), f(2, 20), f(3, 0)$.

12. Let $y = f(x, z, u) = 3 + 10x - 4z + u^2$.
    Find $f(1, 1, 1), f(0, 2, 2), f(3, 4, 3), f(0, 0, 0)$.

CHAPTER 2

Graphs of Functions

The analytic expression of functions—their expression as mathematical equations—can be transformed into geometric representations. These are the visual counterparts to the equations. From the study of economic theory, one becomes familiar with demand curves, cost curves, supply curves, etc. Whenever a demand schedule is pictured by a curve in a diagram, this geometric presentation implies the existence of an equivalent analytic statement of demand: some mathematical equation which corresponds to the curve. A verbal statement of a relationship between quantity demanded and price or quantity produced and marginal cost of production (or a relationship among any economic magnitudes) can in principle be reduced to a mathematical expression. We shall, therefore, want to consider the transformation of functions into graphs.

A. RECTANGULAR COORDINATES

The graphical representation or "picture" of relationships between two variables is very important in economics. To represent a pair of related numbers, which may be positive or negative, we first draw two axes, one horizontal and one vertical. The point at which the two axes intersect is labeled zero and is called the *origin*. The horizontal axis is called the *x axis* and the vertical axis is the *y axis* (see Figure 2.1)

The two-dimensional plane (called the *xy plane*) is divided into four parts by the two axes. On the *x* axis all distances measured from the origin to the right are positive, and all distances to the left are negative. Likewise, all distances measured upward on the *y* axis are positive and all distances measured downward are negative (see Figure 2.1). The four parts into which the plane is divided by the two axes are called *quadrants;* they are labeled in Figure 2.1. In the first quadrant any pair of numbers x, y are both positive; in the second quadrant the number x in the pair is negative and the number y is positive, and so forth.

Convenient units of x and y are chosen. These units need not be the same since x and y may represent entirely different types of quantities. The units in which x and y are measured will depend upon the ranges of the values of x and y which are to be included in the "picture." A complete rectangular coordinate system is shown in Figure 2.1.

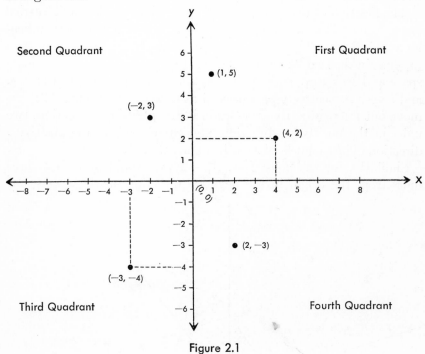

Figure 2.1

The geometric representation of a pair of related numbers x and y upon an axis system is a *point*. Construction of an axis system permits us to translate a pair of numbers into a visual expression of the numbers, for it is possible to locate points in space by means of numbers. A point in the xy plane is denoted by (x, y). In Figure 2.1 the point $(4, 2)$ is plotted by moving four units to the right on the x axis and two units up on the y axis. Note that $x = 4$ and $y = 2$. We proceed from the origin four units to the right (the positive x direction) and two units up (the positive y direction). This yields the required point $(4, 2)$. The point $(-3, -4)$ is plotted by moving three units to the left of the origin on the x axis and four units down from the origin on the y axis. Four other points have been plotted in Figure 2.1, and the reader would do well to trace through the procedure by which they were located. Any pair of related numbers (x, y) can be located by the conjunction of units measured on the two axes. The x number is said to be the x coordinate or *abscissa* of the point, and the y number is the y coordinate or *ordinate* of the point. The origin itself is also a point in the plane; its coordinates are seen to be $(0, 0)$.

The location of points in space of three dimensions can be carried out in exactly the same way. A system of three mutually perpendicular axes is drawn. Then a point is represented by (x, y, z) rather than (x, y) as in the two-dimensional case. If we have a three-dimensional space and seek to plot the point $(4, 2, 3)$ corresponding to the x, y, and z axes respectively, we proceed as follows (see Figure 2.2). We move out four units from the origin in the positive x direction, two units in the positive y direction, and three units in the positive z direction. This point is plotted in Figure 2.2.

Similarly, for the point $(-3, 1, -2)$ we would move out three units from the origin in the negative direction on the x axis, one

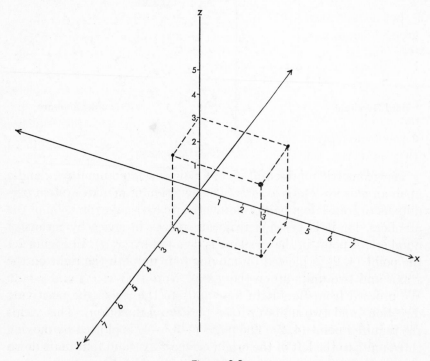

Figure 2.2

unit in the positive direction on the y axis, and two units in the negative direction on the z axis. It follows that the point at the origin in a three-dimensional space is represented by $(0, 0, 0)$.

In the geometric counterpart to an analytic formula there is a dimension for each different variable included in the equation. An explicit function of one variable includes, say, x and y in the equation which specifies it. The geometric counterpart will have two dimensions like that shown in Figure 2.1. Similarly, an explicit function of two variables whose equation includes x, y, and z will have a three-dimensional geometric counterpart like Figure 2.2. Some equations involve more than three variables. Of course, we cannot visualize more than three dimensions, but we can conceive of more than three. It is possible, by giving up visual representation, to extend the geometry to spaces of more than three dimensions with the same properties as those having two or three dimensions. In general, an equation having n variables has a (conceived) corresponding space of n dimensions.

B. GRAPHS OF LINEAR FUNCTIONS OF ONE VARIABLE

Let us now expand the procedure for plotting a point to include a group of points instead of a single point. Suppose that an explicit function, $y = f(x)$, is given by means of an equation. It is possible to learn the simultaneous behavior of x and y by plotting a set of points (x, y), where each x is one of the permissible values selected arbitrarily, and the y in each case is the corresponding value of y determined by the function $y = f(x)$. The result is a *graph*, showing a group of plotted points, from which the relative changes in the two quantities can be traced. The two-way connection between points and numbers provides a link between geometry and analysis. This link enables us to translate an analytical problem into a geometrical or diagrammatic one and conversely.

From the definition of a given function, $f(x)$, a table of the corresponding values of the two variables, x and y, can be constructed and made as detailed as we wish. It is a matter of assigning values to one of the variables (the independent variable) and solving the formula of the function for the corresponding values of the other variable (the dependent variable). If the range of variation is continuous, there is no limit to the number of entries that can be inserted.

Let $y = f(x) = 2 + 3x$. We would like to know about the behavior of x and y for the range $x = -5$ to $x = 6$. Therefore, we construct the following table for the choices, $x = -5, -4, -3, -2,$ $-1, 0, 1, 2, 3, 4, 5, 6$ along with the corresponding values of y.

x	$y = f(x) = 2 + 3x$
-5	$2 + 3(-5) = -13$
-4	$2 + 3(-4) = -10$
-3	$2 + 3(-3) = -7$
-2	$2 + 3(-2) = -4$
-1	$2 + 3(-1) = -1$
0	$2 + 3(0) = 2$
1	$2 + 3(1) = 5$
2	$2 + 3(2) = 8$
3	$2 + 3(3) = 11$
4	$2 + 3(4) = 14$
5	$2 + 3(5) = 17$
6	$2 + 3(6) = 20$

1. The Nature of a Linear Function Graph

The related values of x and y from this table, namely $(-5, -13)$, $(-4, -10)$ and so forth, determine a set of points that are plotted on the same set of axes and connected by a line. The points and the line are shown in Figure 2.3.

If we were to choose our x values at smaller intervals (say -5, $-4\frac{9}{10}$, $-4\frac{8}{10}$, ...) more points would result and they would lie closer to one another. If the range of variation is continuous, there is no limit to the number of entries that can be put in the table. Our function is assumed to be continuous, which means that we could choose values of x at indefinitely small intervals so that the points would all touch each other and we would have a continuous straight line without gaps or broken segments. A *line* is a locus of points. Just as the variables are related in an ordered way by the function, so the corresponding points must display a definite characteristic, that is, they must make up a specific line. Hence to each given linear function relating variables x and y, there corresponds a set of points comprising a line. The analytical property defined by the function is reflected in the geometrical property common to all points on the line. It is important to remember, however, that the uniqueness of the connection depends on fixing the coordinate axes. A given curve has different equations when different axes are selected.

We can now see why functions which involve only the first power of the variables are called linear functions. They give rise to straight lines when plotted on coordinate axes. Any function of the general

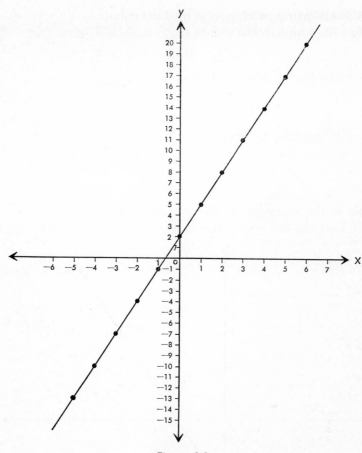

Figure 2.3

form $y = a + bx$, where a and b are any arbitrary constants, is said to be a *linear function*—the graph corresponding to a linear function shows a straight line.

2. The Slope of a Line

Consider now a straight line which goes through two given points. This condition enables us to determine the particular line. The equation of a line which passes through the two fixed points (x_1, y_1) and (x_2, y_2) is given by:

$$y - y_1 = \frac{y_2 - y_1}{x_2 - x_1} (x - x_1) \tag{2.1}$$

It is easy to show that such a line passes through the two points (x_1, y_1) and (x_2, y_2) by merely substituting the pair $x = x_1$, $y = y_1$

and also the pair $x = x_2$, $y = y_2$ into the equation. For example, the straight line through the points $(2, 2)$ and $(4, 8)$ gives:

$$x_1 = 2, \; y_1 = 2, \; x_2 = 4, \; y_2 = 8$$

Then the above equation becomes:

$$y - 2 = \frac{8 - 2}{4 - 2}(x - 2) = 3(x - 2)$$

Simplifying this, we get:

$$y = 3x - 6 + 2$$
or
$$y = -4 + 3x$$

This is the equation of the straight line shown in Figure 2.4. Notice that the line passes through the two points $(2, 2)$ and $(4, 8)$.

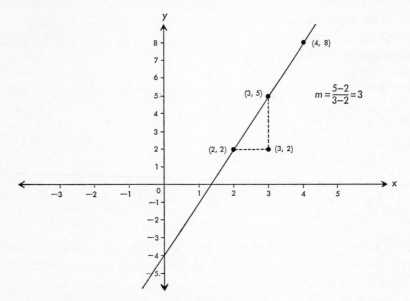

Figure 2.4

The expression

$$m = \frac{y_2 - y_1}{x_2 - x_1}$$

is known as the *slope* of the line. With this change in notation the equation (2.1) can be written:

$$y - y_1 = m(x - x_1) \tag{2.2}$$

The geometric interpretation of the slope is the ratio of the vertical rise (or fall) of the line to the horizontal run. From any point on the line one proceeds horizontally by one unit to the right. Then from the new point one proceeds vertically by m units. The point determined in this way is also seen to be on the line. In Figure 2.4 we arbitrarily pick the starting point at (2, 2). Move one unit to the right to the point (3, 2). Since the slope, $m = 3$, is positive (see the equation for this line), we move upward three units from (3, 2) to the point (3, 5). This point is also on the line.

If our equation had been

$$y - 2 = -3(x - 2)$$

which simplifies to

$$y = 8 - 3x$$

we would have moved downward m units instead of upward. The slope in this case is said to be negative. The line corresponding to this equation is shown in Figure 2.5 and has a slope of -3.

Picking an arbitrary starting point at (1, 5) and moving one unit horizontally to the right entails a movement downward of three units. This follows from the fact that the slope is -3. The point thus obtained is (2, 2), and again this point is found to be on the line.

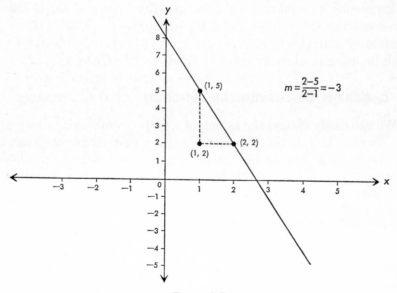

Figure 2.5

The equation

$$y - y_1 = m(x - x_1)$$

is called the *point-slope form of the equation for a straight line*. Given the point (x_1, y_1) and the slope m, the line can be plotted over any permissible range of x and y. It goes through the point (x_1, y_1) with a slope of m. If m is positive, the line goes upward to the right: y is an *increasing function* of x (as in Figure 2.4). If m is negative, the line goes downward to the right: y is a *decreasing function* of x (as in Figure 2.5).

We can write $y - y_1 = m(x - x_1)$ as $y = (y_1 - mx_1) + mx$. Since y_1, x_1, and m are constant numbers, this equation can be expressed as

$$y = f(x) = a + bx$$
$$\text{where } a = (y_1 - mx_1) \text{ and } b = m$$

Hence, in this general linear form b is the slope of the function. By taking $x = 0$ we find that:

$$f(0) = a + b(0) = a$$

We say that a is the y *intercept*. It is the value of y which corresponds to $x = 0$. Consequently, it is the ordinate of a point on the y axis or, stated another way, it is the point at which the straight line cuts the y axis. In Figure 2.5 the y intercept is 8. This general form of expressing an equation for a straight line, $y = a + bx$, is called the *slope-intercept equation* and is the one most often used. Complete familiarity with this form of the linear equation is important, for we shall be using it when we come to treat statistical analysis.

C. GRAPHS OF CURVILINEAR FUNCTIONS OF ONE VARIABLE

We can easily extend the notion of a graph to functions which are not linear. The function expressed by the equation $y = 2 + x^2$ will not result in a straight-line graph. Suppose we make a graph indicating the behavior of this function from $x = -3$ to $x = 4$. We proceed exactly as we did for a linear function. A table is constructed as follows, and the points are plotted as a curve in Figure 2.6.

x	$y = f(x) = 2 + x^2$
-3	$2 + (-3)^2 = 11$
-2	$2 + (-2)^2 = 6$
-1	$2 + (-1)^2 = 3$
0	$2 + (0)^2 = 2$
1	$2 + (1)^2 = 3$
2	$2 + (2)^2 = 6$
3	$2 + (3)^2 = 11$
4	$2 + (4)^2 = 18$

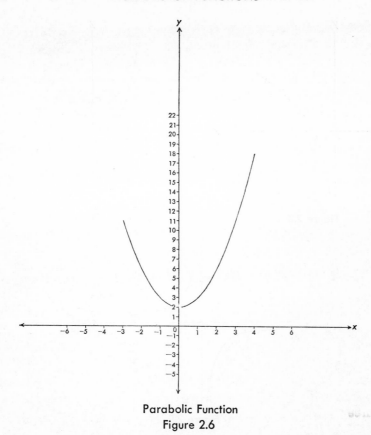

Parabolic Function
Figure 2.6

Incidentally, this particular type of quadratic function is called a *parabolic function*, and its curve is a parabola. Three other types of curvilinear functions and their graphs are shown in Figures 2.7, 2.8, and 2.9. To determine the values of y in Figure 2.7 the table of logs at the end of the book was used. By looking up the log of each value of x to the base e (the base e will be explained later) and inserting it in the equation, the corresponding values of y are determined.

The difference between linear and curvilinear functions is now apparent. Whereas a curvilinear function, when plotted on a set of axes, reveals a curve, a linear function shows up as a straight line. The following general conclusion applies to all functions: the graph of a function is a locus of points called a curve. In the special case where the explicit function happens to include only the first power of the independent variable, the function is called linear because the locus of points assumes the form of a line. A line is a particular kind of curve.

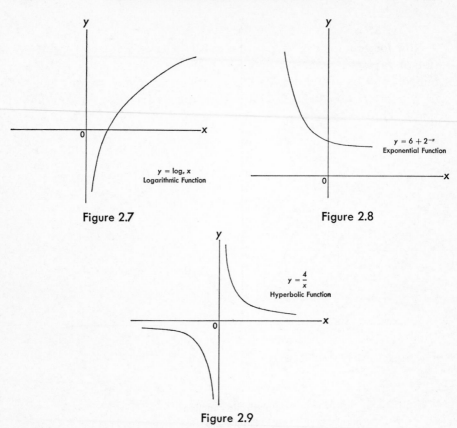

Figure 2.7   Figure 2.8

Figure 2.9

D. GRAPHS OF FUNCTIONS OF TWO VARIABLES

We have already seen that a dependent variable may be a function of several other independent variables. But graphing extends to functions of no more than two variables. Pure geometry as an abstract study is just as possible in four or more dimensions as in two or three dimensions, and the correspondence between analysis and the concepts of geometry persists no matter how many variables are related. A set of values of n variables is described as a "point" in n-dimensional space referred to n mutually perpendicular axes; any relation among the variables is known as a *hyper-surface*. Actual diagrammatic or graphical representations are, however, no longer possible when more than three variables are involved. In this section we shall discuss the graphing of functions of two variables.

Consider an explicit function of two variables which takes the form of a simple linear equation:

$$z = f(x, y) = 1 + x - y$$

Now for each pair of values of x and y, that is, for each combination of values of x and y, a point in three-dimensional space is determined. Assume we know $x = 2$ and $y = 1$. Then for the point (x, y, z) we obtain $(2, 1, 2)$. The value of z is derived from the function f. This point is represented in Figure 2.10.

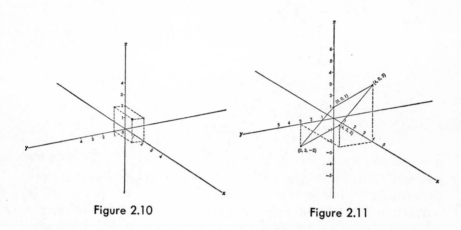

Figure 2.10   Figure 2.11

Figure 2.11 depicts the type of figure (a plane) that would result if all points were plotted between $x = 0$ and $x = 4$ and $y = 0$ and $y = 3$. Note that when y is held constant at a given value, we get a relationship between x and z represented by a line in a two-dimensional xz plane. The plane in which the line falls depends on which value we assign to y—and hold that value of y constant. The same would be true if we held x constant; we would then get a relationship between z and y. This relationship is "pictured" by a line in the yz plane. By holding z constant, we get a relationship between x and y, and a line in the xy plane defining this relationship. When x, y, and z are all allowed to vary, we generate a surface rather than a line.

It now becomes obvious that the two-dimensional presentation is a special case of three-dimensional geometry. If we let $z = 4$, the equation becomes $4 = 1 + x - y$. This is an implicit function involving x and y only as variables. Therefore, we can write y as an explicit function of x (or x as an explicit function of y). Letting y be the dependent variable, we obtain $y = -3 + x$. Note that this is a particular equation under the general linear form $y = a + bx$, where

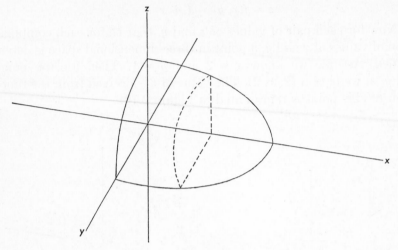

Figure 2.12

$a = -3$ and $b = 1$. By assigning a different value to z, we obtain a different value for a. The student can demonstrate this for himself by letting $y = 8$ or some other constant.

When a function of two variables involves nonlinearities, the surface is no longer flat; it is curved just as the graph of the two-dimensional case is curved rather than a straight line. Figure 2.12 shows one kind of curved surface for chosen intervals of x, y, and z. The general equation for this surface is

$$\frac{x^2}{a^2} + \frac{y^2}{b^2} + \frac{z^2}{c^2} = 1$$

Notice again, for each different value of z chosen and held constant, a different relation between x and y results. There are many diverse kinds of curved surfaces resulting from nonlinear functions of two variables—as many kinds as there are types of nonlinear functions.

E. PARAMETERS AND CURVES

When specifying the general forms of functions, the letters a, b, c, etc. have been used as arbitrary constants. In the quadratic equation $y = a + bx + cx^2$, the a, b, and c are constant values—for various values of x the corresponding values of y are determined. But in algebra we represent unspecified numbers by letters. Hence, when we use a, b, c, etc. for constants, we must recognize that there is a sense in which they are also variables. They are different from the x, y, z variables, however.

Suppose we are dealing with the general linear function $y = f(x) = a + bx$. Two points of view can be adopted. From the first point of view we examine the relation between the variables x and y, and the numbers a and b must be taken as fixed. We have seen that this generates a graph relating y to x. Any change in the values of x and y results in movements along the curve pictured in the diagram. From the other point of view the function is treated as a whole. As a matter of fact, the general formulation represents any function of a linear form since a and b are not specified to be particular numbers. Here the entire function is made to vary by changing the values of a and/or b. The whole curve shifts when a and b are varied. These numbers are fixed within one (linear) function but variable from one (linear) function to another. In the preceding section we have seen that the whole graph in the xy plane shifts position as the constants in the equation are changed. These "variable constants" are called *parameters*.

Let us consider the function given by the equation $y = 2 + 3x$. Its graph is depicted as I in Figure 2.13. This is a particular linear equation of the type $y = a + bx$, where a is the y intercept and b is

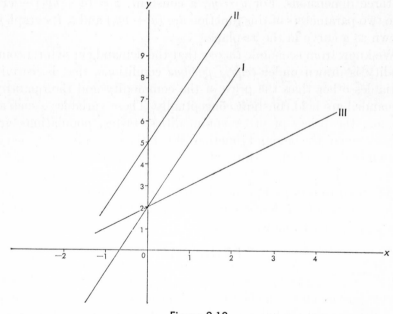

Figure 2.13

the slope of the function. Now suppose we were to change a from 2 to 5. Then the entire straight line shifts upward to II, which is parallel to I. The slope has remained unchanged. If, on the other hand, b were to change from 3 to 1, while a remains equal to 2, the graph will shift from position I to position III. If both a and b are allowed to change, both the y intercept and the slope will change. Consequently, we see that when particular values are assigned to the parameters a and b, a unique linear function is specified. For different values of the parameters different linear functions are specified.

This is true not only for linear functions but for all functions. If the function is given by the equation $y = a + bx + cx^2 + dx^3$, then a change in the value assigned to any of the parameters a, b, c, or d will change the entire function, and the graph of the function will change accordingly. In the preceding section we have seen that when dealing with functions of two variables, $z = f(x, y)$, one of the independent variables may be held constant. The result is an explicit function of one variable. If y is held constant at y_1, then $z = g(x)$; if y is held constant at y_2, then $z = h(x)$. For the functions g and h, the value of y is a parameter, but it is not a parameter for the function f. For example, suppose the function f is specified as $z = a + by - cx^2$, with a, b, and c as parameters. The graph of this function is a surface in three dimensions. For $y = y_1$, a constant, $z = (a + by_1) - cx^2$. The two parameters of this function are $(a + by_1)$ and c. Its graph is shown as a curve in the xz plane.

We know from economic theory that the demand curve for a commodity is drawn under *ceteris paribus* conditions, that is, certain variables other than the price of the commodity and the quantity demanded are held constant conceptually. These variables—such as income, the prices of other commodities, tastes, population—are parameters of the demand function. When they are allowed to vary, the whole demand curve shifts. Similar applications of the parameter concept can be made to cost curves, supply curves, and all other curves used to interpret economic theory. The concept of a parameter is very important in econometrics and will be used extensively in the chapters that follow.

PROBLEMS

GROUP I:

1. Let (x, y) represent a point in the xy plane. Draw rectangular coordinates and plot the following points: $(1, 5)$, $(6, 2)$, $(3, 3)$, $(0, 0)$.

2. Plot the function $y = f(x) = 3 + 2x$ for the range $x = -2$ to $x = 6$.

3. Plot the function $y = f(x) = -3 + x$ for the range $x = -3$ to $x = 10$. Compute the slope of the line.

4. Graph the function $y = f(x) = 5 - .5x$ for the range $x = -4$ to $x = 8$.

5. Graph the function $y = f(x) = -2 - 4x$ for the range $x = 0$ to $x = 4$. Compute the slope of the line.

6. Plot a smooth curve corresponding to the function $y = f(x) = x^2 - 4$ for the range $x = -4$ to $x = 4$.

GROUP II:

7. Plot a smooth curve corresponding to the function $y = f(x) = x^3$ for the range $x = 0$ to $x = 5$.

8. Plot a smooth curve corresponding to the function $y = f(x) = 1^x$ for the range $x = -2$ to $x = 6$.

9. Plot a smooth curve corresponding to the function $y = f(x) = 2 - 2^x$ for the range $x = 0$ to $x = 8$.

10. Plot a smooth curve corresponding to the function $y = f(x) = \dfrac{10}{x}$ for the range $x = 1$ to $x = 10$.

11. Let (x, y, z) represent a point in three-dimensional space. Draw three mutually perpendicular axes and plot the points $(1, 3, 2)$, $(4, 4, 4)$, $(6, 1, 8)$.

12. Graph the function $z = f(x, y) = 2 - 2x + 3y$ from $x = 0$, $y = 0$ to $x = 4$, $y = 4$.

13. Graph the function $z = f(x, y) = \dfrac{x}{y}$ from $x = 1$, $y = 1$ to $x = 4$, $y = 4$.

14. (a) Graph the function $y = f(x) = 6 + 2x$ for the range $x = -3$ to $x = 3$. The constants 6 and 2 are parameters of this function. Label this line I.

    (b) Allow the parameter 6 to change to 9, while the parameter 2 is unchanged. Plot the resulting function for the same range on the same diagram. Label this line II.

    (c) Allow the parameter 2 to change to 1, while the parameter 6 remains unchanged. Plot the resulting function for the same range on the same diagram and label this line III.

15. (a) Graph the function $y = f(x) = \dfrac{100}{x^2}$ for the range $x = 1$ to $x = 10$.

    The constant 100 is a parameter of this function. Label this curve I.

    (b) Allow the parameter to change to 200. Graph the resulting function for the same range on the same diagram. Label this curve II.

    (c) Allow the parameter to change to 50. Graph this function for the same range on the same diagram and label the curve III.

CHAPTER 3

Economic Applications
of Functions and Graphs

Since most propositions of economic theory can be stated in mathematical terms, analytical methods are directly applicable to economic problems. Diagrammatic methods are also of great service. Any economic proposition capable of symbolic representation can be illustrated, in general, with the aid of graphs. There is a graph corresponding to each function we use to interpret a relationship among economic variables; there are demand and supply curves as well as demand and supply functions. These curves can be represented on a set of axes, and the relationships among several curves can be displayed in one diagram. Diagrams serve the purpose of clarifying and emphasizing the relationships stated in an analytical exposition. In this chapter we shall illustrate the mathematical formulation of theoretical economic propositions by means of several examples.

A. DEMAND FUNCTIONS

We have seen in the previous chapter that the quantity of a commodity demanded can be represented as a function of several variables. Assuming that income, other prices, and all other determinants of demand are constant, we can express the quantity demanded as a function of the price of that commodity only. This is the usual meaning given to the demand schedule in economics. It is shown as a table which records for each price of the commodity the quantity that consumers would take. All other variables assumed to affect the quantity demanded, such as consumers' income, other prices and tastes, are parameters of the demand function so expressed. Let the amount of commodity X demanded in the market be denoted by the symbol x, and let the price of the commodity be denoted by p. Now

x and p are variables—they are magnitudes that may assume various values. In the language of functional relationships the dependence of x upon p can be written:

$$x = d(p)$$

Incidentally, the demand function might be written implicitly as:

$$f(x, p) = 0$$

From this formulation the demand function can be converted to an explicit function.

In order to specify this demand function, we must give it a particular form in terms of an equation. Once we have done that, it is possible to represent the demand function as a demand curve and draw the graph in a plane referred to as the p and x axes, along which prices and quantities demanded are respectively measured in some chosen units. For example, the units of x may be pounds, dozens, tons, etc.; the units of p will be dollars or cents. The units in which the quantities are measured is a matter of convenience and clarity of exposition. There are no negative prices and no negative quantities demanded. Since both of these variables assume only positive values, we shall use only the first quadrant in plotting the relationship. We have taken price as the independent variable and quantity demanded as the dependent variable, so we should draw the p axis horizontally and the x axis vertically according to mathematical convention. Nevertheless, it is a convention in economics to represent the quantity demanded on the horizontal axis and price on the vertical axis, and we shall follow the economic convention.

In Figure 3.1 are shown the equations for three selected types of demand functions together with their corresponding demand curves. In each case the demand curve was plotted by the same technique used in the preceding chapter. A table was constructed for chosen values of p. The corresponding value of x was obtained for each of these values of p by solving the demand equation for x. The set of values of p and corresponding values of x is precisely what is meant by a demand schedule. From each of the three demand schedules the demand curves were plotted in their respective diagrams.

It ought to be emphasized that the demand function and curve represent a set of hypothetical quantities demanded at alternative hypothetical prices. They are not actual observable prices and quantities existing in the market. These remarks also apply to the variables in all functions in economics—cost functions, supply functions,

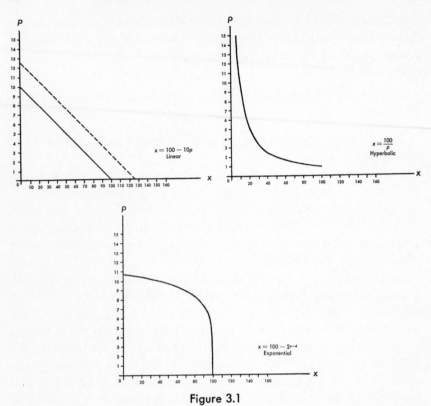

Figure 3.1

consumption functions, production functions, etc. For example, a total cost function states the total cost that would result if output were equal to various quantities.

Before proceeding to other economic functions, let us take a somewhat closer look at the operation of the demand parameters. In the linear demand function illustrated in Figure 3.1, the constants 100 and 10 are demand parameters. In order to simplify the explanation of the effects of parameter changes, let us assume that income is the only other determinant of the quantity demanded and, further, that the quantity demanded is a linear function of income. We might have, for example:

$$x = -10p + .5y$$

where y signifies income. Assuming income to be constant at a level of 200 units, we get

$$x = .5(200) - 10p = 100 - 10p$$

the equation for the linear function represented by the solid line in Figure 3.1.

Now suppose income were to change to 250 units; our demand function becomes:

$$x = .5(250) - 10p = 125 - 10p$$

The demand curve will shift to the right and rest at a position in which it is parallel to the original demand curve, as is shown by the broken line in Figure 3.1. The new x intercept is 125, and the new p intercept is 12.5. This shift in the demand curve is like the movement from I to II in Figure 2.13. Similar arguments apply to the other parameters of the demand function. Indeed, they apply to the parameters of any function.

B. SUPPLY FUNCTIONS

The general principles of mathematical formulation refer also to the expression of supply functions. The symbolic statement

$$x = s(p)$$

may be used to express the market supply function. Figure 3.2 depicts three different supply functions and their corresponding supply curves. Notice that the slopes of the supply functions are positive, whereas the demand functions are negatively sloped. This follows from the principles of economic theory.

The prices of factors of production and technological conditions (coefficients in the production functions) are the parameters of the supply function. When the values of these parameters change, the supply curve will shift in the xp plane.

C. COST FUNCTIONS

In the first two examples we have been dealing with market relationships. Let us now turn to the behavior of the individual firm; in particular, let us consider the short-run costs of production for the firm (certain inputs are assumed to be fixed). Let us call the product in question commodity X. The symbol x will be used to denote the amount of X produced by the firm. Finally, the total cost of production will be signified by the letter y. Now consider the typical relationship between total cost and the quantity produced by the firm. This can be written in functional notation as $y = f(x)$. In implicit form the total cost function might be represented as $g(y, x) = 0$.

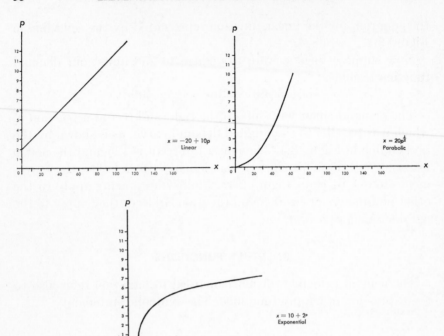

Figure 3.2

Average cost of production is the cost per unit of the commodity produced. If the total cost function is known, we get the average cost by dividing total cost by the quantity produced. Let z signify average cost (z is a variable just as y is); thus:

$$z = \frac{y}{x} = \frac{f(x)}{x} = h(x)$$

Hence, we have another function: the average cost function. If, on the other hand, the average cost function is known, we can derive the total cost function by multiplying the average cost function by the quantity produced; that is:

$$y = zx = h(x)x = f(x)$$

In Figure 3.3 a short run total cost function and its corresponding average cost function are exhibited. They have the typical shapes generally assumed in economic theory. We shall defer discussion of the marginal cost function to a later chapter.

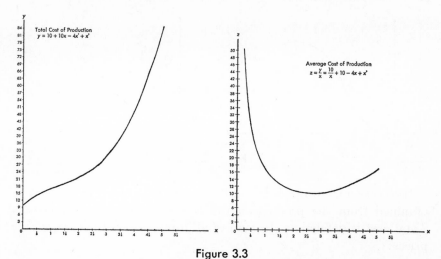

Figure 3.3

D. PRODUCTION FUNCTIONS

The production function plays a key role in the theory of the firm. It is from knowledge of the production function and the (given) prices of factors of production that we obtain the cost curves. This relationship among physical units tells us how much of the commodity will be produced for varying hypothetical quantities of inputs used. Assume that we have two inputs, labor and capital, represented by L and K respectively, engaged in the production of commodity X. Let l, k, and x signify the quantities of L, K, and X respectively (measured in some appropriate units). The production function may be written:

$$x = j(l, k)$$

If the amount of capital is fixed in the short run (that is, $k = k_1$, a constant) but the amount of labor utilized is variable, then the quantity of X produced is a function of the amount of labor employed. In the language of functional relationships

$$x = r(l)$$

A total product curve and its corresponding average product curve are depicted in Figure 3.4. The average product function is derived from the total product function in exactly the same way that average cost was derived from total cost. Let z represent the average product; then we have

$$z = \frac{x}{l} = \frac{r(l)}{l} = q(l)$$

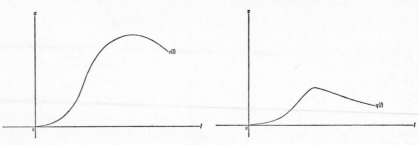

Figure 3.4

It has been mentioned that the total cost function of a firm can be obtained from the production function and the prices of inputs. Total cost is defined as the sum of all inputs times their respective prices:

$$c = l \cdot p_l + k \cdot p_k$$

where, for two inputs, c is the total cost, l is the quantity of labor, p_l is the price of labor (the wage rate), k is the quantity of capital, and p_k is the price per unit of capital. For a fixed quantity of capital, k_1, we have the production function expressed by the relationship $x = r(l)$ with the prices of the inputs given. If $x = r(l)$, then $l = s(x)$ is the inverse of this function. In order to express total cost as a function of output, we merely substitute the fixed quantity of capital and this inverse function in the above definition of total cost; thus we obtain:

$$c = s(x) \cdot p_l + k_1 \cdot p_k$$

For any given (constant) p_l and p_k, we have:

$$c = f(x)$$

This is total cost as a function of output. Diagrammatically, it yields the total cost curve—and, by dividing through by x, the average cost curve. The prices of inputs and the coefficients of the production function are parameters of the total and average cost functions; for example, any change in their values will produce a shift in the total cost curve in the cx plane.

If we had not assumed the quantity of capital to be fixed, the production signified by $x = j(l, k)$ could have been "pictured" by a surface in three dimensions. Had production been expressed as a function of more than two inputs, we could not represent it diagrammatically, but we could still treat it analytically.

E. THE CONSUMPTION FUNCTION

Passing out of the area of price theory, let us take an example from national income analysis. In particular, let us assume that the aggregate consumption function for the economy as a whole is linear; that is, aggregate consumption is a linear function of disposable income. With C denoting consumption, Y income, and T total income tax payments (all measured in, say, billions of dollars), the consumption function may be written:

$$C = f(Y - T) = 20 + .8(Y - T)$$

We make the further assumption that taxes are exogenous, that is, they are given by legislative action. Setting T equal to five billion dollars, this consumption function can be rewritten as:

$$C = 16 + .8Y$$

Its graph is shown in Figure 3.5.

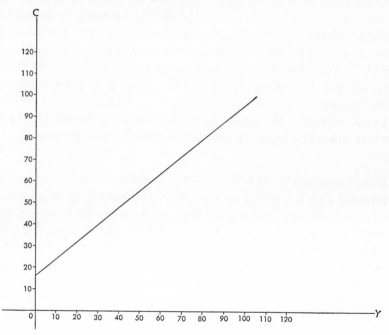

Figure 3.5

Were we to introduce other independent variables that affect consumption, such as the interest rate and the value of total consumers' assets, we would have a function of more than one variable Using functional notation, we would express this as follows:

$$C = g(Y, i, A)$$

where i denotes the relevant interest rate and A denotes the value of consumers' assets. This function may be linear in all three variables, linear in one or two variables, or linear in none of the variables, depending upon theoretical reasoning and perhaps certain factual information.

F. THE LIQUIDITY PREFERENCE FUNCTION

Another concept drawn from national income analysis is liquidity preference—an economic relationship existing in the money market rather than in the commodity market. Two motives are usually postulated as an explanation of the holding of money balances: the convenience motive and the liquidity motive (sometimes broken down into the precautionary and speculative motives). Given the amount held for the convenience motive (assumed to depend upon income or some other variable), the demand for money to hold for liquidity purposes is dependent upon the interest rate. The lower the interest rate, the greater the quantity of money demanded for liquidity. In other words, the demand for money to hold for all purposes is a decreasing function of the interest rate, given convenience balances.

Let M represent the total quantity of money demanded and i the interest rate. The liquidity preference function is expressed as

$$M = f(i)$$

Diagrammatically the dependent variable is measured on the horizontal axis according to economic convention, as was done in the case of demand and supply curves for commodities. Figure 3.6 shows a liquidity preference curve and its corresponding equation. Notice that the curve approaches a horizontal straight line (called an asymptote) at an interest rate of 1 per cent. Consequently, this particular liquidity preference function includes an assumption of the so-called "liquidity trap." In the neighborhood of an existing interest rate of 1 per cent, changes in the money supply by the monetary authority are practically ineffective in altering the interest rate. An extremely large change in the money supply is required to have even a small effect upon the interest rate.

Convenience balances were assumed to be constant for the given liquidity preference function. Therefore, any change in the amount of convenience balances will shift the liquidity preference curve in the iM plane. For instance, if it is assumed (1) that the amount of convenience balances is an increasing function of income and (2) that income increases, then the liquidity preference curve will shift upward and to the right. It will shift downward and to the left for a decrease in income.

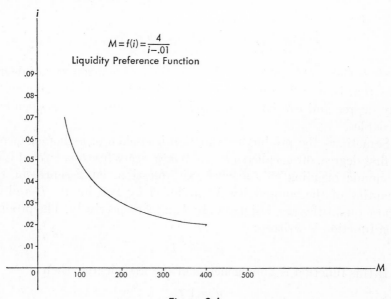

Figure 3.6

G. HOMOGENEOUS FUNCTIONS

A special type of function that is important in several areas of economics is the homogeneous function. It has peculiar properties which are extremely useful in many economic problems. We shall discuss the homogeneous function itself and then its applications to economics.

Let us suppose we have a function of two variables:

$$z = f(x, y)$$

This function is said to be a homogeneous function of degree n if the following relationship holds:

$$f(ax, ay) = a^n f(x, y)$$

A function is homogeneous of degree n if when each of the independent variables is multiplied by a constant a, the new function is a^n times the original function.

Consider the function signified by:

$$z = f(x, y) = x^2 + y^2$$

Multiply each of the independent variables by an arbitrary constant a:

$$f(ax, ay) = (ax)^2 + (ay)^2$$
$$= a^2x^2 + a^2y^2$$
$$= a^2(x^2 + y^2)$$
$$= a^2f(x, y)$$

Since $f(ax, ay) = a^2f(x, y)$, this function is homogeneous of degree two, that is, $n = 2$. Homogeneous functions may be homogeneous of any degree and can be generalized for any number of independent variables.

Sometimes the production function is spoken of as homogeneous of first degree, often called a *linear homogeneous function*.[1] What is its economic meaning? To answer this question, let x represent the quantity of the commodity X produced by two inputs L and K, whose quantities are designated by l and k respectively. The production function is written:

$$x = f(l, k)$$

If this function is homogeneous of the first degree, then:

$$n = 1$$
$$\text{and}$$
$$f(al, ak) = af(l, k) = ax$$

By multiplying each of the inputs by an arbitrary positive constant,[2] output is multiplied by the same constant. For example, if we were to double all inputs ($a = 2$), we would double output. If we were to reduce all inputs by one-half ($a = \frac{1}{2}$), output would be reduced by one-half. The production function given by the equation

$$x = f(l, k) = 10 \, l^{\frac{1}{2}} \, k^{\frac{1}{2}}$$

is homogeneous of the first degree. To illustrate, multiply each independent variable by the arbitrary positive constant a:

---

[1] This should not be confused with a linear function since the independent variables need not enter linearly for a linear homogeneous function. As we shall see, it is the constant a which enters linearly.

[2] We restrict the constant here to be positive; otherwise total output would turn out to be negative. To discuss decreases in output when all inputs are reduced we merely let $0 < a < 1$, that is, we restrict the positive a to values less than one. For the constant greater than one, we increase all inputs and output. For the constant less than one, we decrease all inputs and output.

$$f(al,\ ak) = 10(al)^{\frac{1}{2}}(ak)^{\frac{1}{2}}$$
$$= 10a^{\frac{1}{2}}l^{\frac{1}{2}}a^{\frac{1}{2}}k^{\frac{1}{2}}$$
$$= a(10l^{\frac{1}{2}}k^{\frac{1}{2}})$$
$$= af(l,\ k)$$

Production functions assumed homogeneous of degree one are very useful methodologically. We want ultimately to distinguish between two sets of forces affecting the costs of the firm: (1) the proportions in which it combines factors of production or inputs, and (2) the scale on which it operates. The law of variable proportions is concerned with the first set, and we can abstract from the influence of scale (changes in all inputs at once) by provisionally supposing it to have no influence. This is precisely what is involved in assuming the production function is homogeneous of first degree in all inputs. Then the output per unit of one input will be a function solely of the ratio of the inputs, and we can ignore the question of scale.

Incidentally, the first-degree homogeneous production function used in our illustration is called a *Cobb-Douglas production function*.[3] Its general representation is

$$x = bL^cC^d$$

where x is total production, L is the quantity of labor, C is the quantity of capital, and b, c, and d are constants. If, as is usually assumed, $c = 1 - d$, the production function is homogeneous of the first degree. Its graph has the shape normally attributed to the production function in economic theory. (See Figure 3.4.)

To examine another application of homogeneous functions to economic problems, suppose that the quantity demanded of a commodity X is given as a function of the price of X, p_x, and the prices of two substitutes, p_y and p_z:

$$x = d(p_x,\ p_y,\ p_z) = 40\,\frac{p_y}{p_x} + 10\,\frac{p_z}{p_x}$$

This demand function is homogeneous of degree zero in all prices, which can be shown by multiplying each of the independent variables by a constant number a. Thus

$$f(ap_x,\ ap_y,\ ap_z) = 40\,\frac{ap_y}{ap_x} + 10\,\frac{ap_z}{ap_x}$$
$$= \frac{a}{a}\left(40\,\frac{p_y}{p_x} + 10\,\frac{p_z}{p_x}\right)$$
$$= a^0 f(p_x,\ p_y,\ p_z) = f(p_x,\ p_y,\ p_z)$$

[3] C. W. Cobb and P. H. Douglas, "A Theory of Production," *American Economic Review*, Vol. XVIII (Supplement, 1938), pp. 139–156.

since any number to the zero power equals one. If *all* of the prices are multiplied by an arbitrary constant, the quantity demanded remains unchanged. The importance of relative prices is emphasized. If all prices change in the same direction by the same proportionate amount, there will be no substitution of one commodity for another in consumption.

H. CYCLES AND TRENDS

The functions and graphs illustrated up to this point have dealt with the usual relationships among typical economic magnitudes— demand and supply relations, costs, and production. Let us now consider a somewhat different type of relationship for the exposition of which functions and graphs are of value.

Often economists are interested in describing the movements of economic magnitudes over time rather than their relationships to other economic magnitudes (as of an instant of time). For certain problems it is useful to know the way in which monthly prices or production fluctuate. For others, it is desirable to know what the typical seasonal pattern of inventories of a commodity is like. Movements of national income over time might be used as an index of the "business cycle." The economics of long-term growth and development has claimed increased attention in recent years. Consequently, functions describing the growth of enterprise or of population over relatively long periods of time may be required. This involves the notion of long-run trends as opposed to short-run variations. The common element in functions used to describe these various movements is that they relate some economic magnitude to time rather than to some other economic magnitude.

1. Cycles

Suppose we are interested in a simple function of time which results in cyclical behavior of the dependent variable. Our problem might be that of describing the monthly variations in butter production, which have a regular seasonal pattern determined by the seasonal fluctuations in milk produced on farms. For simplicity, let us assume that there is no trend in butter production—the annual average level of butter production is 130 million pounds and does not change from year to year. The seasonal cycle of butter production might be described by the following equation:

$$x = f(t) = 130 - 40 \cos \frac{\pi t}{6} - 6 \sin \frac{\pi t}{6}$$

where t is time measured in months and x is total monthly production. This is a trigonometric function. The values of the sines and cosines can be looked up in tables that are contained in practically all textbooks on trigonometry. The symbol π has the conventional mathematical value of $\frac{22}{7}$. A table giving the values of the dependent variable for selected values of the independent variable has been constructed.

t	$x = f(t)$
0	$130 - 40(\ 1.000) - 6(\ \ .000) = \ \ 90.00$
1	$130 - 40(\ \ .866) - 6(\ \ .500) = \ \ 92.36$
2	$130 - 40(\ \ .500) - 6(\ \ .866) = \ \ 94.80$
3	$130 - 40(\ \ .000) - 6(\ 1.000) = 124.00$
4	$130 - 40(-.500) - 6(\ \ .866) = 144.80$
5	$130 - 40(-.866) - 6(\ \ .500) = 161.64$
6	$130 - 40(-1.00) - 6(\ \ .000) = 170.00$
7	$130 - 40(-.866) - 6(-.500) = 167.64$
8	$130 - 40(-.500) - 6(-.866) = 155.20$
9	$130 - 40(\ \ .000) - 6(-1.00) = 136.00$
10	$130 - 40(\ \ .500) - 6(-.866) = 115.20$
11	$130 - 40(\ \ .866) - 6(-.500) = \ \ 98.36$
12	$130 - 40(\ 1.000) - 6(\ \ .000) = \ \ 90.00$

The graph of this function is exhibited in Figure 3.7. The unbroken curve shows the values of x for the values of t included in the table. If the table were to include values of t beyond twelve, we would get the continuation of this curve shown by the broken segment.

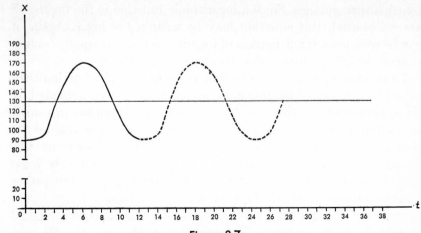

Figure 3.7

The oscillation of x is said to be periodic with a twelve-month period. Notice that identical cycles continue indefinitely (without variation in amplitude or duration as time is extended). It is called a *harmonic oscillation*. A function that describes oscillations which get smaller with increases in time and approach some fixed value (such as the annual average value, 130) would be called a *damped harmonic oscillation*. If, on the other hand, the cycles were to grow larger, the movement would be called *explosive*.

2. Trend

We have assumed in this example that there is no trend in the behavior of production. We can introduce a linear trend by replacing the constant term, 130, with a linear function of time, for example, $130 + .4t$. This suggests that the annual average level of production around which the cycles occur itself increases at a (constant absolute) rate of .4 million pounds per month. Not all long-run trends are linear, however. The economic magnitude in question may not increase or decrease by a constant absolute amount during each time interval. We shall now consider some typical nonlinear trends which have found application in econometric analysis.

Suppose that an industry is assumed to grow by a constant percentage each year rather than by a constant absolute amount. Then the growth of the industry, measured by its output, can be described by an exponential function such as $x = a^t$, where the variable x is output, the variable t is time, and a is a constant. It can be seen from this equation that as t increases by equal increments, x will increase by equal percentages. Since a logarithmic function is the inverse of an exponential, this equation may be written $t = \log_a x$. Again, it can be seen from the definition of logarithms that for equal absolute changes in t there are equal percentage changes in x.

To be more specific, let us assume that the growth of an industry beyond an output of 100,000 units per year can be approximated by the exponential function $x = 99 + 2^t$, where x is output measured in thousands of units and t is time measured in years. Figure 3.8 shows the graph of this function. Note that in absolute terms this function increases at an increasing rate. If we were to use the logarithmic form $t = \log_2 (x - 99)$ and measure $\log_2 (x - 99)$ rather than x on the vertical axis, as in Figure 3.9, this same relation would appear as a straight line. The reason is that the t axis shows equal absolute changes for equal distances whereas the $\log_2 (x - 99)$ axis shows equal percentage changes for equal distances.

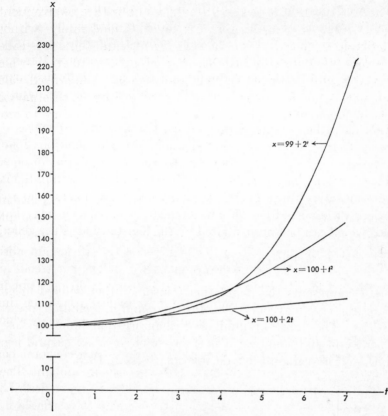

Figure 3.8

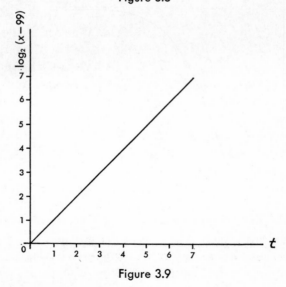

Figure 3.9

A power function might also be used to describe the growth of industry, such as $x = 100 + t^2$, $x = 100 + t^3$, or $x = 100 + t^4$. For purposes of comparison Figure 3.8 also shows the graphs corresponding to two other growth functions: $x = 100 + t^2$ and $x = 100 + 2t$. The choice of a mathematical equation to express growth will depend upon economic theory and the peculiarities of the industry under investigation.

Another rather common function used to describe a trend is the logistic. It has been demonstrated that animal populations follow the logistic law of growth under certain conditions, and it (or one of its modifications) is sometimes used to express the growth of human populations over time. Therefore, many economic magnitudes that are closely connected to the development of population may have trends which can be approximated by the logistic. It has the general form

$$P = \frac{a}{1 + be^{-ct}}$$

where P represents the population (or some other defined magnitude as the case may be), t denotes time, and a, b, and c represent constants. The constant number e is an irrational number used frequently in mathematics; it is the base of so-called natural logarithms, and its value to five decimal places is 2.71828.

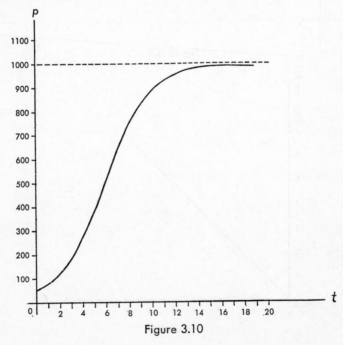

Figure 3.10

The graph of the logistic

$$P = \frac{1,000}{1 + 19e^{-.5t}}$$

is presented in Figure 3.10. The property which recommends this function as compared with polynomial or exponential trends is the fact that it has an upper asymptote; this asymptote is a in the general formula. The upper asymptote, 1,000, is drawn as a broken line in Figure 3.10 in order to clearly indicate the upper boundary of the function.

I. DIFFERENCE EQUATIONS

We treat now a special kind of function—that involving a difference equation. We shall make use of difference equations in later chapters. For the present, let us define them and present some simple examples. Assume we have a known function $y = f(x)$. If we subtract the value of y at the point x, that is, $f(x)$, from the value of y at the point $(x + 1)$, that is, $f(x + 1)$, we obtain the first difference:

$$\Delta y = f(x + 1) - f(x)$$

In general equations that involve $f(x)$ and $f(x + t)$, where t is an integer, are known as *difference equations*. The equation

$$af(x + 1) + bf(x) = 0$$

where the coefficients a and b are constants is called a *linear homogeneous difference equation of the first order with constant coefficients*. A *nonhomogeneous linear first-order difference equation* is an equation of the form

$$af(x + 1) + bf(x) = c$$

where a, b, and c may or may not be constant. We shall treat only the case of constant coefficients.

1. Linear Homogeneous Difference Equation

Let us consider first the linear homogeneous difference equation of the first order with constant coefficients. The equation

$$af(x + 1) + bf(x) = 0$$

may be written

$$f(x + 1) = -\frac{b}{a}f(x)$$

To find its solution, we must know the value of the function at one point. Suppose this is the point corresponding to $x = 0$, so that

$f(0) = Q$, a known number. To arrive at the general solution for this difference equation, we proceed step by step; thus

$$f(1) = \left(-\frac{b}{a}\right) f(0) = \left(-\frac{b}{a}\right) Q$$

$$f(2) = \left(-\frac{b}{a}\right) f(1) = \left(-\frac{b}{a}\right)^2 Q$$

$$f(3) = \left(-\frac{b}{a}\right) f(2) = \left(-\frac{b}{a}\right)^3 Q$$

.

.

.

$$f(x) = \left(-\frac{b}{a}\right)^x Q$$

where x is an integer. The reader can easily check this general solution by substituting $(-b/a)^{x+1}$ for $f(x + 1)$ and $(-b/a)^x$ for $f(x)$ in the difference equation.

To illustrate, assume we are dealing with a compound interest problem. Let P indicate the principal, i the interest rate, and $R(x)$ the amount paid in the year x. For convenience let $r = 1 + i$. We know that $R(0) = P$. The amount $R(x)$ paid in the year x satisfies the difference equation $R(x + 1) - rR(x) = 0$. To arrive at this, we can again proceed step by step:

$$R(0) = P$$
$$R(1) = rR(0) = rP$$
$$R(2) = rR(1) = r^2P$$
.
.
.
$$R(x) = r^x P$$

Hence in the year n the amount paid in that year is $R(n) = r^n P$. The general solution can be checked by substitution in the difference equation. The student will find this to be a valuable exercise.

2. Nonhomogeneous Linear Difference Equation

Consider next the nonhomogeneous linear first-order difference equation with constant coefficients. We have seen that this equation has the form $af(x + 1) + bf(x) = c$ with a, b, and c as constants. It can be written:

$$f(x + 1) = \left(-\frac{b}{a}\right) f(x) + \frac{c}{a}$$

Again let the initial value $f(0) = Q$. By successive application of the difference equation, we have

$$f(1) = \left(-\frac{b}{a}\right)f(0) + \frac{c}{a} = \left(-\frac{b}{a}\right)Q + \frac{c}{a}$$

$$f(2) = \left(-\frac{b}{a}\right)f(1) + \frac{c}{a} = \left(-\frac{b}{a}\right)^2 Q + \left(-\frac{b}{a}\right)\frac{c}{a} + \frac{c}{a}$$

$$= \left(-\frac{b}{a}\right)^2 Q + \frac{c}{a}\left[\left(-\frac{b}{a}\right) + 1\right]$$

$$= \left(-\frac{b}{a}\right)^2 Q + \frac{c}{a}\left[\frac{\left(-\frac{b}{a}\right)^2 - 1}{\left(-\frac{b}{a}\right) - 1}\right]$$

$$\cdot \quad \cdot \quad \cdot \quad \cdot$$
$$\cdot \quad \cdot \quad \cdot \quad \cdot$$
$$\cdot \quad \cdot \quad \cdot \quad \cdot$$

$$f(x) = \left(-\frac{b}{a}\right)^x Q + \frac{c}{a}\left[\frac{\left(-\frac{b}{a}\right)^x - 1}{\left(-\frac{b}{a}\right) - 1}\right]$$

where x is an integer. This last expression is the general solution of the difference equation.

To take a simple economic application, assume an economy in which all income is consumed. Assume further that the additional consumption in year $x + 1$ is a constant proportion a of the income in year x. If the initial income (consumption) is C, a constant number, then we have the difference equation:

$$Y(x + 1) = aY(x) + C$$

with $Y(0) = C$, where Y denotes income. This difference equation tells us that the income in year $x + 1$ is the initial consumption plus a constant proportion of income in the preceding year. The solution of this difference equation (which we shall not trace through) is

$$Y(x) = \frac{C}{1 - a} - \frac{aCa^x}{1 - a}$$

Therefore, for known values of C and a we can forecast income in any year by using this formula. Difference equations are very useful in economic dynamics, and we shall return to them in Chapter 15.

In this chapter we have shown that a variety of theoretical propositions in economics are translatable into mathematical formulation. Since all branches of economic theory deal with relationships among quantities, widespread applications of analysis and geometry are possible. Whether one wishes to relate one economic magnitude to another or one economic magnitude to time (which is also a magnitude), these magnitudes can be represented symbolically. The symbols which stand for economic (or other) variables are related by functional notation. The functions are then specified by mathematical equations. To each equation corresponds a graph which represents the curve or surface determined by the equation.

PROBLEMS

GROUP I:

1. Assume that the market demand function for electric shavers in the United States is given by
$$q = f(p) = 500 - 25p$$
where q denotes the quantity demanded per year (in thousands of shavers) and p denotes the price (in dollars per shaver).
   (a) Construct the market demand schedule for electric shavers for the range $p = 10$ to $p = 1$ inclusive. Make the price entries in the table at $1 intervals.
   (b) Plot the demand curve for electric shavers for the same price range.

2. Assume that the market demand function for a college education in the United States is given as
$$e = f(p, y) = -2p^2 + .3y$$
where e is measured in thousands of college entrants per year, p represents the average price per year of education in thousands of dollars (tuition plus room, board, fees, etc.), and y denotes national income in the United States in billions of dollars. It is known that y is equal to $300 billion per year.
   (a) Construct the demand schedule for college education for the range $p = 1$ to $p = 6$ inclusive, at $1,000 intervals, assuming $y = 300$.
   (b) Plot a smooth demand curve for college education for the same price range. Label this curve I.
   (c) Assume national income increases to $360 billion. Plot the new demand curve and label it II.
   (d) Assume national income decreases to $200 billion. Plot the new demand curve and label it III.

3. The consumption for the American economy as a whole is assumed to be given as
$$C = f(Y, T, A) = 10 + .5(Y - T) + .1A$$
where C represents aggregate consumption by households in the United States, T signifies total tax payments to the government, and A denotes the asset holdings of households. All variables are measured in billions of dollars. Assume it is known that total tax payments equal $10 billion and total asset holdings equal $400 billion.

(a) Graph the consumption as a function of income for the range $Y = 0$ to $Y = 200$ inclusive, assuming $T = 10$ and $A = 400$. Label this curve I.

(b) Assume taxes are increased to $30 billion, while asset holdings do not change. Graph the new consumption curve for the same income range and label it II.

(c) Assume asset holdings increase to $600 billion, while taxes remain, as they were originally, equal to $10 billion. Graph the new consumption curve for the same income range and label it III.

(d) Suppose $T = 10$ and $A = 400$ as for consumption curve I. Now suppose both change simultaneously: taxes increase to 30 and asset holdings increase to 600. Graph the new consumption curve for the same income range and label this curve IV.

4. Given the difference equation $f(x + 1) - 2f(x) = 0$ and the condition that $f(0) = 20$.

Find $f(2), f(4), f(5)$, and the general solution.

GROUP II:

5. Assume that the market supply function for wheat in the United States is given as

$$s = f(p) = -2 + 2^p$$

where s denotes the quantity of wheat supplied measured in millions of bushels per year and p denotes the price of wheat in dollars per bushel.

(a) Construct the supply schedule for wheat for the range $p = 1$ to $p = 7$ inclusive, at $1 intervals.

(b) Plot a smooth supply curve for wheat for the same price range.

6. Assume that the market demand function for unskilled labor in a certain city is given by

$$l = f(w) = \frac{400}{2w^2}$$

where l represents thousands of labor hours per month and w signifies the wage rate per hour in dollars.

(a) Construct the demand schedule for unskilled labor for the range $w = 1$ to $w = 4$ inclusive, at $1 intervals.

(b) Plot the smooth demand curve for unskilled labor for the same wage range.

7. The total cost of production function for a firm producing commodity X is given as

$$c = f(x) = 50 + 3x - 2x^2 + x^3$$

where c denotes total cost in thousands of dollars and x denotes the output of the firm in hundreds of units per month.

(a) Plot the smooth total cost of production curve for the range $x = 0$ to $x = 8$ inclusive.

(b) Plot the smooth average cost curve for the same range of output.

8. The following production function is given for a firm:

$$x = f(l, k) = 10(l + k)$$

where x measures the firm's output per year in thousands of units l denotes the amount of labor used by the firm in hours per year, and k denotes the capital input of the firm measured in thousands of units per year. Prove that this production function is homogeneous of the first degree.

9. The demand function for a commodity X is given as

$$x = f(p_x, p_y) = 25 \frac{p_y}{p_x}$$

where x denotes the quantity of X per unit of time and p_x and p_y denote respectively the price of X and the price of Y, a substitute commodity. Is this demand function homogeneous? If so, of what degree is it homogeneous? How would you give a common-sense explanation of this characteristic of the demand function?

10. Assume that there are three industries producing three different commodities: X, Y, and Z. The long-run trend of production in each industry is described by the following equations:

$x = f(t) = 10 + 3t - .01t^2$ (Consult the table of logarithms
$y = g(t) = \log_e t$ at the back of this textbook.)
$z = h(t) = .01(2^t - t)$

The quantities x, y, and z measure production of X, Y, and Z respectively in thousands of units per year and t measures time in years. The origin is 1900 (that is, $t = 0$ at 1900). Plot the smooth trend curve corresponding to each of the equations for the range $t = 1$ to $t = 10$ inclusive (that is, plot the trend curve from 1901 to 1910 inclusive).

11. For the economy as a whole it is given that aggregate United States consumption can be described by the equation

$$C(t + 1) = aC(t)$$

where $C(t)$ denotes consumption at time t and a is a constant. It is also given that the initial consumption is 100. Hence, we have the difference equation

$$C(t + 1) = aC(t) + 100$$

It is known $C(0) = 100$.

(a) Assume $a = .8$.
    Find $C(2)$, $C(5)$, $C(7)$.

(b) Assume $a = 2$.
    Find $C(2)$, $C(5)$, $C(10)$.

CHAPTER 4

Systems of Equations

One of the most common principles of economic theory is that the market price of a commodity is determined by demand and supply: the equilibrium price and quantity traded are determined as those amounts at which the quantity demanded is just equal to the quantity supplied. The equilibrium output for a single firm is set by the decision to equate marginal cost of production to marginal revenue. Statements like these are found throughout economic theory. In general, one function alone will not enable the economist to arrive at a prediction. In order to derive a conclusion about observable economic behavior, it is necessary to take account of two or more functions, such as both the demand function and the supply function. Consequently, we are led to the consideration of a system of two or more simultaneous equations and their solution. This discussion will, no doubt, be familiar to the student from his knowledge of elementary algebra.

A. SYSTEMS OF TWO LINEAR EQUATIONS

Assume that we have the following system of two equations with two unknowns, x and y:

$$4x + 6y = 16$$
$$2x + \ y = \ 2$$

To solve this system for the two unknowns is to find the values of x and y that will satisfy both of the equations. We arrive at the solution by first eliminating one of the two variables. Suppose that we choose to eliminate x; we multiply the members of one of the equations by some number that will enable us to eliminate x. This number is seen to be 2; that is, by multiplying the members of the second equation by 2, we obtain:

$$4x + 6y = 16$$
$$4x + 2y = \ 4$$

Now we subtract the second equation from the first, thereby obtaining:

$$4y = 12$$

Dividing both sides of this equation by 4 yields the value of y:

$$y = 3$$

To obtain the value of x, substitute this value of y in one of the original equations. Choosing the first equation, we have:

$$4x + 6(3) = 16$$
$$4x = -2$$
$$x = -\tfrac{1}{2}$$

The solution for our original system of two linear equations is therefore $x = -\tfrac{1}{2}$, $y = 3$. This solution can be checked by substituting these values in the original equations, thus:

$$4(-\tfrac{1}{2}) + 6(3) = 16$$
$$2(-\tfrac{1}{2}) + \quad 3 = 2$$

B. SYSTEMS OF MORE THAN TWO LINEAR EQUATIONS

An extension of this method can be used to solve a system of more than two linear equations. For example, assume that the system contains three linear equations in three unknowns:

$$4x + 6y - 3z = 16$$
$$2x - 8y + 7z = 22$$
$$-x + 3y + \quad z = 5$$

To solve this system of equations for x, y, and z, we first treat two of the equations, say the first and the second, to eliminate one variable. To eliminate x, we multiply the members of the second equation by 2:

$$4x + \quad 6y - \quad 3z = 16$$
$$4x - 16y + 14z = 44$$

Subtracting the first from the second leaves one equation in two unknowns:

$$-22y + 17z = 28$$

Next we treat the second and third equations together, and multiply the members of the third equation by 2 to eliminate x, thus:

$$2x - 8y + 7z = 22$$
$$-2x + 6y + 2z = 10$$

Adding these equations, we obtain

$$-2y + 9z = 32$$

We now have two equations in two unknowns, y and z:

$$-22y + 17z = 28$$
$$- 2y + 9z = 32$$

By repeating the same process, y can be eliminated from these two equations. Multiply the second equation by 11 and subtract the first from the second, which yields:

$$82z = 324$$
$$z = 3.95 \text{ carried out to two decimal places.}$$

To obtain the value for y, we now substitute this value for z into one of the two equations in two unknowns. Suppose that we choose the first of these:

$$-22y + 17(3.95) = 28$$
$$y = 1.78$$

We now know y, also, to two decimal places. Of course, to complete the solution, we must substitute these values for y and z in any one of the three original equations in three unknowns. Let us make the substitution in the first of the three:

$$4x + 6(1.78) - 3(3.95) = 16$$
$$4x = 17.17$$
$$x = 4.29$$

The solution for the system of three equations is $x = 4.29$, $y = 1.78$, and $z = 3.95$. This solution for the system can be checked by substituting the values found for x, y, and z in the original three equations. The solution will satisfy the equations only approximately because we have solved for the unknowns to only two decimal places.

We can generalize this solution procedure to a system of n linear equations in n unknowns. Except for the rare occurrence when one equation is essentially a restatement of one or more of the other equations, such a system has a solution. The system of n equations is reduced to a system of $n - 1$ equations in $n - 1$ unknowns by eliminating one of the original n variables, that is, by combining the n equations two by two and adding or subtracting after multiplying them by suitable constants.

The new system can be treated in the same way. Combine the $n - 1$ linear equations two by two after multiplying by appropriate constants. This leaves a system of $n - 2$ linear equations in $n - 2$

unknowns. The process can be repeated until we have left one linear equation in one unknown. This equation can be solved by simple algebra to yield the value of that one unknown. Using one of the two equations in the system of two equations in two unknowns, we derive the value of another unknown. The third unknown is found from an equation in the system of three equations in three unknowns, and so forth until all of the n unknowns have been determined. The complete system can be checked by substitution into the n equations of the original system.

C. SYSTEMS INVOLVING QUADRATIC EQUATIONS

A quadratic equation is an equation of second degree. Suppose that our system of two equations involves a quadratic equation and a linear equation:

$$x^2 - 2y = 2$$
$$x + 3y = 1$$

We eliminate y by multiplying the first equation by 3 and the second equation by 2 and obtain:

$$3x^2 - 6y = 6$$
$$2x + 6y = 2$$

Adding the first to the second equation results in a quadratic equation in one unknown:

$$3x^2 + 2x = 8$$

It is demonstrated in algebra textbooks that the general quadratic equation $ax^2 + bx + c = 0$ has the solution:

$$x = \frac{-b \pm \sqrt{b^2 - 4ac}}{2a}$$

Rewriting our quadratic equation in this form,

$$3x^2 + 2x - 8 = 0$$

we obtain the following *two* solutions for x by letting $a = 3$, $b = 2$, and $c = -8$:

$$x = \tfrac{4}{3} \quad \text{and} \quad x = -2$$

Inserting each of these values of x in either one of the two original equations, we can solve for the two values of y. These turn out to be $y = -\tfrac{1}{9}$ for $x = \tfrac{4}{3}$, and $y = 1$ for $x = -2$. The student should perform this operation as an exercise.

It is not necessary that one of the equations be linear. For example, a pair of solutions exists for the following system of two quadratic equations:

$$x^2 + y^2 + 4x - 6y - 10 = 0$$
$$x^2 + y^2 + 2x + 2y - 4 = 0$$

These equations can be solved most easily by subtracting the second from the first to obtain the linear equation:

$$2x - 8y - 6 = 0$$

One can then solve this linear equation for one unknown in terms of the other. Let us solve it for x; then

$$x = 4y + 3$$

We next substitute this linear expression in one of the two original equations. By substituting into the second so that

$$(4y + 3)^2 + y^2 + 2(4y + 3) + 2y - 4 = 0$$

and expanding and simplifiying, the problem is reduced to the solution of a quadratic equation in one unknown:

$$17y^2 + 34y + 11 = 0$$

The solution for this type of equation has been explained in the previous illustration. It yields the following two solutions for y to three decimal places:

$$y = -1.594 \quad \text{and} \quad y = -.406$$

Since these values must satisfy our linear equation, we merely substitute $y = -1.594$ and $y = -.406$ in the linear equation $x = 4y + 3$. This substitution gives

$$x = -3.376 \quad \text{and} \quad x = 1.376$$

as the corresponding solutions for x.

The solutions for systems of three or more quadratic equations, if there is a solution, can be accomplished by an extension of these methods. It should be emphasized that we have no guarantee that in all cases a solution exists. This is true whether we are dealing with linear or nonlinear equations. In this text we will treat only that very large class of cases in which solutions do exist.

D. GRAPHIC INTERPRETATION OF THE SOLUTIONS

We have seen in Chapter 2 that each function has a graph which corresponds to it. We shall now demonstrate that the solution of a system of equations also has a geometric counterpart. Let us first take the system of two linear equations that were solved in Section A of this chapter:

$$4x + 6y = 16$$
$$2x + y = 2$$

Each of these expresses an implicit function involving x and y. We may write them explicitly as:

$$y = f(x) = \tfrac{8}{3} - \tfrac{2}{3}x$$

and

$$y = g(x) = 2 - 2x$$

We saw in Section A that the solution of this system is $x = -\tfrac{1}{2}$ and $y = 3$. If we construct a table and plot the graphs of these two functions, as in Figure 4.1, we see that they intersect at the point $(-\tfrac{1}{2}, 3)$, which is the solution to the system derived analytically.

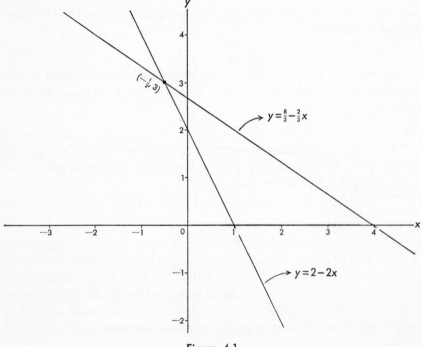

Figure 4.1

The solution of a system of two linear equations yields the point at which the two straight lines, corresponding to the two equations, intersect. It is only at this point that the values of x and y will satisfy both equations. Therefore, we can readily see that when the two straight lines are parallel, there will be no solution to the system of equations.

To illustrate the geometric interpretation of a pair of solutions, let us consider the system solved in Section C:

$$x^2 - 2y = 2$$
$$x + 3y = 1$$

We write these as the explicit functions:

$$y = -1 + \tfrac{1}{2}x^2$$
$$y = \tfrac{1}{3} - \tfrac{1}{3}x$$

We can construct two tables, each showing the values of y corresponding to chosen values of x. The graphs of these two functions are depicted in Figure 4.2. Note that they intersect at the points $(\tfrac{4}{3}, -\tfrac{1}{9})$ and $(-2, 1)$. These two pairs of values were seen to be the two solutions for this system of equations in Section C.

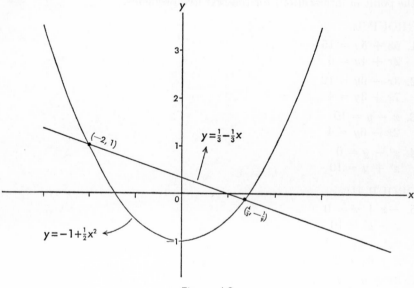

Figure 4.2

Again we can see from this figure the geometric interpretation of a system of two equations which does not have a solution. If the straight line were shifted downward sufficiently, parallel to its present position, there would be no point at which it would intersect the parabola. For instance, if the equation for the linear function were $y = -2 - \tfrac{1}{3}x$, there would be no solution for this system. No point common to both curves and no values of the variables common to both equations would exist.

For the system of three equations in three unknowns, which has a unique solution, the geometric interpretation is similar. Three surfaces intersect at one point in three-dimensional space. The point at which the three surfaces intersect corresponds to the set of values of the three variables derived by solving the three equations simultaneously. Likewise, for a system of n equations in n unknowns the set of n or more values of the variables is interpreted as one or more points in n-dimensional space.

PROBLEMS

Solve the following systems of equations and check your answers. Give a graphic interpretation of the solution (plot the curves or lines and show the point of intersection) for the first five problems.

GROUP I:

1. $5x + 5y = 15$
   $2x + 4y = 6$

2. $3x - 9y = 12$
   $7x + 3y = 4$

3. $x - y = 10$
   $2x - 6y = 4$

4. $x^2 - y = 0$
   $x^2 + y = 10$

GROUP II:

5. $-x + y^2 = 0$
   $x - y^2 = 10$

6. $2x^2 - 4y = 4$
   $x + 6y = 2$

7. $3x + y + z = 6$
   $x - 4y - 2z = 8$
   $-x + 3y + 4z = 3$

8. $x + y + z = 1$
   $-x - \frac{1}{2}y - \frac{2}{3}z = 4$
   $2x + 2y - z = 5$

9. $4x^2 + y^2 + 6x - 4y = 15$
   $4x^2 + y^2 - 2x + 4y = -1$

CHAPTER 5

Economic Applications of Systems of Equations

Intuitively it can be seen that the solution of a system of equations corresponds to what is meant by equilibrium in economics. The intersection of a demand curve and a supply curve gives the equilibrium price of a commodity and the quantity exchanged on the market. Since the intersection of two curves yields the values of two unknowns in two equations, the geometric presentation of economic theory can be converted into an analytic presentation. In place of demand and supply curves one has demand and supply equations. And in place of the intersection point one has the values of price and quantity that satisfy both equations simultaneously. In the present chapter we shall show by several examples how economic theory can be expressed in terms of systems of simultaneous equations.

A. MARKET EQUILIBRIUM FOR ONE COMMODITY

Assume that the market demand schedule for a commodity is known and can be described by the equation $q_d = 2,000 - 100p$, where q_d is the quantity demanded (measured in thousands of pounds) and p is the price (measured in cents per pound). Furthermore, assume that the supply schedule is also known and that it is described by the equation $q_s = -100 + 50p$, where q_s is the quantity supplied (also measured in thousands of pounds). What we have, therefore, is a system of two linear equations in two unknowns, quantity and price. Since the demand equation indicates that the slope of the demand function is negative (the price coefficient is negative) and the supply equation indicates that the slope of the supply function is positive, this system will have a solution.

The condition for market equilibrium is that the quantity demanded equal the quantity supplied. Consequently, we set $q_d = q_s$, which results in one equation in one unknown, p. The solution of this equation is the equilibrium price.

$$2,000 - 100p = -100 + 50p$$
$$150p = 2,100$$
$$p = 14$$

Since this equilibrium price must satisfy both the demand and supply equations, substitution of this value of p in either the demand or the supply equation gives us the quantity traded on the market. Let us substitute in the demand equation:

$$q_d = 2,000 - 100(14) = 600$$

Therefore, we predict that the equilibrium quantity of 600 thousand pounds is supplied and demanded at the equilibrium price of 14 cents per pound. We derive this prediction from knowledge of the two functions. It will be a valuable exercise for the student to plot the demand curve given by the demand equation and the supply curve given by the supply equation in the same diagram. It will be seen that the intersection of these curves occurs at the point $p = 14$, $q = 600$.

B. MARKET EQUILIBRIUM FOR SEVERAL COMMODITIES

Frequently the demand for a commodity depends not only on the price of that particular commodity but also on the prices of other related commodities. The effect of the price of oleomargarine on the demand for butter is a classic example. In general, when treating the demand for a commodity that has close substitutes or complements in consumption, one ought to take into account the effects of the prices of these substitutes and/or complements.

Sometimes the quantity of a commodity supplied is also influenced by the prices of other commodities. Dairy products manufactured from whole milk are substitutes in production. Whole milk may be used by the same firm to produce fluid milk; butter; and nonfat, dry milk solids. Consequently the price of butter, as well as the price of fluid milk, will likely influence the amount of fluid milk supplied.

In such cases the condition for equilibrium in the market is: For all commodities the quantity supplied is equal to the quantity demanded. With the aid of this condition we can determine the equilibrium prices and quantities exchanged of all commodities being studied.

Suppose that there are two commodities whose demand and supply functions are interrelated. Denote by P_x the price of commodity X and by P_y the price of commodity Y. Let D_x and D_y be the quantities demanded of X and Y respectively; let S_x and S_y be the quantities supplied. The demand functions for X and Y are given as

$$D_x = 26 - P_x + P_y$$
$$D_y = 8 + P_x - P_y$$

The respective supply functions are:

$$S_x = -4 + 3P_x - P_y$$
$$S_y = -2 - P_x + 5P_y$$

By setting $D_x = S_x$ and $D_y = S_y$, we get two linear equations in P_x and P_y:

$$4P_x - 2P_y = 30$$
$$-2P_x + 6P_y = 10$$

Solving this system of equations by the method shown in the preceding chapter, we find the equilibrium prices $P_x = 10$ and $P_y = 5$. By substituting these equilibrium prices in the original demand or supply equations, we compute $D_x = S_x = 21$ and $D_y = S_y = 13$.

If we had information about the demand and supply functions for every commodity in the economy, we could compute the so-called Walrasian general equilibrium. For n commodities we would have n demand functions and n supply functions. By combining the equations two by two and successively eliminating variables, the equilibrium prices and quantities traded of each of the n commodities could be determined.

C. THE EFFECTS OF CHANGES IN PARAMETERS

We saw in Chapter 2 that every economic relationship or function has parameters—magnitudes that are held constant for any given function and which cause the whole function to change for any change in their values. For example, for any given demand function relating the quantity demanded to the price of the commodity, income of consumers, prices of other commodities, etc. are parameters. For any given supply function relating quantity supplied to the price of the commodity, the prices of factor inputs, technological coefficients, the prices of other commodities, etc. are parameters. Many times we are interested in what will happen to certain economic magnitudes when there are changes in the values of the parameters.

Let us suppose that a demand function is given by the equation:

$$q_d = \frac{100}{p} + .5y$$

where q_d is the quantity demanded, p is the price of the commodity, and y is consumer income. For income assumed to be known and equal to 200 (appropriately defined units), the demand function may be written:

$$q_d = 100 + \frac{100}{p}$$

Let us further suppose that the supply function is given by the equation

$$q_s = 40 + 16p$$

where q_s is the quantity supplied. We solve this system of equations by first setting $q_d = q_s$:

$$40 + 16p = 100 + \frac{100}{p}$$

To solve this equation for p, multiply both sides of the equation by p and combine terms to obtain a quadratic equation in one unknown:

$$16p^2 - 60p - 100 = 0$$

Using the methods outlined in Chapter 4 for the solution of quadratic equations, we find the pair of solutions for this equation is $p = 5$ and $p = -1.25$. Since it is impossible to have negative prices in practice, we reject the second solution. Substitution of the equilibrium price, $p = 5$, in either the demand or supply equation yields the equilibrium quantity exchanged, $q_d = q_s = 120$. We now have the equilibrium; it is shown in Figure 5.1.

Now let us see what happens when a parameter of the demand function changes. Suppose that consumer income increases from 200 to 300. Then the demand curve will shift to the right, and the new system of two equations is:

$$q_d = 150 + \frac{100}{p}$$
$$q_s = 40 + 16p$$

Solving this system in the same way (the student should do this as an exercise) we arrive at the new equilibrium values: $p = 7.69$, exact to two decimal places, and $q_d = q_s = 163$, rounded to whole numbers. The new demand curve is shown as $D'D'$ in Figure 5.1.

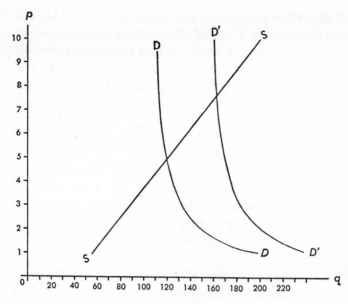

Figure 5.1

Exactly the same sort of argument applies to other functions in economic theory. For example, a change in the prices of factor inputs or in the technological conditions of production would cause a shift in the cost curves of the producing firms, and consequently in the market supply curve. When the supply curve shifts, it intersects the demand curve at a new point—a new equilibrium is achieved.

D. NATIONAL INCOME EQUILIBRIUM

The examples we have used so far have all been in the area of price theory. Let us now discuss an example drawn from national income analysis. It is a familiar proposition that total consumption of goods and services for the economy as a whole is an increasing function of national income. The definition, total consumption plus total investment equals national income, is also familiar. We shall combine these two propositions with a third, namely that investment is a known constant, in order to derive the equilibrium national income for the economy.

We have a system of three equations in three unknowns:

$$C = 10 + .6Y$$
$$I = 30$$
$$Y = C + I$$

where C denotes consumption as a linear function of income Y, and I denotes investment. Each of these might be measured in billions of dollars. In this theory we have two statements describing economic behavior. The first states that consumption is a given increasing linear function of income, and the second states that investment is a known constant. The third equation is the definition of equilibrium and serves the same purpose as the statement, "The quantity demanded equals the quantity supplied," in our previous examples.

In order to solve this system of equations, we substitute the first and the second in the third. This results in a linear equation in one unknown, Y. We proceed to solve this equation as follows:

$$Y = 10 + .6Y + 30$$
$$(1 - .6)\ Y = 40$$
$$Y = 100$$

With the equilibrium value of Y known, the equilibrium value of C can be determined by merely substituting this value of Y in the first equation of the original system. This yields $C = 70$. Of course, the equilibrium value of I is already known to be 30.

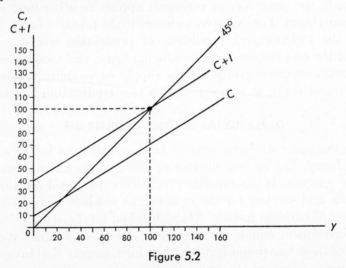

Figure 5.2

The graphic presentation of this solution is shown in Figure 5.2. The equilibrium value of income is determined at that point where the curve labeled $C + I$ intersects the 45-degree line. A 45-degree line bisects a two-dimensional space in such a way that at every point on the line the value of the variable on the horizontal axis is exactly equal to the value of the variable on the vertical axis. In elementary national income analysis it is shown that the 45-degree line out of the origin is a very useful device. It does not describe the behavior of consumers or investors, but it is convenient for depicting the solution geometrically.

A careful examination of the line reveals that when the value on the vertical axis corresponding to a point is 20, the value on the horizontal axis corresponding to the same point on the line is also 20. The same is true for all other values on the axes corresponding to points on the 45-degree line. Notice that the $C + I$ curve cuts the 45-degree line when $C + I$, measured on the vertical axis, is 100. It follows that Y, measured on the horizontal axis, must also be 100. Hence, when the $C + I$ curve intersects the 45-degree line, at that point and only at that point the equilibrium equation, $C + I = Y$, is satisfied. At all other points in the diagram the equation is not satisfied, which is to say the other points are not equilibrium points.

Notice that the method used to arrive at the equilibrium solution is essentially the same as that used to arrive at the equilibrium solution in problems of price theory. Once the equilibrium is defined by an equation, the problem reduces to one of simultaneously solving the equations in the system. The solution of the simultaneous equations yields the equilibrium values of the variables that the theory seeks to predict. Corresponding to this analytical solution is the geometric solution, visualized by the intersection of the curves plotted from the equations. The simultaneous solution of the equations gives the values of the variables that correspond to the point of intersection. This is true regardless of the area of economic theory with which we may be concerned.

The solution of a demand equation and a supply equation analytically is tantamount to finding the point of intersection of the demand curve and the supply curve. The simultaneous solution of two equations, one of which describes the marginal cost of the firm as a function of output and the other describes the marginal revenue of the firm as a function of output, gives the equilibrium output of the firm. This equilibrium output is that output at which the marginal cost and marginal revenue curves intersect.

Our example from national income theory follows the same procedure. When the equilibrium equation, $C + I = Y$, is satisfied, the $C + I$ curve intersects the 45-degree line, so that $C + I$ must equal Y. Other examples from all areas of economic theory could be illustrated. Only the substance of the theory changes from one application to another. The method for finding the equilibrium values of the variables remains the same.

PROBLEMS

GROUP I:

1. Let q denote the quantity of a commodity demanded or supplied and p its price. Find the equilibrium price and quantity traded for each of the following demand and supply functions. Give a graphic interpretation of the solution.

   (a) $q = 100 - 20p$ (demand equation)
        $q = -5 + 15p$ (supply equation)
   (b) $800 - 2q - 20p = 0$ (demand equation)
        $5q - 50 - 200p = 0$ (supply equation)
   (c) $q = 1,000 - p^2$ (demand equation)
        $q = 30p$ (supply equation)
   (d) $q = 20 - p$ (demand equation)
        $p = .10q^2$ (supply equation)

   NOTE: Solve for q first.

2. Let the aggregate consumption function for the United States be given as:

$$C = 100 + .5Y$$

where C and Y denote consumption and income respectively in billions of dollars per year. Aggregate investment is known to equal \$20 billion:

$$I = 20$$

   (a) Find the equilibrium national income.
   (b) Show the equilibrium graphically.

3. Assume United States aggregate consumption and investment are both functions of national income. They are given as

$$C = 100 + .5Y$$
$$I = 10 + .1Y$$

   (a) Find the equilibrium level of national income.
   (b) Show the equilibrium graphically.

4. Let D_x and S_x represent the quantities demanded and supplied respectively of the commodity X. Let D_y and S_y denote the quantites demanded and supplied of the commodity Y. Let p_x and p_y denote the prices of X and Y respectively. The demand and supply functions for the two commodities are interrelated:

$$D_x = 100 - 10p_x - 20p_y$$
$$S_x = -30 + 10p_x + 10p_y$$
$$D_y = 60 - 10p_x - 10p_y$$
$$S_y = -20 + 10p_y$$

(a) Find the equilibrium prices of X and Y.

(b) Find the equilibrium quantities exchanged.

5. Let the consumption for the United States be given as

$$C = 60 + .5Y + .1A$$

where C denotes consumption, Y income, and A the liquid asset holdings of households, all measured in billions of dollars. Let investment in billions of dollars as a function of income be given as:

$$I = 10 + .1Y$$

Assume asset holdings equal \$300 billion.

(a) Find the equilibrium level of national income. Show it graphically.

(b) Assume asset holdings increase to \$400 billion. Find the new equilibrium national income and illustrate it on the same diagram.

GROUP II:

6. Find the new equilibrium prices and quantities traded if the following changes in parameters occur. Show the new equilibriums graphically.

(a) In problem 1 (a) the demand increases and the new demand equation is given as: $q = 155 - 25p$

(b) In problem 1 (c) the supply increases and the new supply equation is given as: $q = 40p + 500$

(c) In problem 1 (d) the demand decreases and the new demand equation is given as: $q = 10 - p$

the supply decreases also and the new supply equation is given as:

$$p = .05q^2$$

7. The demand and supply functions for three commodities are interrelated. Let the symbols have the same meaning as in Question 2. The equations are given as:

$$D_x = 21 - 5p_x + 3p_y - 3p_z$$
$$S_x = 3 + p_x$$
$$D_y = 12 + 3p_x - 6p_y + 3p_z$$
$$S_y = 15 + 6p_y$$
$$D_z = 64 - 3p_x - 3p_y - 9p_z$$
$$S_z = 10 + 6p_z$$

Find the equilibrium prices and equilibrium quantities exchanged for all three commodities.

CHAPTER 6

Determinants and Matrices

In this chapter we will present some elementary mathematical ideas that will prove valuable in understanding econometric theories. The solution of a system of linear equations can be accomplished by combining the equations two by two and by successively eliminating variables. This method was explained in Chapters 4 and 5. Determinants can be viewed as an alternative way to solve a system of linear equations. They serve, however, an additional purpose. It was pointed out in the Introduction that econometric theories are formulated with statistical analysis in mind. We shall see in Chapter 23 that determinants are useful for stipulating the conditions under which a theory is amenable to statistical measurement and testing. In addition, knowledge of determinants is helpful in the modern treatment of statistical problems proper.

We shall also discuss the formulation of a system of equations in matrix notation. Matrix notation is frequently used as a convenient way to express a system of equations in short form. Although the operations of matrix algebra are beyond the scope of this book, a method for the solution of a system of equations in matrix form will be presented.

A. SECOND-ORDER DETERMINANTS

As our first example, in Chapter 4 we solved the following system of two linear equations in two unknowns:

$$4x + 6y = 16$$
$$2x + \ y = \ 2$$

By the process of elimination, the values of x and y that satisfy both equations were found as follows. We first solved for y. To obtain the value of y, we multiplied the second equation by 2 and subtracted the second equation from the first (see Chapter 4). This eliminated x and yielded the value of y. Then this value of y was substituted in either of the two original equations to find x. The solution turned out to be:

$$x = -\tfrac{1}{2} \quad \text{and} \quad y = 3$$

We shall now demonstrate that this solution can be obtained by the use of determinants. The procedure employed is called the solution by determinants. A *second-order determinant* is a square array of elements consisting of two rows (horizontal) and two columns (vertical). We define the second order determinant

$$\begin{vmatrix} q & r \\ s & t \end{vmatrix}$$

as having the value $qt - sr$. The solution of our system of two linear equations can be written

$$x = \frac{\begin{vmatrix} 16 & 6 \\ 2 & 1 \end{vmatrix}}{\begin{vmatrix} 4 & 6 \\ 2 & 1 \end{vmatrix}} \quad \text{and} \quad y = \frac{\begin{vmatrix} 4 & 16 \\ 2 & 2 \end{vmatrix}}{\begin{vmatrix} 4 & 6 \\ 2 & 1 \end{vmatrix}}$$

Notice that the elements of the determinant in both denominators are the coefficients of x and y in the original two equations. The values of x and y differ only by the determinant that appears in the numerator of each. Looking first at x, we see that the determinant in the numerator is obtained by substituting for the coefficients of x (4 and 2) the constants on the right side of the equations (16 and 2). For y, the constants 16 and 2 are substituted for the coefficients of y (6 and 1) in the numerator. Next, we shall compute the actual values of x and y. We have seen that the value of a second-order determinant is found by multiplying the element in the upper left-hand corner by the element in the lower right-hand corner and by subtracting from this product the product of the element in the lower left-hand corner multiplied by the element in the upper right-hand corner. Therefore, the solution of the system of equations by determinants is:

$$x = \frac{\begin{vmatrix} 16 & 6 \\ 2 & 1 \end{vmatrix}}{\begin{vmatrix} 4 & 6 \\ 2 & 1 \end{vmatrix}} = \frac{(16 \cdot 1 - 2 \cdot 6)}{(4 \cdot 1 - 2 \cdot 6)} = -\tfrac{1}{2}$$

$$y = \frac{\begin{vmatrix} 4 & 16 \\ 2 & 2 \end{vmatrix}}{\begin{vmatrix} 4 & 6 \\ 2 & 1 \end{vmatrix}} = \frac{(4 \cdot 2 - 2 \cdot 16)}{(4 \cdot 1 - 2 \cdot 6)} = 3$$

We can generalize this solution by determinants for the general system of any two linear equations in two unknowns

$$ax + by = m$$
$$cx + dy = n$$

where a, b, c, d, m, and n are constants. The determinants for the values of x and y are immediately seen to be

$$x = \frac{\begin{vmatrix} m & b \\ n & d \end{vmatrix}}{\begin{vmatrix} a & b \\ c & d \end{vmatrix}} \quad \text{and} \quad y = \frac{\begin{vmatrix} a & m \\ c & n \end{vmatrix}}{\begin{vmatrix} a & b \\ c & d \end{vmatrix}}$$

We derive the solution without eliminating variables by finding the values of the determinants:

$$x = \frac{(md - nb)}{(ad - cb)} \quad \text{and} \quad y = \frac{(an - cm)}{(ad - cb)}$$

B. THIRD-ORDER DETERMINANTS

A third-order determinant has three rows and three columns. In general form it has the following appearance:

$$\begin{vmatrix} a_1 & a_2 & a_3 \\ b_1 & b_2 & b_3 \\ c_1 & c_2 & c_3 \end{vmatrix}$$

It is convenient to use subscripts on the letters in this case, rather than different letters, to denote different numbers. We find the value of this determinant by a process known as *expansion* in terms of the elements of a row or a column. The *minor* of any element is the second-order determinant obtained by striking out the row and the column that contain the particular element. The portion of the original determinant which then remains constitutes the minor.

Suppose we wish to expand the third-order determinant given above in terms of the elements in the first column, that is, in terms of a_1, b_1, c_1. To get the minor of a_1, we strike the first column and row:

$$\begin{array}{ccc} \cancel{a_1} & a_2 & a_3 \\ \cancel{b_1} & b_2 & b_3 \\ \cancel{c_1} & c_2 & c_3 \end{array}$$

We have as the minor of a_1 the second-order determinant:

$$\begin{vmatrix} b_2 & b_3 \\ c_2 & c_3 \end{vmatrix}$$

The minor of the element b_1 is obtained by striking out the first column and the second row, which gives:

$$\begin{vmatrix} a_2 & a_3 \\ c_2 & c_3 \end{vmatrix}$$

Likewise, to get the minor of c_1, we strike out the first column and third row. This yields the second-order determinant:

$$\begin{vmatrix} a_2 & a_3 \\ b_2 & b_3 \end{vmatrix}$$

We now have the minors of each of the elements in the first column. The value of the original determinant is given by:

$$\begin{vmatrix} a_1 & a_2 & a_3 \\ b_1 & b_2 & b_3 \\ c_1 & c_2 & c_3 \end{vmatrix} = a_1 \begin{vmatrix} b_2 & b_3 \\ c_2 & c_3 \end{vmatrix} - b_1 \begin{vmatrix} a_2 & a_3 \\ c_2 & c_3 \end{vmatrix} + c_1 \begin{vmatrix} a_2 & a_3 \\ b_2 & b_3 \end{vmatrix}$$

That is, each element in the first column is multiplied by its minor. Note carefully the alternating signs in the development by minors.

Next the values of the second-order determinants are obtained by the procedure outlined in the preceding section. The complete expansion is

$$a_1(b_2c_3 - c_2b_3) - b_1(a_2c_3 - c_2a_3) + c_1(a_2b_3 - b_2a_3)$$

Once the method for deriving the value of a third-order determinant is known, it can be used to solve a system of three linear equations in three unknowns, say x, y, and z. The procedure is like that used to solve two linear equations in two unknowns. Each unknown is set equal to one determinant divided by another, and the denominator determinant is the same for all three unknowns. To get the denominator, form the determinant of the coefficients of the unknowns in the equations. To find the value of x, form the numerator determinant by replacing the coefficients of x in the denominator determinant by the constants on the right side of the equations. To find y, replace the coefficients of y in the denominator determinant by these three constants on the right side of the equations. To find the value of z, proceed in a similar fashion: replace the coefficients of z in the denominator determinant by the three constants. We then have each of the three unknowns equal to the ratio of one third-order determinant to another. Third-order determinants are usually developed by minors.

Let us solve the following system of equations by determinants:

$$2x + y - z = 3$$
$$x + 4y + 2z = 10$$
$$-2y - 3z = 5$$

The three unknowns will each have the same denominator determinant. It is formed from the coefficients of the equation as follows:

$$\begin{vmatrix} 2 & 1 & -1 \\ 1 & 4 & 2 \\ 0 & -2 & -3 \end{vmatrix}$$

To find the value of x, replace the column of the coefficients of x (the first column) by the column of the three constants on the right side of the equations—this gives the numerator determinant. Thus

$$x = \frac{\begin{vmatrix} 3 & 1 & -1 \\ 10 & 4 & 2 \\ 5 & -2 & -3 \end{vmatrix}}{\begin{vmatrix} 2 & 1 & -1 \\ 1 & 4 & 2 \\ 0 & -2 & -3 \end{vmatrix}}$$

Similarly the values of y and z are given by:

$$y = \frac{\begin{vmatrix} 2 & 3 & -1 \\ 1 & 10 & 2 \\ 0 & 5 & -3 \end{vmatrix}}{\begin{vmatrix} 2 & 1 & -1 \\ 1 & 4 & 2 \\ 0 & -2 & -3 \end{vmatrix}} \quad \text{and} \quad z = \frac{\begin{vmatrix} 2 & 1 & 3 \\ 1 & 4 & 10 \\ 0 & -2 & 5 \end{vmatrix}}{\begin{vmatrix} 2 & 1 & -1 \\ 1 & 4 & 2 \\ 0 & -2 & -3 \end{vmatrix}}$$

Each of these determinants is then expanded in terms of minors. This expansion for x in terms of the elements in the first column yields:

$$x = \frac{3\begin{vmatrix} 4 & 2 \\ -2 & -3 \end{vmatrix} - 10\begin{vmatrix} 1 & -1 \\ -2 & -3 \end{vmatrix} + 5\begin{vmatrix} 1 & -1 \\ 4 & 2 \end{vmatrix}}{2\begin{vmatrix} 4 & 2 \\ -2 & -3 \end{vmatrix} - 1\begin{vmatrix} 1 & -1 \\ -2 & -3 \end{vmatrix} + 0\begin{vmatrix} 1 & -1 \\ 4 & 2 \end{vmatrix}}$$

$$= \frac{-24 + 50 + 30}{-16 + 5 + 0} = -\frac{56}{11}$$

By the same type of expansion for y and z, we obtain:

$$y = \frac{76}{11} \quad \text{and} \quad z = -\frac{69}{11}$$

The solution can be checked by substitution in the original equations.

Expansion of a third-order determinant has been carried out here in terms of the elements in the first column of the determinant. But the expansion could be carried out in terms of any row or column. The solution would not be changed thereby. In our illustration we could have expanded the determinant in terms of the second or third column—or any one of the three rows. It can be shown that any one of these alternative procedures would give identically the same expression for the completed expansion.

One caution must be emphasized. The alternating signs in the expansion have been noted. Each element in the first column was multiplied by its minor with alternating plus and minus signs attached. We started with $+a_1$, then $-b_1$, and finally $+c_1$. Now in consideration of expansion in terms of other rows or columns, the order of sequence of the alternating signs depends on which row or column is used to develop the minors. Using the second row instead of the first column, for example, would have given us a minus, then a plus, and finally a minus.

C. DETERMINANTS OF ORDER n

A general rule can be developed to cover expansion of a third-order determinant by any row or column. Indeed, the rule applies to a determinant of any order and expansion of that determinant in terms of any row or column. Evaluation of second- and third-order determinants are then seen to emerge as special cases of the general rule. As a consequence, the rule can in principle be used as a method for solving any number of equations.

A determinant of order n can be represented as

$$|A| = \begin{vmatrix} a_{11} & a_{12} \cdots a_{1n} \\ a_{21} & a_{22} \cdots a_{2n} \\ \cdot & \cdot \quad\quad \cdot \\ \cdot & \cdot \quad\quad \cdot \\ \cdot & \cdot \quad\quad \cdot \\ a_{n1} & a_{n2} \cdots a_{nn} \end{vmatrix}$$

consisting of n rows and n columns. Each element has two subscripts attached, the first indicating the row and the second indicating the column in which the element appears. The typical element is written

$$a_{ij}, \qquad\qquad \begin{aligned} i &= 1, 2, \ldots, n \\ j &= 1, 2, \ldots, n \end{aligned}$$

That is, i runs from 1 to n and j runs from 1 to n. By proper substitution of values for i and j, a_{ij} can be taken to represent any one of the elements.

In order to expand this general determinant, two concepts must be defined: (1) the complementary minor of an element, and (2) the cofactor of an element.

The *complementary minor* of element a_{ij} is another determinant of order less than n. It is obtained from $|A|$ by striking the ith row and the jth column of $|A|$. We shall denote the complementary minor of element a_{ij} by m_{ij}.

The *cofactor* of element a_{ij} is the complementary minor of a_{ij} multiplied by $(-1)^{i+j}$. Let c_{ij} denote the cofactor of a_{ij}. Then

$$c_{ij} = (-1)^{i+j} m_{ij}$$

Since cofactors will be used in the evaluation of a determinant, an example of a third-order determinant will prove helpful. Let

$$|A| = \begin{vmatrix} a_{11} & a_{12} & a_{13} \\ a_{21} & a_{22} & a_{23} \\ a_{31} & a_{32} & a_{33} \end{vmatrix} = \begin{vmatrix} 1 & 2 & 6 \\ 2 & -4 & 1 \\ 3 & 5 & -2 \end{vmatrix}$$

Then

$$c_{11} = (-1)^{1+1} \begin{vmatrix} -4 & 1 \\ 5 & -2 \end{vmatrix} = (-1)^2 (8 - 5) = 3$$

Also

$$c_{12} = (-1)^{1+2} \begin{vmatrix} 2 & 1 \\ 3 & -2 \end{vmatrix} = (-1)^3 (-4 - 3) = 7$$

and

$$c_{23} = (-1)^{2+3} \begin{vmatrix} 1 & 2 \\ 3 & 5 \end{vmatrix} = (-1)^5 (5 - 6) = 1$$

We are now in a position to find the value of the determinant of order n. To do so we introduce the operator Σ. This Greek letter, sigma, means "the summation of." For instance,

$$\sum_{i=1}^{4} i^2 = (1)^2 + (2)^2 + (3)^2 + (4)^2.$$

The determinant can be expanded according to any given row or any given column, and its value turns out to be the same. For any row i

$$|A| = \sum_{j=1}^{n} a_{ij} c_{ij}$$

Note that for any row chosen, the summation is over the columns. Similarly, for any column j

$$|A| = \sum_{i=1}^{n} a_{ij} c_{ij}.$$

That is, summation is over the rows.

To illustrate, consider the third-order determinant presented above:

$$|A| = \begin{vmatrix} 1 & 2 & 6 \\ 2 & -4 & 1 \\ 3 & 5 & -2 \end{vmatrix}$$

The determinant can be expanded according to any row or column. By expanding $|A|$ according to the second row (i.e., $i = 2$):

$$|A| = \sum_{j=1}^{3} a_{2j} c_{2j} = a_{21} c_{21} + a_{22} c_{22} + a_{23} c_{23}$$

$$= 2c_{21} - 4c_{22} + 1c_{23}$$

$$= 2(-1)^3 \begin{vmatrix} 2 & 6 \\ 5 & -2 \end{vmatrix} - 4(-1)^4 \begin{vmatrix} 1 & 6 \\ 3 & -2 \end{vmatrix} + 1(-1)^5 \begin{vmatrix} 1 & 2 \\ 3 & 5 \end{vmatrix}$$

$$= -2(-4-30) - 4(-2-18) - 1(5-6)$$

$$= 68 + 80 + 1 = 149$$

To show the value of $|A|$ is not altered by expanding according to some other row or column, we expand $|A|$ according to the third column (i.e., $j = 3$):

$$|A| = \sum_{i=1}^{3} a_{i3} c_{i3} = a_{13} c_{13} + a_{23} c_{23} + a_{33} c_{33}$$

$$= 6(-1)^4 \begin{vmatrix} 2 & -4 \\ 3 & 5 \end{vmatrix} + 1(-1)^5 \begin{vmatrix} 1 & 2 \\ 3 & 5 \end{vmatrix} - 2(-1)^6 \begin{vmatrix} 1 & 2 \\ 2 & -4 \end{vmatrix}$$

$$= 6(10+12) - 1(5-6) - 2(-4-4) = 149$$

If the order of a determinant is very large, the formula for $|A|$ will yield other determinants of smaller order, which can in turn be evaluated by successive applications of the rule. For $|A|$ a fifth-order determinant, c_{ij} will involve fourth-order determinants, and each fourth-order determinant is expanded to yield third-order determinants. These in turn are expanded to find second-order determinants until the final formula is reduced to a single number.

The method of evaluating a determinant can be used to solve large systems of equations. Suppose a system of n linear equations in n unknowns is given by

$$a_{11}x_1 + a_{12}x_2 + \cdots + a_{1n}x_n = b_1$$
$$a_{21}x_1 + a_{22}x_2 + \cdots + a_{2n}x_n = b_2$$
$$\dots\dots\dots\dots\dots\dots\dots\dots\dots\dots\dots\dots$$
$$a_{n1}x_1 + a_{n2}x_2 + \cdots + a_{nn}x_n = b_n$$

Each a_{ij} is the known coefficient of the unknown x_j in the ith equation, and each b_i is a known constant in the ith equation. The value of each unknown can be found by an extension of the methods described in connection with second- and third-order determinants.

To find the value of x_1, for example, form the determinant from the coefficients in the n equations. This is the denominator determinant having n columns and n rows. To get the numerator determinant, replace the coefficients of x_1 in the denominator determinant by the n constants on the right side of the equations. Proceed in the same fashion for the other $n - 1$ unknowns. By solving for the values of the determinants, the values of the unknowns are obtained. The properties of determinants of order two or three hold in general for any determinant of order n.

In more general symbolic notation, we wish to find x_j for any j. Let $|A_j|$ denote the determinant obtained by deleting from $|A|$ the jth column of coefficients and replacing them by the constant terms b_i. Then

$$x_j = \frac{|A_j|}{|A|} \qquad\qquad j = 1, 2, \cdots, n$$

can be evaluated to find x_j for all j.

D. ELEMENTS OF MATRICES

1. Matrix Notation

From one viewpoint the symbolic notation of ordinary algebra, like that used in Chapters 4 and 5, is a system of shorthand. The notation of matrices carries this shorthand another step. A general system of n linear equations can be written in terms of one expression rather than n expressions. And just as certain operations are performed in ordinary algebra, similar operations are performed on matrices.

A matrix is simply an array of numbers, usually represented by enclosing the array by brackets. The number of rows and columns determine the size or dimensions of a matrix. For example, the matrix

$$\begin{bmatrix} 2 & 3 & -4 & 2 \\ 8 & -7 & 6 & 9 \\ 4 & 1 & 5 & -3 \end{bmatrix}$$

has the elements 2, 3, −4, etc. There are three rows and four columns, so this matrix is said to be of size 3 by 4.

We deal here only with square matrices, those in which the number of rows equals the number of columns. A matrix is expressed by a single upper-case letter. Thus the $n \times n$ matrix A written

$$A = \begin{bmatrix} a_{11} & a_{12} & \cdots & a_{1n} \\ a_{21} & a_{22} & \cdots & a_{2n} \\ & \cdot & & \cdot \\ & \cdot & & \cdot \\ & \cdot & & \cdot \\ a_{n1} & a_{n2} & & a_{nn} \end{bmatrix}$$

is comprised of the elements a_{ij}, for $i = 1, 2, \ldots , n$ and $j = 1, 2, \ldots , n$.

A special case is that of a matrix consisting of only one row or one column. In such a case the matrix is called a *vector*. Lower case letters without subscripts will be used to signify vectors. Thus

$$b = \begin{bmatrix} b_1 \\ b_2 \\ \cdot \\ \cdot \\ \cdot \\ b_n \end{bmatrix}$$

is an n dimensional *column vector*, while

$$c = [c_1 \, c_2 \, \cdots \, c_n]$$

is an n dimensional *row vector*.

Let us now use this notation to show how a system of linear equations may be conveniently expressed. A system of n linear equations in n unknowns $x_1, x_2, \ldots, x_n$ is written out explicitly as

$$a_{11}x_1 + a_{12}x_2 + \cdots + a_{1n}x_n = b_1$$
$$a_{21}x_1 + a_{22}x_2 + \cdots + a_{2n}x_n = b_2$$
$$\ldots\ldots\ldots\ldots\ldots\ldots\ldots\ldots\ldots$$
$$a_{n1}x_1 + a_{n2}x_2 + \cdots + a_{nn}x_n = b_n$$

Let A be the $n \times n$ matrix of coefficients. These, of course, are known constants, as are the numbers $b_1, b_2, \ldots, b_n$. The unknowns and the constant terms can be expressed as vectors:

$$x = \begin{bmatrix} x_1 \\ x_2 \\ \cdot \\ \cdot \\ \cdot \\ x_n \end{bmatrix} \qquad b = \begin{bmatrix} b_1 \\ b_2 \\ \cdot \\ \cdot \\ \cdot \\ b_n \end{bmatrix}$$

With the aid of these two vectors and the matrix of coefficients, the above system of linear equations is written in matrix notation as

$$Ax = b.$$

2. Solutions of Equations

Methods for solving systems of equations in matrix form are available. Most methods involve several operations of matrix algebra —matrix addition, matrix multiplication, the transpose and inverse of a matrix—all of which are beyond the scope of this book. The interested student can find a discussion of these methods in textbooks on matrices.[1]

We shall treat here only one method of solution that utilizes the determinants already discussed and which has a bearing on later discussions of econometric models in Chapters 23 and 24. It is im-

---

[1] A. C. Aitken, *Determinants and Matrices* (5th ed.; Edinburgh: Oliver & Boyd, Ltd., 1948). R. A. Frazer, W. J. Duncan, and A. R. Collar, *Elementary Matrices* (Cambridge: Cambridge University Press, 1946). R. G. D. Allen, *Mathematical Analysis for Economists* (New York: The Macmillan Co., 1939), pp. 372 ff. W. L. Ferrar, *Algebra* (London: Oxford University Press, 1941).

portant that a distinction be made clear at the outset. A determinant is a value or a number whereas a matrix is only an array of numbers rather than a value. Nevertheless, from a matrix the determinant of that matrix can be formed. For instance, from the matrix A the determinant $|A|$ can be formed and operations performed on the determinant.

When a square matrix yields a determinant whose value is zero, the matrix is said to be *singular*. Given A, if $|A| = 0$, then A is singular. If the determinant is nonvanishing, if $|A| \neq 0$, then A is said to be *nonsingular*. To say that A is singular means that its columns (and rows) are linearly dependent; one column is a linear combination of some other column. The vanishing of the determinant $|A|$ is a criterion for determining whether the system of equations $Ax = b$ has a unique solution. For if A is singular, it can be shown that the system $Ax = b$ *does not* have a unique solution.

Granted that A is nonsingular, the question of a unique solution hinges upon the rank of the matrix A. The rank of a matrix may be regarded as the number of linearly independent columns in the matrix. And determinants can be used to find the rank of a matrix. The rank of a matrix A is equal to the order of the largest nonzero minor of the determinant $|A|$. Given that $|A| \neq 0$, if the rank of A is n, then a unique solution can be found for $Ax = b$.

Let us suppose that the system $Ax = b$ does indeed have a unique solution. Then Cramer's rule, a method of solution, is applicable to

$$Ax = b$$

where A is $n \times n$ and b is not zero. This is the method already described in connection with determinants:

$$x_j = \frac{|A_j|}{|A|} \qquad\qquad j = 1, 2, \cdots, n$$

where $|A_j|$ is the determinant obtained by substituting the column vector b for the column vector of coefficients of x_j in A.

The simple two-equation system

$$2x_1 + 4x_2 = 7$$
$$x_1 - 5x_2 = 12$$

is written in matrix form as

$$\begin{bmatrix} 2 & 4 \\ 1 & -5 \end{bmatrix} \begin{bmatrix} x_1 \\ x_2 \end{bmatrix} = \begin{bmatrix} 7 \\ 12 \end{bmatrix}$$

so that

$$x_1 = \frac{\begin{vmatrix} 7 & 4 \\ 12 & -5 \end{vmatrix}}{\begin{vmatrix} 2 & 4 \\ 1 & -5 \end{vmatrix}} \quad \text{and} \quad x_2 = \frac{\begin{vmatrix} 2 & 7 \\ 1 & 12 \end{vmatrix}}{\begin{vmatrix} 2 & 4 \\ 1 & -5 \end{vmatrix}}$$

PROBLEMS

Solve the following systems of equations by determinants. Check your answers.

1. $x + 3y = 5$
   $2x + y = 1$

2. $2x - 2y = 3$
   $x + y = 4$

3. $4x + 12y = 18$
   $6x - 2y = -1$

4. $-x - y = 3$
   $2x + y = 5$

5. The equations of Problem 1, Chapter 5, parts (a) and (b).
Find the values of the following determinants.

6. $\begin{vmatrix} 1 & 2 & 3 \\ 3 & 2 & 1 \\ 0 & 1 & 2 \end{vmatrix}$

7. $\begin{vmatrix} 1 & 3 & 8 \\ 2 & 1 & -4 \\ 1 & 0 & 1 \end{vmatrix}$

Solve the following systems of equations by determinants. Check your answers.

8. The equations of Problem 8, Chapter 4.

9. $x + 3y - z = 0$
   $3x + 4y - 2z = 10$
   $y + z = -6$

Write the following systems of equations in matrix notation.

10. $5x + 3y = 6$
    $2x - y = 7$

11. $a_{11}x_1 + a_{12}x_2 + a_{13}x_3 + \cdots + a_{1n}x_n = b_1$
$a_{21}x_1 + a_{22}x_2 + a_{23}x_3 + \cdots + a_{2n}x_n = b_2$

$\qquad \cdot \qquad\quad \cdot \qquad\quad \cdot \qquad\quad\quad \cdot \qquad\quad\quad \cdot \qquad\quad\quad \cdot$
$\qquad \cdot \qquad\quad \cdot \qquad\quad \cdot \qquad\quad\quad \cdot \qquad\quad\quad \cdot \qquad\quad\quad \cdot$
$\qquad \cdot \qquad\quad \cdot \qquad\quad \cdot \qquad\quad\quad \cdot \qquad\quad\quad \cdot \qquad\quad\quad \cdot$

$a_{n1}x_1 + a_{n2}x_2 + a_{n3}x_3 + \cdots + a_{nn}x_n = b_n$

PART II

Elements of Calculus.

CHAPTER 7

Limits and Derivatives

In the previous chapters, we have discussed some of the fundamental ideas of mathematics and their application to economics. We are now in a position to attack one of the most important problems of applied mathematics—the problem of the differential calculus. It has already been shown that if y is given as a function of x, the value of y is determined by the value assigned to x. When x and y represent economic variables, the relationship between them can be expressed by a mathematical equation, and the value of one economic variable is determined from knowledge of the other. But since we are also interested in *changes* in the value of y, it is important to devise a systematic method for comparing the changes in y with those in x. Such a method will permit us to measure the rate at which y changes whenever x changes. For example, in economics it is extremely valuable to have a measure of the rate at which the quantity of a commodity demanded changes in response to a change in the price of the commodity. It is also very useful to know the rate at which the total costs of a firm change when output changes, or the rate at which total United States consumption changes in response to a change in national income.

In the differential calculus, we define precisely what is meant by the rate of increase or decrease of a function. By introducing convenient symbols, we spell out a technique for evaluating these rates of change for various functions. In Part II we shall present the laws of differentiation and their applications to economics. Exact mathematical definitions and rigorous proofs are beyond the scope of the book, and intuitive explanations will be used whenever required. The interested student can find exact definitions and proofs of the theorems in any textbook on the calculus.

A. TANGENTS

In Chapter 2, we saw that the slope of a straight line is the rate of vertical rise or fall in the line for any given horizontal movement. The line through the points (x_1, y_1) and (x_2, y_2) has the slope m, where

$$m = \frac{y_2 - y_1}{x_2 - x_1}$$

assuming x_2 is not equal to x_1 (to express this symbolically we write $x_2 \neq x_1$). The equation of the line was seen to be

$$y - y_1 = m(x - x_1)$$

and the geometric interpretation is presented in Figure 7.1. We let the symbol Δy represent the finite change in y. Hence, $\Delta y = y_2 - y_1$. To denote the finite change in x, $x_2 - x_1$, the symbol Δx is used.

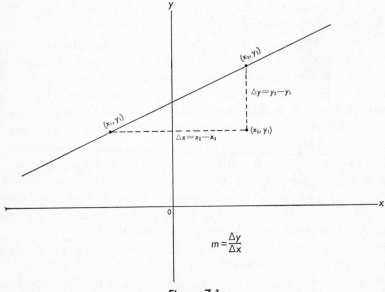

Figure 7.1

Any two points on a straight line can be chosen to measure the slope of the line. Regardless of which segment of the line is used and regardless of how close together or how far apart the two points are, the numerical value of the slope is the same. This is merely another way of saying that the slope of a line is identically the same at every point on the line. But this is not true for a *curve* in contrast to a straight line. Its rate of rise or fall is not the same at all points on the curve. The curve may be rising over one segment and falling over another. Even if it is rising over all segments, it need not rise at the same rate. One can see this immediately by referring to Figures 2.6 through 2.9 in Chapter 2. Consequently, we need a measure of the rate of change which occurs at different points on a curve. In order to arrive at this measure, we shall find it helpful to examine first the so-called *tangent* to a curve.

Since a parabola, similar in form to that depicted in Figure 2.6, is one type of curve, it will serve to illustrate the meaning of tangency. On the parabola having the equation $y = x^2$, consider the two points having abscissas 2 and 4. It is apparent from the equation that the values of y corresponding to these two values of x are 4 and 16 respectively. Therefore, the two points are (2, 4) and (4, 16). Next, let us consider a straight line which connects these two points on the parabola. From the above definition of a slope, it is seen that the line through these two points has a slope given by

$$m = \frac{\Delta y}{\Delta x} = \frac{16 - 4}{4 - 2} = \frac{12}{2} = 6$$

Furthermore, the equation of the line passing through these two points is

$$y - 4 = 6(x - 2)$$

Simplifying this equation, we get

$$y = -8 + 6x$$

Now let us choose another point on the parabola to connect with the point (2, 4). The point (4, 16) lies a certain distance from (2, 4). We shall choose as our next point one that lies closer to (2, 4). Suppose we let this point be (3, 9). A line passing through these two points has slope and equation given by

$$m = \frac{\Delta y}{\Delta x} = \frac{9 - 4}{3 - 2} = \frac{5}{1} = 5$$

and

$$y = -6 + 5x$$

In this illustration, we first chose two points on the parabola and determined the slope and equation of a line that connects the points. These points were (2, 4) and (4, 16). We then chose another point on the parabola to join with the point (2, 4); that point was (3, 9) which lies closer to the point (2, 4). This second set of points determined a line with a different equation and a different slope.

The geometric interpretation of this procedure is presented in Figure 7.2. The broken lines in the figure illustrate the straight lines obtained by joining sets of points. For the moment we shall ignore the unbroken straight line. When the point (2, 4) is joined to the point (4, 16) on the parabola, the line with equation $y = -8 + 6x$ emerges. Then by choosing a point closer to our starting point, namely the point (3, 9) on the parabola, the line with equation $y = -6 + 5x$ is obtained.

Suppose we were to continue this process. We would choose a third point on the parabola to join with (2, 4), and we would choose it so that it is situated even closer to (2, 4). It might be the point

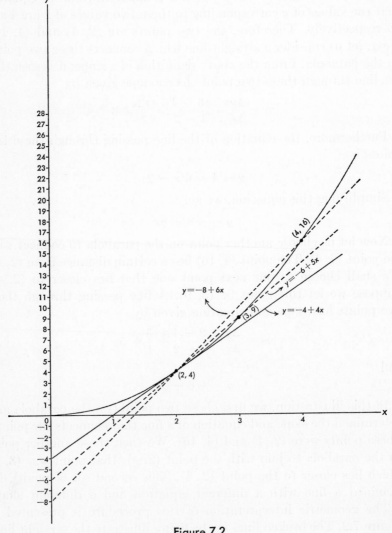

Figure 7.2

(2.50, 6.25), for example. Then we would choose a fourth point, closer to (2, 4) then a third, and so on. As we find the lines which connect each of these points to (2, 4), where each point is progressively closer to (2, 4) than the previous one, we would see that the lines so determined approach closer and closer to the solid (unbroken) straight line in the figure. And naturally, the equations of these lines approach the equation $y = -4 + 4x$.

The solid straight line obtained in this way, and having equation $y = -4 + 4x$, is called the tangent to the parabola having equation $y = x^2$ at the point on the parabola having abscissa 2. That is, the line is tangent to the parabola at the point (2, 4) on the parabola. It touches the parabola at the point (2, 4) but does not "cross over" the parabola as do the other lines. The slope of the curve is equal to the slope of the line at the point of tangency. Hence, in our illustration we know that the slope of the parabola at the point (2, 4) is 4, because this is the slope of the line tangent to the parabola at that point.

To arrive at the line tangent to the parabola, we began with a point to the right of (2, 4) and moved closer and closer to (2, 4). Notice that we could have started with a point to the left of (2, 4) and moved toward (2, 4) from the opposite direction. For example, we might have joined the point (0, 0) on the parabola to the point (2, 4), then the point (1, 1), then (1.50, 2.25), and so on. The line tangent to the parabola at (2, 4) would be identically the same. It does not matter from which direction we approach the fixed point.

The line given by the equation $y = -4 + 4x$ is tangent to the parabola given by $y = x^2$ only at the point (2, 4). If a different point on the parabola were chosen, a different tangent would be obtained. That is to say, the slope varies from point to point on the parabola. A straight line has the same slope at all points on the line, but in general a curve has different slopes at different points. Consequently, the equations of lines tangent to a curve at different points on the curve will be different. For instance, in Figure 7.2, we could find the equation of a line tangent to the parabola at the point (4, 16). This line would have a different equation than the line tangent to the parabola at the point (2, 4). This is true in general for all different points on the same curve. The meaning of tangency, moreover, has been carried through for a single parabola only. The argument applies in general for any single-valued continuous function. Tangents can be found at each point on a curve corresponding to the function, and at each of these points the slope of the tangent gives also the slope of the curve at that point. A grasp of the meaning of tangency will facilitate understanding the limit of a function, and that will be our next step.

B. LIMITS

In order to arrive at a precise definition of rates of change, we must first consider a concept that was implicit in our discussion of tangents. This is the concept of a *limit*. To arrive at the line tangent to the parabola given by $y = x^2$, we first chose a specific point $(2, 4)$ on the parabola. We then considered points in the neighborhood of this point, approaching closer and closer to $(2, 4)$. We found that the equation for the line tangent to the parabola at $(2, 4)$ is $y = -4 + 4x$. Since the slope of this line is 4, the slope of the parabola at the point $(2, 4)$ is 4.

We shall now go beyond one specific point and restate the problem in more general terms. Let the point in question be denoted by (x, y)—for which we can substitute any values of the variables in order to talk about any one specific point, such as $(2, 4)$. A point in the neighborhood of (x, y) is denoted by $(x + \Delta x, y + \Delta y)$, where Δx and Δy represent small (positive or negative) increments of x and y respectively. It follows that when we join any two points by a line, we are joining (x, y) with $(x + \Delta x, y + \Delta y)$. For example, in our illustration, if we let $\Delta x = 1$ and $\Delta y = 5$, we join $(2, 4)$ with $(2 + 1, 4 + 5)$ or $(3, 9)$. In the previous section, we let the other points considered on the parabola approach the fixed point $(2, 4)$. Consequently, what we did, stated in more general terms, was to let Δx approach zero. As Δx approached zero, $(x + \Delta x)$ approached x. Furthermore, as Δx approached zero, so did Δy; hence, $(y + \Delta y)$ approached y.

Having stated the movement on the curve toward the fixed point in general terms, let us rephrase our statements about the curve itself in more general terms also. The equation corresponding to the parabola was $y = f(x) = x^2$. More generally, we can write simply $y = f(x)$ to denote *any* continuous function—not just a parabolic one. The slope of the tangent to the curve given by $y = f(x)$ at a given point (x, y) is

$$\frac{\Delta y}{\Delta x} = \frac{(y + \Delta y) - y}{(x + \Delta x) - x}$$

Since $y = f(x)$, we can write this in functional notation as

$$\frac{f(x + \Delta x) - f(x)}{(x + \Delta x) - x} = \frac{f(x + \Delta x) - f(x)}{\Delta x}$$

But we have seen that Δx must be allowed to approach zero. It is a convention in mathematics to use a horizontal arrow to indicate that one magnitude approaches another. Thus, in our case we can say symbolically that "Δx approaches zero" by writing

$$\Delta x \to 0$$

There is also a mathematical notion called a limit. Leaving this word undefined for the moment, we present the conclusion that the slope of the tangent to a curve given by $y = f(x)$ at the point (x, y) is

$$\lim_{\Delta x \to 0} \frac{f(x + \Delta x) - f(x)}{\Delta x}$$

We can interpret this as follows. In the limit as Δx approaches zero, the slope of the tangent to the curve given by $y = f(x)$ at the point (x, y) is

$$\frac{f(x + \Delta x) - f(x)}{\Delta x}$$

We shall return to the relationship between the slope of a tangent and a limit in a moment. We must first define a limit. Let k be some number, and let $y = f(x)$ be a function whose permissible values of x include all numbers close to k and may or may not include k. If there is a number L such that $f(x)$ may be made as close to L as we please merely by choosing for x any number whatsoever close enough to k, but different from k, we write the following:

$$\lim_{x \to k} f(x) = L$$

We read this symbolic statement as follows: "the limit of $f(x)$ as x approaches k is L." If no such number L exists, the function does not have a limit. For example, if it is known that the value of a function $y = f(x)$ approaches 10 when x approaches 3, we write

$$\lim_{x \to 3} f(x) = 10$$

To grasp the import of a limit, consider the function specified by the equation

$$y = f(x) = \frac{1 - x^2}{2 - \sqrt{x^2 + 3}}$$

If $x = 1$, then it is seen that $1 - x^2 = 1 - 1 = 0$. Also if $x = 1$, then $2 - \sqrt{x^2 + 3} = 2 - \sqrt{4} = 2 - 2 = 0$. Therefore, $f(1)$ is not defined at all by this equation, because the formal substitution of 1 (or for that matter of -1) for x leads to $0/0$, a number which is not defined. We can, however, substitute for x a number very close to 1 and thereby obtain a value for the function which is defined. By choosing for x a number sufficiently close to 1 (either positive or negative), both the numerator and the denominator would be close to zero. But neither would be equal to zero. The closer is x to 1, the closer the numerator and the denominator are to zero, but so long as x is not equal to 1, the function will be defined.

One problem remains, however. It is not clear what fraction the function is close to when x is close to 1. Suppose we rationalize the denominator:

$$f(x) = \frac{1 - x^2}{2 - \sqrt{x^2 + 3}} = \frac{1 - x^2}{2 - \sqrt{x^2 + 3}} \cdot \frac{2 + \sqrt{x^2 + 3}}{2 + \sqrt{x^2 + 3}}$$

$$= \frac{(1 - x^2)(2 + \sqrt{x^2 + 3})}{4 - (x^2 + 3)} = \frac{(1 - x^2)(2 + \sqrt{x^2 + 3})}{1 - x^2}$$

$$= \frac{2 + \sqrt{x^2 + 3}}{1} \cdot \frac{1 - x^2}{1 - x^2} \qquad x^2 \neq 1$$

Now the same function is expressed in a way that permits us to see the value it approaches as x approaches 1. Clearly $\dfrac{1 - x^2}{1 - x^2} = 1$ for any value of x not equal to 1. Since $2 + \sqrt{x^2 + 3}$ is as close to 4 as we please to make it whenever x is sufficiently close to 1, we see that $f(x)$ may be made as close to 4 as we please by choosing x sufficiently close to 1 but different from 1.

The statement "$f(x)$ is as close to 4 as we please whenever x is sufficiently close to 1 (but different from 1)" is symbolized by

$$\lim_{x \to 1} f(x) = 4$$

This notation is read, "the limit of $f(x)$ as x approaches 1 is 4." It is important to note it is the limit that is 4, and the function itself is not equal to 4.

Consider another example. Let

$$y = f(x) = x^2$$

Now by letting x approach as close to 2 as we wish, but not equal to 2, we see that x^2 approaches 4. Hence, we can write

$$\lim_{x \to 2} f(x) = 4$$

The limit of $y = f(\text{x}) = x^2$ as x approaches 2 is 4.

Having defined the limit, let us return to the relationship between tangents and limits. The slope of the tangent to a curve at a chosen point on the curve is essentially a limit, for the attainment of the slope of the tangent involves the notion of approaching closer and closer to some specified value. In particular, we let $\Delta x \to 0$. We can write the notation for the slope of the tangent to the curve given by $y = f(x)$ at the point (x, y) as

$$\lim_{\Delta x \to 0} \frac{f(x + \Delta x) - f(x)}{\Delta x}$$

If we consider the parabolic function $y = f(x) = x^2$, then $f(2) = 4$, and the slope of the tangent at $x = 2$ is

$$\lim_{\Delta x \to 0} \frac{(2 + \Delta x)^2 - 2^2}{\Delta x} = \lim_{\Delta x \to 0} \frac{4 + 4\Delta x + (\Delta x)^2 - 4}{\Delta x}$$

$$= \lim_{\Delta x \to 0} \frac{4\Delta x + (\Delta x)^2}{\Delta x} = \lim_{\Delta x \to 0} (4 + \Delta x) \frac{\Delta x}{\Delta x}$$

As Δx approaches zero, but is not equal to zero, it is seen that the limit is 4. In the previous section, the slope of the tangent to this parabola when $x = 2$ was seen to be 4.

From the general formula for a limit and the added condition that Δx be allowed to approach zero, the slope of the tangent at a point (x, y) can be found. The slope of the tangent is equal to the slope of the curve at that point of tangency, and at different points the curve will have different slopes. In each case, however, the concept of a limit is involved.

C. DERIVATIVES

One of the most fundamental definitions in calculus is the definition of the derivative of a function. The process of calculating the derivative is called *differentiating the function*. Much work in calculus (and in its application to economics) centers around this notion. The definition of a derivative follows immediately upon the definition of the slope of a tangent as a limit. It is the concept toward which we have been working in the previous pages of this chapter. The derivative of a function given by $y = f(x)$ measures the rate of change of the variable y with respect to a change in the variable x. In the previous two sections we let Δx represent an increment or decrement of x—some finite change in the value of x. We let Δy represent a finite change in the value of y. For the function $y = f(x)$, it was seen that

$$\frac{\Delta y}{\Delta x} = \frac{f(x + \Delta x) - f(x)}{\Delta x}$$

That is, $\dfrac{\Delta y}{\Delta x}$ shows the *average* rate of change in y with respect to x.
Now let the change in x become smaller: let $\Delta x \to 0$. Then we can say

$$\lim_{\Delta x \to 0} \frac{\Delta y}{\Delta x} = \lim_{\Delta x \to 0} \frac{f(x + \Delta x) - f(x)}{\Delta x}$$

is called the derivative of the function $f(x)$.

As Δx becomes smaller, Δy will also in general decrease (see Figure 7.2). The smaller Δx becomes, the closer together will be the two points having the abscissas x and $x + \Delta x$ and the ordinates y and $y + \Delta y$, respectively. The line connecting the points (x, y) and $(x + \Delta x, y + \Delta y)$, which cuts the curve in at least two points, approaches the position of the tangent to the curve $y = f(x)$ at (x, y) as $\Delta x \to 0$. This follows from the fact that, as $\Delta x \to 0$, the point $(x + \Delta x, y + \Delta y)$ approaches the point (x, y). Therefore, the line joining them approaches the tangent to the curve $y = f(x)$ at the point (x, y).

The symbol most commonly used to denote the derivative of $y = f(x)$ is

$$\frac{dy}{dx} \quad \text{or} \quad \frac{df(x)}{dx}$$

Another very common symbol is $f'(x)$. For the function denoted by $y = f(x)$, we write[1]

$$\frac{dy}{dx} = \frac{df(x)}{dx} = f'(x) = \lim_{\Delta x \to 0} \frac{f(x + \Delta x) - f(x)}{\Delta x}$$

The entire function f' so defined, for each number x for which the limit exists, is sometimes called the derived function of x.

There are two viewpoints on terminology. The first is that the derivative may be obtained as a definite value for a given x (rather than an entire function of x)—the derivative at a given point. The second point of view is that the derivative may be taken as a function of x (the derivative at a variable point). When the former view is adopted, the "derived function" is distinguished from the "derivative" and is the term applied to the derivative at a variable point rather than a fixed point. We find the derived function by the process of finding derivatives of $f(x)$ for all the permissible values of x. In order to remain as close as possible to the terms introduced in Chapter 1 on values and functions, we shall regard the derivative

[1] Other symbols sometimes used are y' and $D_x y$.

itself as another function of x; we shall adopt the second point of view and say the terms "derivative" and "derived function" refer to one and the same thing. When we want to know the rate of change of the original function $f(x)$ at one chosen point, we shall speak of the *value of the derivative* at that point. For example, we will use the notation $\frac{dy}{dx}$ or $\frac{df(x)}{dx}$ or $f'(x)$ to indicate the derivative, and we will use the notation $\frac{df(3)}{dx}$ or $f'(3)$ to denote the value of the derivative at the point on the function $f(x)$ with abscissa 3, that is, when $x = 3$, a chosen fixed value.

The relation between tangency and the derivative is now obvious. The problem of finding the tangent and its slope at any one point on a curve is equivalent to the problem of finding the value of the derivative of the function $y = f(x)$ at that point. The slope of the tangent to the curve at the point (x, y) is equal to the value of the derivative of the function at that point. The value of the derivative measures the rate of change of y with respect to x at that one point. When we took finite changes in y and x and considered the ratio $\frac{\Delta y}{\Delta x}$, we were measuring the average rate of change in y with respect to x, that is, the average change in the value of y relative to a given change in x over some finite section of the curve. This was indicated, in Figure 7.2, by a chord that connected two points, (2, 4) and (4, 16). The derivative measures the rate of change in y in the limit as the change in x approaches zero. Because it measures the slope of the tangent at a point, and because the slope of the tangent is equal to the slope of the curve at that point, the value of the derivative measures the slope of the curve at that point of tangency.

A straight line through a fixed point (x_1, y_1) on the curve given by $y = f(x)$, and with slope m has the equation

$$y - y_1 = m(x - x_1)$$

This line is tangent at the point (x_1, y_1) if the slope m is equal to $f'(x_1)$. Therefore, the equation of the tangent to the curve corresponding to $y = f(x)$ at the point with coordinates (x_1, y_1) is

$$y - y_1 = f'(x_1)(x - x_1)$$

By choosing different points on the curve, we get different values of the derivatives if the slope of the curve changes. For a linear function, the slope is unchanged over the entire straight line, so the value of the derivative is the same regardless of the point at which the measurement is taken.

D. HIGHER DERIVATIVES

Suppose we are given a function denoted by $y = f(x)$. Suppose, further, that we differentiate this function at the point with co-ordinates (x_1, y_1). For the value x_1 of the variable x, the value of the derivative is obtained and denoted by $f'(x_1)$. Then for the point (x_2, y_2), the value of the derivative is also obtained at this point on the curve represented by $y = f(x)$; that is, $f'(x_2)$. If we continue this process for all permissible values of x, we have another function—the derivative of f. That is, the function f' defined, for each number for which the limit exists, is called the derivative of f and denoted by $f'(x)$. This function too yields a curve on any point of which, for a given value of x on the horizontal axis, the value of f' is read off the vertical axis. Figures 7.3a and 7.3b show the curves corresponding to a function $f(x)$ and its derivative $f'(x)$ for a chosen range of x. We see that the positive slope of the tangent to the curve, in Figure 7.3a, [given by $y = f(x)$] gets smaller and smaller as the value of x gets larger—the value of the derivative gets smaller (but is always positive) as x gets larger. Hence, the curve corresponding to the derivative $f'(x)$ is negatively sloped at all points.

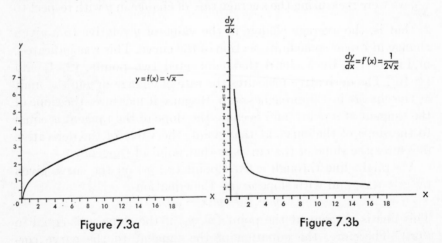

Figure 7.3a   Figure 7.3b

We can pursue the application of derivatives to another stage. We can determine the tangents to the curve represented by $f'(x)$ for all permissible values of x. The derivative of the original function given by $f(x)$ is called the *first derivative* and, as we have already seen, is symbolized by

$$\frac{dy}{dx} = f'(x) = \lim_{\Delta x \to 0} \frac{\Delta y}{\Delta x}$$

In general, $f'(x)$ is another function of x that can be differentiated in turn. The derivative of the derivative gives what is called the *second derivative* of the original function $f(x)$; it is symbolized by

$$\frac{d^2y}{dx^2} = f''(x) = \lim_{\Delta x \to 0} \frac{\Delta f'(x)}{\Delta x}$$

The notations $\dfrac{d^2y}{dx^2}, \dfrac{d^2f(x)}{dx^2}$, or $f''(x)$ may be used to symbolize the second derivative. The second derivative shows the rate of change of the first derivative with respect to x, just as the first derivative shows the rate of change of the original function with respect to x.

We can repeat the process and differentiate the second derivative, which yields the third derivative:

$$\frac{d^3y}{dx^3} = f'''(x) = \lim_{\Delta x \to 0} \frac{\Delta f''(x)}{\Delta x}$$

Likewise, by differentiating this function, we obtain the fourth derivative, and so on.

The geometric interpretation of the first derivative is the graph of a curve that shows the slope of the original function for all permissible values of x. The first derivative of $y = \sqrt{x}$ is shown in Figure 7.3b. The second derivative has the same relation to the first derivative as the first has to the original. Notice that the slope of the function $f'(x)$, in Figure 7.3b, is negative, but the slope gets smaller (in absolute value) and approaches zero as x gets larger. Consequently, if we were to plot the second derivative of $y = \sqrt{x}$, we would see that its value is negative for all permissible values of x. As x gets larger, moreover, the function $f''(x)$ approaches zero. Its graph would show a curve in the fourth quadrant, but rising to the horizontal axis as x gets larger.

In our economic applications, we shall have occasion to use only the first and second derivatives of a function. It is well, however, to keep in mind the existence and meaning of higher derivatives. To summarize, once a variable y is stated to be a function of another variable x, $y = f(x)$, this function can be specified by an equation in y and x. We may wish to know the rate at which y changes with respect to changes in x. The first derivative of y with respect to x is another function that tells us this for all permissible values of x. For a single chosen *value* of x, we obtain the value of the derivative at that value of x, or the rate at which y changes with respect to x at that value of x only. Geometrically, the curve corresponding to $y = f(x)$ can be represented in a diagram. Suppose we wish to know the slope of this curve at the point with abscissa x_1. Then the value of the derivative, $f'(x_1)$, tells us the slope of the curve at that point. In general, for any chosen value of x (for any point on the curve) the slope of the curve can be computed. The second derivative of a function bears the same relation to the first derivative that the first derivative bears to the original function.

PROBLEMS

1. Let $y = 3 + x^3$.
   (a) Graph the function from $x = 0$ to $x = 7$.
   (b) Connect by a straight line the point $(3, 30)$ with each of the following points: $(6, 219)$; $(5, 128)$; $(4, 67)$.
   (c) By computing $f(6)$, $f(5)$, $f(4)$, $f(3.5)$, $f(3.1)$, and $f(3.001)$ show that
   $$\lim_{x \to 3} = 30$$

2. Let $y = \dfrac{x + 3}{x - 1}$.
   (a) Graph the function from $x = 0$ to $x = 10$.
   (b) By computing $f(6)$, $f(5.5)$, $f(5.1)$, $f(4.9)$, and $f(4)$ show that
   $$\lim_{x \to 5} = 2$$

3. Find each of the following limits:
   (a) $\displaystyle\lim_{x \to 2} (2 - x)$
   (b) $\displaystyle\lim_{x \to 2} (2 + \sqrt{2x})$
   (c) $\displaystyle\lim_{x \to 2} \dfrac{2 - x}{2 - \sqrt{2x}}$

CHAPTER 8

Rules of Differentiation

In Chapter 7, the definition of a derivative as a limit was established. It is possible to calculate the value of the derivative of a function $y = f(x)$ at a point, by taking a finite difference in x and the corresponding difference in y defined by the function. When we let the difference in x approach zero, the equation and slope of a line tangent to the curve at a point are determined. The slope of this tangent is equal to the value of the derivative of the function at that point on the curve. By repeating this process again and again, for all points on the curve, the derivative (a function) can be obtained. But this is a slow and cumbersome procedure. In order to avoid going through many computations of limits every time we want the derivative of a function, formulas have been discovered that may be applied in a variety of cases. These formulas yield the derivative, so that for any permissible value of the independent variable, the rate of change of the function at that value can easily be determined. We shall now present these formulas or rules without giving the proofs. Again, the proofs can be found in any textbook on calculus.

A. DERIVATIVE OF A POWER

Rule 1: If k is constant, n is any number whatever, and f is the function defined for each number x by $f(x) = kx^n$, then the derivative $f'(x)$ is defined by:

$$f'(x) = knx^{n-1}$$

Let us consider some examples. Suppose the function f is given by:

$$y = f(x) = x^2$$

Applying the rule where $k = 1$ and $n = 2$, we get

$$\frac{dy}{dx} = f'(x) = 1 \cdot 2x^{2-1} = 2x$$

Hence, we have the derivative of the function $f(x)$. If we were to plot the graph of this derivative, it would appear as a straight line going through the origin with a positive slope. We can calculate the value of the derivative of the original function f for any value of x by merely substituting that value for x in the derivative. In this case, we now know that the value of the derivative (the rate of change) of f when $x = 2$ is 4; the value of the derivative when $x = 6$ is 12, and so on for any value of x. That is, the curve corresponding to the function f has a slope of $+4$ at the point with abscissa $+2$, and a slope of $+12$ at the point with abscissa $+6$. At the point with abscissa -3, the curve has a slope of -6. In other words, the curve corresponding to the derivative shows the rate of change of the original function for all permissible values of x.

Consider another function $y = f(x) = 10x^5$. Here $k = 10$ and $n = 5$ in the rule. Consequently,

$$\frac{dy}{dx} = 10 \cdot 5 \cdot x^{5-1} = 50x^4$$

If we want to know the value of the derivative of the function f when $x = 2$, we substitute 2 for x in the derivative; we see that the value of the derivative is

$$f'(2) = 50(2)^4 = 800$$

The functions given by the following equations have the derivatives shown in the column on the right. As an exercise, the reader should apply the rule of differentiation to each function and obtain the derivative shown in the right-hand column.

Function	*Derivative*
$y = 2x^7$	$\dfrac{dy}{dx} = 14x^6$
$y = 3\sqrt{x} = 3x^{\frac{1}{2}}$	$\dfrac{dy}{dx} = \dfrac{3}{2}x^{-\frac{1}{2}} = \dfrac{3}{2\sqrt{x}}$
$y = \dfrac{4}{x^2} = 4x^{-2}$	$\dfrac{dy}{dx} = -8x^{-3} = -\dfrac{8}{x^3}$
$y = \dfrac{3}{x} = 3x^{-1}$	$\dfrac{dy}{dx} = -3x^{-2} = -\dfrac{3}{x^2}$

A special case of this rule is that in which the function equals some constant, that is, $y = f(x) = k$. The graph of this function appears as a straight line parallel to the x axis at the level $y = k$. Applying the rule where $n = 0$ (hence $x^0 = 1$, for any value to the zero power equals 1), we have

$$\frac{dy}{dx} = k \cdot 0 \cdot x^{0-1} = 0$$

The derivative of a constant is zero. The geometrical interpretation is clear. A horizontal line has zero slope at all points on the line. Since the derivative is equal to the slope of the line, it is also zero. For example, if the function f is given by $y = f(x) = 10$, then $\dfrac{dy}{dx} = 0$. The value of the derivative is zero for all values of x.

Another special case of this rule is one in which the function of x is multiplied by a constant. The derivative of a function of x multiplied by a constant is the constant times the derivative of the function. Let $f(x) = kx^n$ be the function of x, and let c be another constant. We have for the constant times the function

$$cf(x) = ckx^n$$

The derivative is

$$\frac{dcy}{dx} = c \cdot \frac{dy}{dx} = c \cdot k \cdot n \cdot x^{n-1}$$

To illustrate, let $f(x) = 2x^3$. If we multiply this by the constant 4, we obtain $4f(x) = 4 \cdot 2x^3$. Then

$$\frac{d\,4f(x)}{dx} = 4\frac{d\,f(x)}{dx} = 4 \cdot 2 \cdot 3x^2 = 24x^2$$

is the derivative.

B. DERIVATIVES OF SUMS AND DIFFERENCES OF FUNCTIONS

Rule 2: The derivative of a sum of functions is equal to the sum of their derivatives. The derivative of a difference of functions is equal to the difference of their derivatives. Let g and h be given functions of x. Define function f by

$$f(x) = g(x) + h(x)$$

If x is a number such that $g'(x)$ and $h'(x)$ both exist, then $f'(x)$ exists and

$$f'(x) = g'(x) + h'(x)$$

Alternatively if $f = g - h$, then $f' = g' - h'$. This rule applies also to a function of x that is the sum or difference of three or more other functions of x.

Up to this point, we have been dealing with the derivatives of functions of x that include only one term. Suppose, however, that we have a function expressed by the following cubic equation:

$$y = f(x) = 10 + 3x - 4x^2 + 2x^3$$

We can treat each of the terms as a function of x. Thus, according to Rule 2, and using Rule 1 on power functions

$$\frac{dy}{dx} = f'(x) = g'(x) + h'(x) - j'(x) + l'(x) = 3 - 8x + 6x^2$$

The value of the derivative when $x = 2$ is

$$f'(2) = 3 - 8(2) + 6(2)^2 = 3 - 16 + 24 = 11$$

Other examples of this rule are presented below. The column on the left gives several functions whose derivatives are shown in the right-hand column. As in the preceding set of examples, and for

Function	*Derivative*
$y = 16 + 3x$	$\dfrac{dy}{dx} = 3$
$y = x^5 - 3x^4 - 2x^3 - x^2 + x$	$\dfrac{dy}{dx} = 5x^4 - 12x^3 - 6x^2 - 2x + 1$
$y = 2x - \frac{1}{2}\sqrt{x}$	$\dfrac{dy}{dx} = 2 - \frac{1}{4}x^{-\frac{1}{2}} = 2 - \dfrac{1}{4\sqrt{x}}$
$y = 24 + \dfrac{4}{x} - \sqrt[3]{x} = 24 + 4x^{-1} - x^{\frac{1}{3}}$	$\dfrac{dy}{dx} = -4x^{-2} - \frac{1}{3}x^{-\frac{2}{3}} = -\dfrac{4}{x^2} - \dfrac{1}{3\sqrt[3]{x^2}}$

others that will be given, it is instructive to trace through the procedure of differentiation as an exercise.

C. DERIVATIVE OF A PRODUCT OF FUNCTIONS

Rule 3: The derivative of the product of two functions is the first factor times the derivative of the second factor plus the second factor times the derivative of the first factor. Let g and h be given functions of x. Define function f by

$$f(x) = g(x) \cdot h(x)$$

If x is a number such that $g'(x)$ and $h'(x)$ both exist, then $f'(x)$ also exists and

$$f'(x) = g(x) \, h'(x) + h(x) \, g'(x)$$

As an illustration, let $g(x) = (2 + 3x)$ and $h(x) = (4 - x)$. Then define the new function $f(x) = (2 + 3x) \, (4 - x)$. Following this rule and utilizing Rule 1 and Rule 2, we obtain

$$\frac{dy}{dx} = g(x) \, h'(x) + h(x) \, g'(x) = (2 + 3x)(-1) + (4 - x)(3) = -2 - 3x$$
$$+ 12 - 3x = 10 - 6x$$

Suppose $g(x) = (x^4 + 3x^2)$ and $h(x) = (x^2 - 2x + 3)$. Then we define the function $y = f(x) = (x^4 + 3x^2) \, (x^2 - 2x + 3)$, and derive

$$\frac{dy}{dx} = (x^4 + 3x^2)(2x - 2) + (x^2 - 2x + 3)(4x^3 + 6x)$$

$$= (2x^5 - 2x^4 + 6x^3 - 6x^2) + (4x^5 - 8x^4 + 18x^3 - 12x^2 + 18x)$$

$$= 6x^5 - 10x^4 + 24x^3 - 18x^2 + 18x$$

The following functions have the derivatives shown on the right.

Function	Derivative
$y = (3x^2)(x^{\frac{1}{3}})$	$\dfrac{dy}{dx} = 7x^{\frac{1}{3}} = 7\sqrt[3]{x^4}$
$y = (3x)(x^2 - \sqrt{x})$	$\dfrac{dy}{dx} = 9x^2 - \frac{9}{2}\sqrt{x}$

D. DERIVATIVE OF A QUOTIENT OF FUNCTIONS

Rule 4: The derivative of a quotient of functions is the derivative of the numerator times the denominator minus the derivative of the denominator times the numerator, all divided by the square of the denominator. Let g and h be given functions of x. Define the function f by

$$f(x) = \frac{g(x)}{h(x)}$$

If x is a number such that $g'(x)$ and $h'(x)$ both exist, then $f'(x)$ also exists and

$$f'(x) = \frac{g'(x)\,h(x) - h'(x)\,g(x)}{[h(x)]^2}$$

For instance, consider the function

$$f(x) = \frac{g(x)}{h(x)} = \frac{2x^2}{3x + 1}$$

Applying this rule and Rules 1 and 2, we have

$$f'(x) = \frac{(4x)(3x + 1) - (3)(2x^2)}{(3x + 1)^2} = \frac{6x^2 + 4x}{(3x + 1)^2}$$

Three examples of derivatives of quotients of functions are presented below.

Function	Derivative
$y = \dfrac{x + 1}{x - 1}$	$\dfrac{dy}{dx} = \dfrac{-2}{(x - 1)^2}$
$y = \dfrac{2x^2 + 3x + 1}{x^2 + 4x + 2}$	$\dfrac{dy}{dx} = \dfrac{5x^2 + 6x + 2}{(x^2 + 4x + 2)^2}$
$y = \dfrac{\sqrt{x}}{x^2 + x}$	$\dfrac{dy}{dx} = \dfrac{-\frac{3}{2}x^{\frac{3}{2}} - \frac{1}{2}x^{\frac{1}{2}}}{(x^2 + x)^2}$

E. DERIVATIVE OF A FUNCTION OF A FUNCTION

Rule 5: When y is a function of g, which is itself a function of x, to find the derivative of y with respect to x multiply the derivative of y with respect to g by the derivative of g with respect to x. Let f and g be functions such that $f'(x)$ and $g'(x)$ exist. If y is the function defined by

$$y = f[g(x)]$$

then $y'(x)$ exists and

$$y'(x) = \frac{dy}{dx} = \frac{dy}{dg} \cdot \frac{dg}{dx}$$

This is called the derivative of a function of a function.

Assume we wish to find the derivative of

$$y = f(x) = (x^2 + 3x + 2)^5$$

We can regard the expression in parentheses, $x^2 + 3x + 2$, as a new function of x and designate it by $g(x)$:

$$g(x) = x^2 + 3x + 2$$

Then the function y can be written

$$y = g^5$$

That is, y is a function of another function. Now according to our rule

$$\frac{dy}{dx} = \frac{dy}{dg} \cdot \frac{dg}{dx}$$

But by Rule 1

$$\frac{dy}{dg} = 5g^4$$

and by Rules 1 and 2

$$\frac{dg}{dx} = 2x + 3$$

Hence, the derivative of y with respect to x is the product

$$\frac{dy}{dx} = (5g^4)(2x + 3) = 5(x^2 + 3x + 2)^4(2x + 3)$$

where the expression in terms of x is substituted for g.

Again as an exercise, some functions are shown in the left-hand column and their derivatives on the right

Function	*Derivative*
$y = (x^2 + x)^2$	$\dfrac{dy}{dx} = 2(x^2 + x)(2x + 1)$
$y = \sqrt{x^3 + 2x^2 + 4}$	$\dfrac{dy}{dx} = \dfrac{3x^2 + 4x}{2\sqrt{x^3 + 2x^2 + 4}}$
$y = \dfrac{(2x + 3)^2}{(x^2 - 1)}$	$\dfrac{dy}{dx} = \dfrac{(8x + 12)(x^2 - 1) - (2x)(2x + 3)^2}{(x^2 - 1)^2}$

NOTE: Use Rules 4 and 5.

F. DERIVATIVE OF A LOGARITHMIC FUNCTION

Rule 6: The derivative of the natural logarithm of x is the reciprocal of x. The reader will recall from Chapter 3, in the discussion of secular trends, that the number designated by e is an irrational number that is taken in mathematics as the base of so-called natural logarithms. Its value to five decimal places is 2.71828. Let y be a function, and let x be a number such that

$$y = f(x) = \log_e x$$

The derivative of the logarithmic function is given as

$$\frac{dy}{dx} = \frac{1}{x}$$

For example, if the function is given by

$$y = 10 \log_e x$$

then

$$\frac{dy}{dx} = 10 \cdot \frac{1}{x} = \frac{10}{x}$$

A frequent combination of rules found in calculus is the combination of Rule 5 with Rule 6. Very often the logarithmic function involves the logarithm of another function of the independent variable. Let us suppose that the function is given by

$$y = \log_e (2x^2 - 3x + 7)$$

Set $(2x^2 - 3x + 7) = g(x)$. Then

$$y = \log_e g$$

and

$$\frac{dy}{dg} = \frac{1}{g} \qquad \frac{dg}{dx} = 4x - 3$$

Hence

$$\frac{dy}{dx} = \frac{dy}{dg} \cdot \frac{dg}{dx} = \frac{1}{g}(4x - 3) = \frac{4x - 3}{2x^2 - 3x + 7}$$

Three illustrative cases of the differentiation of logarithmic functions are shown in the following columns.

Function	*Derivative*
$y = \log_e x + 3 \log_e x$	$\dfrac{dy}{dx} = \dfrac{1}{x} + \dfrac{3}{x} = \dfrac{4}{x}$
$y = 2 \log_e x - \log_e x^2$	$\dfrac{dy}{dx} = \dfrac{2}{x} - \dfrac{2x}{x^2} = 0$
$y = \log_e (2x^2 + 4x - 1)^2$	$\dfrac{dy}{dx} = \dfrac{8x + 8}{2x^2 + 4x - 1}$

NOTE: Use Rule 5 and Rule 6 twice.

G. DERIVATIVE OF AN EXPONENTIAL FUNCTION

There is a special case of logarithmic differentiation that pertains to the derivative of the exponential function

$$y = e^x$$

We have already become somewhat familiar with this type of function in Chapter 3, where secular trends were discussed.

Rule 7: The derivative with respect to x of the exponential function e^x is equal to itself. Let y be a function, and let x be a number such that

$$y = f(x) = e^x$$

The derivative of this exponential function is given as

$$\frac{dy}{dx} = e^x$$

To illustrate, take the logarithm to the base e of both members of the equation. We obtain [1]

$$\log_e y = \log_e e^x = x$$

Then we differentiate these two members with respect to x. For the left side of the equation we have

$$\frac{d \log_e y}{dx} = \frac{1}{y}\frac{dy}{dx}$$

[1] This conclusion should be familiar to the student from elementary algebra. By definition of the logarithm of x, where $x = \log_a y$, x is the power to which a must be raised to give y. Hence, $y = a^x$ has the same meaning as $x = \log_a y$, and $\log_a a^x = x$.

by Rule 6. On the right side of the equation

$$\frac{dx}{dx} = 1$$

Therefore, by differentiating the two members, we obtain

$$\frac{1}{y} \cdot \frac{dy}{dx} = 1$$

so that

$$\frac{dy}{dx} = y = e^x$$

Let us now consider some examples in which functions of functions are involved. Let $y = e^{3x}$ and define the function $g(x) = 3x$. Then

$$\frac{dy}{dx} = \frac{dy}{dg} \cdot \frac{dg}{dx} = (e^g)(3) = 3e^{3x}$$

Suppose $y = f(x) = (2x + 3e^x)^3$. Again using the principle of the derivative of a function of a function, we write

$$g(x) = (2x + 3e^x)$$

so that

$$y = g^3$$

Hence, by Rule 5

$$\frac{dy}{dx} = \frac{dy}{dg} \cdot \frac{dg}{dx}$$

and by Rules 1, 2, and 7

$$\frac{dy}{dg} = 3g^2 \qquad \frac{dg}{dx} = 2 + 3e^x$$

Therefore

$$\frac{dy}{dx} = 3(2x + 3e^x)^2(2 + 3e^x)$$

When $x = 1$, we have $f'(1) = 3136.96$ by the substitution of 1 for x and 2.71828 for e.

Consider another example in which $y = f(x) = \dfrac{1}{2^x}$. We take the logarithm of both members since the operation is most easily done by use of logarithms. Thus

$$\log_e y = \log_e 2^{-x}$$

But $\log_e 2^{-x}$ can be written $(-x \log_e 2)$. We take the derivative of both sides of the equation (noting that $\log_e 2$ on the right side is a constant coefficient of x):

$$\frac{d \log_e y}{dx} = \frac{1}{y} \cdot \frac{dy}{dx} \qquad \frac{d(-x \log_e 2)}{dx} = -\log_e 2$$

By having differentiated the two members, we obtain

$$\frac{1}{y} \cdot \frac{dy}{dx} = -\log_e 2$$

and

$$\frac{dy}{dx} = (-\log_e 2)y = \frac{-\log_e 2}{2^x}$$

Since $-\log_e 2$ is a constant, its value can be found in Table A at the end of the book. We then have

$$\frac{dy}{dx} = -\frac{.6931}{2^x}$$

When $x = 4$, $\dfrac{df(4)}{dx} = \dfrac{.6931}{2^4} = \dfrac{.6931}{16} = .04$

Three additional exponential functions and their derivatives are presented below.

Function	*Derivative*
$y = \dfrac{1}{e^x} = e^{-x}$	$\dfrac{dy}{dx} = -e^{-x} = -\dfrac{1}{e^x}$
$y = (3x^2 - 3e^x)^2$	$\dfrac{dy}{dx} = (6x^2 - 6e^x)(6x - 3e^x)$
$y = \dfrac{2x + 4e^x}{1 + 2e^x}$	$\dfrac{dy}{dx} = \dfrac{2 + 8e^x - 4xe^x}{(1 + 2e^x)^2}$

NOTE: Use Rule 4 and Rule 7.

H. HIGHER DERIVATIVES

The rules for second, third, and higher derivatives are exactly the same as those for first derivatives. The only difference in the procedure is that now the differentiation is performed on a function that is itself already the derivative of another function. This process is best demonstrated by the use of some examples.

Let the function denoted by $f(x)$ be given by the following equation:

$$y = f(x) = 3x^2$$

As we have seen, this is the equation for a parabola similar to that in Figure 7.2. To obtain the first derivative, we use Rule 1:

$$\frac{dy}{dx} = f'(x) = 6x$$

The graph of this function, $f'(x)$, appears as a straight line with a positive slope (equal to 6) going through the origin. Now to get the second derivative of f, we differentiate this function, again using Rule 1. Thus

$$\frac{d^2y}{dx^2} = f''(x) = 6$$

Since the second derivative is a constant, the graph of this function is a straight horizontal line parallel to the x axis at a level of $f''(x) = 6$. Likewise, the third derivative is obtained by differentiating the second derivative:

$$\frac{d^3y}{dx^3} = f'''(x) = 0$$

The derivative of a constant is zero by Rule 1. The graph of the function $f'''(x)$ is shown as a horizontal line lying on top of the x axis—it is zero for all permissible values of x. Higher derivatives will also be zero, because zero is a constant number.

Now consider the function given by

$$y = f(x) = 147 - 2x + 3x^2 + x^3$$

To arrive at the second derivative of f, we first find the first derivative. Using Rules 1 and 2:

$$\frac{dy}{dx} = f'(x) = -2 + 6x + 3x^2$$

Again using Rules 1 and 2, we get

$$\frac{d^2y}{dx^2} = f''(x) = 6 + 6x$$

Higher derivatives are obtained by repetition of this procedure.

An interesting case is that which involves a logarithmic function of a function. Our third example in Section F postulated the function given by

$$y = \log_e (2x^2 + 4x - 1)^2$$

To find the first derivative, we use Rule 6 and Rule 5. According to Rule 5, let

$$2x^2 + 4x - 1 = g(x)$$

and

$$g^2 = h(x)$$

then the function $f(x)$ is defined as

$$y = \log_e h$$

We apply Rule 6 to obtain

(1)
$$\frac{dy}{dx} = \frac{1}{h} \cdot \frac{dh}{dx}$$

But according to Rule 5

(2)
$$\frac{dh}{dx} = \frac{dh}{dg} \cdot \frac{dg}{dx}$$

So, by substituting (2) into (1):

$$\frac{dy}{dx} = \frac{1}{h} \left(\frac{dh}{dg} \cdot \frac{dg}{dx} \right)$$

$$= \frac{1}{h} (2g)(4x + 4)$$

$$= \frac{2(2x^2 + 4x - 1)(4x + 4)}{(2x^2 + 4x - 1)^2} = \frac{8x + 8}{2x^2 + 4x - 1}$$

This gives us the first derivative of the function y, which is shown in Section F. But we have not yet found the second derivative of y. To find the second derivative, we must differentiate the first derivative. In order to do this, we note that the first derivative is a quotient of functions, so we use Rule 4. Let $(8x + 8) = u(x)$ and $(2x^2 + 4x - 1) = v(x)$ so

$$\frac{dy}{dx} = \frac{u(x)}{v(x)}$$

Applying Rule 4:

$$\frac{d^2y}{dx^2} = \frac{u'v - v'u}{v^2}$$

$$= \frac{8(2x^2 + 4x - 1) - (4x + 4)(8x + 8)}{(2x^2 + 4x - 1)^2}$$

$$= \frac{-(16x^2 + 32x + 40)}{(2x^2 + 4x - 1)^2}$$

Three other illustrations of second derivatives follow.

Function	Second Derivative
$u = x^2 + \sqrt{x}$	$\dfrac{d^2y}{dx^2} = 2 - \dfrac{1}{4\sqrt{x^3}}$
$y = (x^3 + 2x^2)^3$	$\dfrac{d^2y}{dx^2} = 3(x^3 + 2x^2)^2 (6x + 4) + 6(x^3 + 2x^2)(3x^2 + 4x)^2$

NOTE: Use Rule 5 for the first derivative and
Rules 3 and 5 for the second derivative.

$y = e^x$	$\dfrac{d^2y}{dx^2} = e^x$

PROBLEMS

GROUP I:

Find the first derivatives and the indicated values of the derivatives for each of the following functions:

1. $y = f(x) = 2 + 4x$.
2. $y = f(x) = 12x$.
   Find $f'(-2), f'(0), f'(2), f'(6)$.
3. $y = f(x) = 14$.
4. $y = f(x) = x^2$.
   Find $f'(0), f'(2), f'(100)$.
5. $y = f(x) = x^5$.
   Find $f'(-2), f'(0), f'(1), 2f'(2)$.
6. $y = f(x) = \dfrac{3}{x^3}$.
7. $y = f(x) = 4\sqrt[3]{x}$.
   Find $f'(-2), f'(0), 4f'(2)$.
8. $y = f(x) = 2x^2 - .5x^3 + 3x - 6$.
9. $y = f(x) = 13 - \dfrac{3}{x} + \sqrt{4x} - \sqrt[3]{x}$.
10. $y = f(x) = (3x + 2)(2x^2 - 2x)$.
    Find $f'(-4), f'(0), f'(1), f'(3)$.
11. $y = f(x) = \dfrac{x - 1}{x^2 + 3}$.
    Find $f'(-3), f'(0), f'(2)$.
12. $y = f(x) = 3(x^2 - 7x + 1)^2$.
    Find $f'(-2), f'(-1), f'(0), f'(4)$.
13. $y = f(x) = \sqrt{x + 1}$.
14. $y = f(x) = \left(\dfrac{x - 1}{x + 3}\right)^3$.
    Find $f'(-2), f'(0), f'(2)$.
15. $y = f(x) = 4 \log_e x$.
16. $y = f(x) = 2 \log_e x - \tfrac{3}{4} \log_e x$.
17. $y = f(x) = 2 \log_e (2x^2 - 3x + 4)$.
18. $y = f(x) = 6e^x$.
    Find $f'(-1), f'(0), f'(1), f'(2)$.
19. $y = f(x) = (x^2 - 2e^x)^{\frac{1}{2}}$.
    Find the second derivatives and the indicated values of the derivatives for each of the following functions:

20. $y = f(x) = 4x + 2x^2 - 6$.

Plot the graphs of the functions $f(x)$, $f'(x)$, and $f''(x)$ from $x = -3$ to $x = 3$.

21. $y = f(x) = e^x + x^2 - (2x - 4)^2$.

GROUP II:

22. $y = f(x) = x^7 - 2x^4 + 6x^2 - x + \dfrac{1}{x} - \dfrac{1}{x^2}$.

Find $f'(-3)$, $f'(-1)$, $f'(0)$, $f'(2)$.

23. $y = f(x) = x^{-2} - 3x^{-1} + 6$.

24. $y = f(x) = (\sqrt{x})(x^2 + 1)$.

25. $y = f(x) = \dfrac{3x^3 + x^2 - 10}{x^2 - 10}$.   26. $y = f(x) = \dfrac{\sqrt{x} + \sqrt[3]{x}}{x + 1}$.

27. $y = f(x) = \dfrac{10x}{x^2 + 3x - 7}$.   28. $y = f(x) = (x + 1)^{-\frac{1}{2}}$.

29. $y = f(x) = 4\left(\dfrac{x^2 + 3x}{3x + 1}\right)^2 - 2(3x^2 + x - 9)^3$.

30. $y = f(x) = (2x - x^2)^{-2} + 4(\sqrt{x} - 9)^2$.

31. $y = f(x) = 3\log_e\left(\dfrac{x + 1}{x - 3}\right) + 2\log_e(x^2 + 2)^2$.

32. $y = f(x) = 2e^x - \log_e(2 - x^2)^2 + \left(\dfrac{2x - 4e^x}{e^x + 1}\right)^2$.

Find the second derivatives and the indicated values of the derivatives for each of the following functions:

33. $y = f(x) = -.5x^3 + 2x^2 + 3x + 10$.

Plot the graphs of the functions $f(x)$, $f'(x)$, and $f''(x)$ from $x = 0$ to $x = 5$.

34. $y = f(x) = \left(\dfrac{x - 2}{x + 4}\right)^3$.

35. $y = f(x) = \log_e(2x^2 + 4x - 1)^2$.

36. $16 + 4y^2 - x + 2x^2 = 0$.

37. $9 - \sqrt[3]{y} + x = 0$.

38. $\dfrac{x}{y} = 6x + 4x^2 - 3$.

Plot the graphs of the functions $f(x)$, $f'(x)$, and $f''(x)$ from $x = -2$ to $x = 4$.

Find the third derivatives of the following functions:

39. $y = f(x) = (x^3 - 2x^2 + 3x - 6)^2$.

40. $y = f(x) = x^3 - x^2 + 3x + 4$.

41. $14 + x^{\frac{1}{2}} - x^2 + 4y = 0$.

42. $y = f(x) = \log_e(2x^2 + 3)^2$.

CHAPTER 9

Economic Applications of
Derivatives

From the study of economic theory, we are already familiar with concepts such as marginal cost, marginal revenue, marginal utility, marginal rates of substitution, and marginal efficiency of capital. Practically all decision processes in economics involve marginals. Should the firm's output be increased, and what would be the effects (in terms of increases or decreases) in cost and revenue? How much more or less labor should be hired in response to a given fall or rise in the wage rate of that labor? In aggregate market relationships also, we are interested in such problems as the rate of change in market quantities demanded or supplied in response to price, income, or cost changes. One might ask, "what is the direction and rate of change in total United States consumption by households when national income changes?" These rates of change are called marginals in economics.

In Chapter 3, we have seen that the relationship between two economic variables can be expressed as a function given by some equation. In this chapter, we shall show that by differentiating the function a measure of the rate of change of the dependent variable with respect to the independent variable can be obtained. For a change in the independent variable, the corresponding change in the dependent variable can be measured. The marginal concept is a derivative. For example, the marginal cost function is the first derivative with respect to output of the total cost function. The first derivative has very widespread use as an operational procedure in economic analyses, and we shall illustrate some of its applications here. The second derivative also has an important role, but its applications will be demonstrated in a later chapter.

A. ELASTICITY OF DEMAND AND SUPPLY

One extremely important measure employed in economic theory is elasticity. Textbooks on economic theory define *price elasticity of demand* as the percentage change in the quantity of a good demanded in response to a percentage change in its price. Likewise, the *price elasticity of supply* is defined as the percentage change in the quantity supplied in response to a percentage change in price. Using the first derivative of calculus, we can give a precise symbolic meaning to elasticity. If y is a continuous function of x denoted by

$$y = f(x)$$

we define the elasticity of the function f as

$$e = \frac{dy}{dx} \cdot \frac{x}{y}$$

Note the comparison of this definition with that often presented without the use of calculus. Let Δ again represent a finite increment or decrement. Then elasticity is presented symbolically as

$$e = \frac{\dfrac{\Delta y}{y}}{\dfrac{\Delta x}{x}} = \frac{\Delta y}{\Delta x} \cdot \frac{x}{y}$$

The change in y divided by the value of y is the percentage change in y; the change in x divided by the value of x is the percentage change in x. But there is a difficulty that arises from this expression. If we choose two points on the curve corresponding to $y = f(x)$, say (x_1, y_1) and (x_2, y_2), then $\Delta y = y_2 - y_1$ and $\Delta x = x_2 - x_1$. Now which point do we choose for the value of x and y in the formula

$$e = \frac{\dfrac{\Delta y}{y}}{\dfrac{\Delta x}{x}} ?$$

We can choose (x_1, y_1) or (x_2, y_2). Suppose (x_1, y_1) is the point on the curve before the change and (x_2, y_2) is the point after the change. If we choose the point before the change has occurred, we substitute x_1 for x and y_1 for y in the formula for elasticity. On the other hand, if we choose x_2 for x and y_2 for y in the formula, we are measuring the percentage change relative to a different base, and we get an entirely different measure for elasticity. Using finite changes results in ambiguity. For example, if in Figure 7.2 we were to choose $(2, 4)$ as (x_1, y_1) and $(4, 16)$ as (x_2, y_2), then $\Delta x = x_2 - x_1 = 4 - 2 = 2$, and

$\Delta y = y_2 - y_1 = 16 - 4 = 12$. These values are unambiguously determined. However, $\dfrac{\Delta y}{y}$ may be $\frac{12}{4}$ or it may be $\frac{12}{16}$; and the corresponding $\dfrac{\Delta x}{x}$ may be $\frac{2}{2}$ or it may be $\frac{2}{4}$. There are no grounds for deciding which of these bases to use in computing the percentage changes. To overcome this difficulty, formulas for *arc elasticity* have been introduced in economics. These formulas are approximations to the definition in terms of derivatives. In an arc formula $\dfrac{\Delta y}{\Delta x}$ measures, not the slope of the curve itself, but the slope of a chord which joins two points on the curve (see the discussion of tangents in Chapter 7).

We can obtain the slope of the curve at a point if we take the limit of $\dfrac{\Delta y}{\Delta x}$ as Δx approaches zero. Thus,

$$e = \lim_{\Delta x \to 0} \frac{\Delta y}{\Delta x} \cdot \frac{x}{y}$$

But, as we have seen, this is the definition of the first derivative of y with respect to x multiplied by x over y. By computing the *value* of the derivative at the point (x_1, y_1), we have a measure of the elasticity of the curve *at that point*. Consequently, the problem of choosing the denominators to calculate the percentage changes is removed. We can compute the elasticity unambiguously at any point on the curve.

1. Elasticity of Demand

Let q signify the quantity demanded of the commodity Q, and let p signify its price. The demand for Q may be written

$$q = f(p)$$

where the function f is assumed to be continuous.

The price elasticity of demand for Q is therefore

$$e = \frac{dq}{dp} \cdot \frac{p}{q}$$

For example, suppose the demand function is given by the equation

$$q = 100 - 5p$$

Then, using Rule 1 of Chapter 8, the elasticity of this demand function is

$$e = \frac{dq}{dp} \cdot \frac{p}{q} = -5\left(\frac{p}{q}\right)$$

To find the elasticity of demand when $p = 3$ and $q = 100 - 5(3) = 85$, we merely substitute these values into the elasticity formula:

$$e = -5(\tfrac{3}{85}) = -\tfrac{3}{17}$$

Since this value is greater than -1 (its absolute value is less than 1), this demand curve is relatively inelastic at the point where $p = 3$ and $q = 85$. By the economic definition of elasticity, a demand curve is said to be relatively inelastic if its elasticity is between zero and -1; it is said to be relatively elastic if its elasticity is between -1 and minus infinity; finally it has unit elasticity if its elasticity equals -1. Had we chosen a different point on the demand curve at which to measure elasticity, it might have turned out to be relatively elastic at that point. Consider the point on the demand curve at which $p = 15$ and $q = 100 - 5(15) = 25$. For the elasticity at this point, we have

$$e = -5(\tfrac{15}{25}) = -3$$

We conclude that the demand curve is relatively elastic at the point where $p = 15$ and $q = 25$.

More generally, a linear demand curve will have different elasticities at different points on the curve. The slope of the curve is constant, but its elasticity is not. This conclusion about the variability of elasticity applies to more than linear functions—in fact it applies to almost all demand functions. Suppose the demand function is specified by the equation

$$q = 1200 - 2p - .8p^2$$

The elasticity of demand is given as

$$e = \frac{dq}{dp} \cdot \frac{p}{q} = (-2 - 1.6p) \cdot \frac{p}{q}$$
$$= -\frac{(2p + 1.6p^2)}{q}$$

This demand function has different elasticities for different values of p and q, which can be shown by choosing various values for p and the corresponding values of q determined by the function.

Constant Elasticity of Demand:

A demand function of the form

$$q = \frac{K}{p^a}$$

where q and p have the same meaning as in previous examples, and K and a are positive constants, is a case in which the demand curve has constant elasticity. Though the slope of the curve changes as p and q change, the elasticity does not; it is the same at every point on the curve. Moreover, this elasticity is equal to $-a$. To demonstrate, we write the above demand function as

$$q = K\,p^{-a}$$

We have, for its first derivative with respect to p,

$$\frac{dq}{dp} = -aK\,p^{-a-1}$$

Substituting this expression in the elasticity formula, we obtain the following:

$$e = \frac{dq}{dp} \cdot \frac{p}{q} = (-aK\,p^{-a-1})\frac{p}{q} = \frac{-aK\,p^{-a}}{q}$$

But $q = Kp^{-a}$, so

$$e = \frac{-aK\,p^{-a}}{K\,p^{-a}} = -a$$

This result may also be demonstrated by the use of logarithms. Take the logarithm to the base e of both sides of the demand equation:

$$\log_e q = -a \log_e p + \log_e K$$

This expression follows from the fact that $\log_e \dfrac{K}{p^a} = \log_e p^{-a} + \log_e K$ and from the fact that $\log_e p^{-a} = -a \log_e p$. Now differentiate both sides with respect to p:

$$\frac{d \log_e q}{dp} = \frac{-a\, d \log_e p}{dp} + \frac{d \log_e K}{dp}$$

Using Rule 6 of Chapter 8 and noting that $\log_e K$ is a constant, we have

$$\frac{1}{q} \cdot \frac{dq}{dp} = -a\,\frac{1}{p}$$

We multiply both sides of this equation by p, so that

$$\frac{dq}{dp} \cdot \frac{p}{q} = -a$$

A function, which is given by an equation that is linear in logarithms for both variables, has constant elasticity.

For instance, consider the demand equation

$$q = \frac{100}{p^3}$$

The elasticity of demand is given by

$$e = 100(-3p^{-4})\,\frac{p}{q}$$
$$= -\,\frac{300p^{-3}}{100p^{-3}} = -3$$

A special case of this general proposition has some interesting properties. This is the case in which $a = 1$ in the preceding proof. Then

$$q = \frac{K}{p}$$

This is the equation for a rectangular hyperbola; it has *unit* elasticity at all points on the curve. Therefore, total expenditure (which is identical to total revenue) remains unchanged for any change in price. The amount spent on the commodity is a constant sum. The percentage changes in price and quantity exactly offset one another so that total expenditure on the commodity remains unchanged.

2. Elasticity of Supply

The meaning of elasticity of supply is essentially the same as elasticity of demand, and of course, the procedure of differentiation is the same. Hence, little need be said of it. The one important difference is that in the case of supply, the elasticity is positive rather than negative. The slope of the supply curve is, in general, positive at every point on the curve—the value of this derivative of the supply function is greater than zero for all values of q and p. This implies, for one thing, that a supply curve of unit (positive) elasticity does not have the same total revenue at all points on the curve. Total revenue rises as price rises.

We still have, however, the property that a supply function, which is linear in logarithms, has constant elasticity. For consider the supply equation

$$s = K\,p^a$$

where s is the quantity supplied of the good S, and p is its price; again a and K are positive constants. This equation can be written

$$\log_e s = a \log_e p + \log_e K$$

and

$$\frac{d \log_e s}{dp} = a \frac{d \log_e p}{dp} + \frac{d \log_e K}{dp}$$

$$\frac{1}{s} \cdot \frac{ds}{dp} = a \frac{1}{p}$$

$$\frac{ds}{dp} \cdot \frac{p}{s} = a$$

We may interpret this constant elasticity as follows: For any point on the supply curve given a one per cent change in price, there is an a per cent change (in the same direction) in the quantity supplied. If a is greater than one, the supply curve is elastic at all points. If a is less than one, the curve is inelastic at all points. If a is equal to one, the supply curve has unit elasticity at all points.

This presentation of elasticity has referred to the demand for and supply of produced commodities only. It should be readily apparent, however, that the properties of elasticity apply to any function. One economically important application refers to the demand for and supply of factors of production. We need merely change the interpretation of our quantity variables from commodities to amounts of factors of production (labor, capital, etc.) and our price variables from prices of commodities to prices of the factors.

B. MARGINAL COST

The total cost of production of a single firm can be expressed as a function of total output; this has been demonstrated in Chapter 3. We can let x represent the units of commodity X produced per week by one firm. Let c denote the total cost, in dollars per unit, of producing x. Then the total cost function of the firm is written

$$c = t(x)$$

Now suppose that the total cost function t is known and given by the equation

$$c = .000167x^3 - .05x^2 + 6x + 10,000$$

The last term, \$10,000, is the total fixed costs of the firm. The *marginal cost of production* is defined as the change in total cost with respect to a change in output. We therefore specify the marginal cost of production as

$$\frac{dc}{dx} = t'(x) = .000501x^2 - .10x + 6$$

The relation of this derivative to economic theory can be clearly seen from the construction of a table that shows the value of $t'(x)$ for chosen values of x, that is, a marginal cost schedule. The graph of $t'(x)$ can then be drawn. It will be seen that the resulting marginal cost *curve* has the approximate shape ordinarily assumed in economic theory. It falls at first and then rises as total output expands. In this case, the marginal cost curve rises at an increasing rate after the minimum point has been reached. Construction of the schedule and the curve is left to the reader as an exercise.

C. MARGINAL REVENUE

Another marginal concept, which is part of the accepted theory of the individual firm, is *marginal revenue*. It is defined as the change in total revenue with respect to a change in output (or more exactly, with respect to a change in sales). Under conditions of pure competition, the marginal revenue is constant and equal to the average revenue or price. *Total revenue* of the firm is defined as the price of the commodity (taken as given independently of the behavior of the firm) times the amount of the commodity sold. Hence, we may write total revenue in functional notation as

$$r = u(x) = p \cdot x$$

where r denotes total revenue from the sale of x units of the commodity X, p denotes the given price of X, and the function u is assumed continuous. To obtain the marginal revenue, we differentiate r with respect to x:

$$\frac{dr}{dx} = p \cdot \frac{dx}{dx} = p$$

The marginal revenue is a constant equal to the price and is drawn diagrammatically as a horizontal line at a level of p units above the x axis. For the individual firm under pure competition, the horizontal marginal revenue curve is also the average revenue curve. This indicates that the demand curve facing the individual firm is perfectly elastic. In fact, the two statements are alternative ways of saying the same thing.

Assume, instead, that the firm under investigation is a monopoly. Then the price cannot be regarded by the firm as a given constant. Rather, the market demand curve is the demand curve (the average revenue curve) facing the monopolist, since he is the only seller. In general, this demand curve will be negatively sloped, so the price is not independent of the behavior of the monopolist; in order to sell more the monopolist must reduce the price.

Let us suppose that the market demand function is given by the equation

$$x = f(p) = 100 - 5p$$

where, again, x denotes the quantity of the good X sold and p denotes its price. Since the price is not taken as constant by the monopolist, from the demand equation we can write its inverse as

$$p = 20 - \tfrac{1}{5}x$$

Now by substituting this expression for p in the total revenue function, we obtain

$$r = px = (20 - \tfrac{1}{5}x)x = 20x - \tfrac{1}{5}x^2$$

Consequently, the marginal revenue function is

$$\frac{dr}{dx} = 20 - \frac{2}{5}x$$

Both the average revenue curve (market demand curve) and the marginal revenue curve are straight lines with negative slopes. The curves can easily be drawn in the same diagram with average and marginal revenues measured on the vertical axis and quantity sold on the horizontal axis. It will be seen that the marginal revenue curve lies below the average revenue curve and declines more rapidly than the average revenue curve as sales expand. Both curves intercept the vertical axis at a value of 20. But the average revenue curve intercepts the x axis at a value of $x = 100$, whereas the marginal revenue curve intercepts the x axis at a value of $x = 50$. Thus, we have the usual types of marginal and average revenue curves of a monopolist.

D. THE MARGINAL PROPENSITIES TO CONSUME AND SAVE

When studying the determination of aggregate variables for the economy as a whole, we study the relationship between total national consumption and national income. This relationship is often called the consumption function or "law of consumption." Stated verbally, the law of consumption states that as income increases (or decreases) consumption increases (or decreases), but by less than the increase (or decrease) in income. Another way of stating this law is as follows: the marginal propensity to consume is greater than zero but less than one, where the marginal propensity to consume is defined as the change in total consumption with respect to a change in income.

Let us write the continuous consumption function as

$$C = f(Y) = 10 + \tfrac{3}{4}Y$$

In this equation C signifies total real consumption measured in, say billions of dollars, and Y indicates total real income measured in the same units. The marginal propensity to consume is the first derivative of the consumption function:

$$\frac{dC}{dY} = \frac{3}{4}$$

When income increases by any given amount, consumption increases by $\frac{3}{4}$ of the amount of the increase in income.

A related concept is the marginal propensity to save. Let S represent total net savings for the economy as a whole. Then

$$Y = C + S$$

defines the disposal possibilities of any level of income. Income must be either consumed or saved. If we know

$$C = 10 + \tfrac{3}{4}Y$$

we can substitute this in the above expression to obtain the savings function:

$$Y = 10 + \tfrac{3}{4}Y + S$$

or

$$S = -10 + (1 - \tfrac{3}{4})Y = -10 + \tfrac{1}{4}Y$$

Therefore, the marginal propensity to save is

$$\frac{dS}{dY} = \frac{1}{4}$$

Furthermore,

$$\frac{dY}{dY} = 1 = \frac{dC}{dY} + \frac{dS}{dY}$$

The value of the marginal propensity to consume for any given level of Y (say Y_1) is seen to be equal to the slope of the consumption curve at the point with abscissa equal to Y_1, and likewise for the marginal propensity to save.

If the consumption function is not linear, that is, if consumption is not a linear function of income, the marginal propensities to consume and save are not constant numbers. Let the consumption function be given by the following equation:

$$C = 10 + 5\sqrt{Y} = 10 + 5Y^{\frac{1}{2}}$$

Then the marginal propensity to consume is given by

$$\frac{dC}{dY} = \frac{5}{2}Y^{-\frac{1}{2}} = \frac{5}{2\sqrt{Y}}$$

Under this formulation, the value of the marginal propensity to consume is smaller for larger chosen levels of income. Consider, for example, the value of the marginal propensity to consume when national income is 100. By the substitution of 100 for Y in the formula for the marginal propensity to consume, we find that the marginal propensity to consume is $\frac{1}{4}$. When income is 225, however, the marginal propensity to consume emerges from the formula as $\frac{1}{6}$. It follows that the value of the marginal propensity to save is larger as greater levels of income are considered. We have already seen that

$$\frac{dS}{dY} = 1 - \frac{dC}{dY}$$

In this case, therefore,

$$\frac{dS}{dY} = 1 - \frac{5}{2\sqrt{Y}}$$

When income is 100, the marginal propensity to save is $1 - \frac{1}{4} = \frac{3}{4}$; and when income is 225, the marginal propensity to save is $1 - \frac{1}{6} = \frac{5}{6}$.

These examples represent but a few cases in which derivatives are used for purposes of economic analysis. This mathematical notion has much wider applicability. Many of the functions with which economists deal are derivatives—both in the analysis of the behavior of individual entities in the economy (single households, firms, etc.) and in specifying certain properties of functions that describe group behavior. Moreover, derivatives are of use in determining the conditions for passing from the individual units to the behavior of groups in the economy. We shall have opportunity in later chapters to make further applications of this very important mathematical concept.

PROBLEMS

Let q denote the quantity demanded or supplied and let p denote the price of a commodity. Compute the price elasticity of demand or supply as indicated at the prices and quantities specified.

1. Demand equation:

$$q = 200 - 20p$$

Compute elasticity when
   (a) $p = 8$
   (b) $p = 5$
   (c) $p = 2$

2. Demand equation:
$$q = \frac{100}{p}$$
Compute elasticity when
(a) $p = 100$
(b) $p = 20$
(c) $p = 2$

3. Demand equation:
$$q = 1000 - p^2$$
Compute elasticity when
(a) $p = 30$
(b) $p = 20$
(c) $p = 10$

4. Supply equation:
$$q = -10 + 30p$$
Compute elasticity when
(a) $p = 1$
(b) $p = 10$
(c) $p = 100$

5. Supply equation:
$$q = 20 - .05p + p^{\frac{1}{2}}$$
Compute elasticity when
(a) $p = 4$
(b) $p = 16$
(c) $p = 100$

6. Supply equation:
$$q = 5 + e^p$$
Compute elasticity when
(a) $p = 1$
(b) $p = 2$
(c) $p = 3$

7. The total cost function of a firm is given as
$$c = 1000 + 8x + .006x^2$$
where c denotes total cost and x denotes the quantity produced per unit time.
(a) Graph the total cost function from $x = 0$ to $x = 100$.
(b) Find the marginal cost of production.
(c) Graph the marginal cost of production from $x = 0$ to $x = 100$.

8. The total cost of production of a firm is given as
$$c = 2000 + 10x - .02x^2 + .001x^3$$
where c denotes total cost and x denotes the quantity produced per unit time.

(a) Graph the total cost function from $x = 0$ to $x = 200$.

(b) Find the marginal cost of production.

(c) Find the average cost of production.

(d) Graph in the same diagram the average and marginal costs of production from $x = 0$ to $x = 200$.

9. The market demand function for a commodity X is given as

$$x = 200 - 20 \sqrt{p}$$

where x denotes the quantity of X demanded and p its price.

(a) Find the marginal revenue function for a monopolist who produces X.

(b) Graph the average revenue curve and the marginal revenue curve from $p = 36$ to $p = 100$.

10. The aggregate consumption function for the economy as a whole is given as

$$C = 15 + .8Y - .5Y^{\frac{1}{2}}$$

where C denotes total consumption and Y denotes national income.

(a) Find the marginal propensity to consume.

(b) Find the marginal propensity to save.

(c) Find the values of the marginal propensities to consume and save for $Y = 9$, $Y = 49$, $Y = 100$, $Y = 196$.

CHAPTER 10

Partial Derivatives and Their Applications

Our explanation of derivatives and their applications to economics has dealt solely with functions of one independent variable. We have been measuring the rate of change of y with respect to x when our functions are assumed to be of the form $y = f(x)$. Yet we know from our discussion of functions in Chapter 1 that one variable may be a function of any number of other variables. Therefore, there are some important questions that are still unanswered. We must extend the notion of a derivative to cover the cases that involve functions of two or more independent variables. If, for instance, the function f is defined by

$$u = f(x, y, z)$$

how do we measure the rate of change of u with respect to x? How do we measure its rate of change with respect to y? In order to answer questions such as these, we introduce the concept of the partial derivative. Given an explicit function of two or more variables, a *partial derivative* measures the rate of change of the dependent variable with respect to one of the independent variables, when all the other independent variables are conceptually held constant.

Obviously this concept is very important in economic analysis. In economics, we frequently have a given quantity depending not just on one other variable but on several. In general, the output of one commodity depends upon the quantities of more than one factor input. To find the behavior of output when the amount of one of the variable inputs changes and others do not, we calculate the partial derivative of output with respect to that one input. Often the quantity demanded of a commodity is expressed as a function of the price of that commodity, other prices, and consumer income. When the demand function is given in this form and we wish to find the rate of change in the quantity demanded with respect to its own price, given other prices and income, we calculate the partial derivative of the quantity demanded with respect to the price of that commodity. Several applications of partial derivatives to economic problems will be presented in this chapter. First, however, let us take a closer look at the meaning of a partial derivative.

A. PARTIAL DERIVATIVES

If the variable z is stated as a function of two variables x and y, we write

$$z = f(x, y)$$

By this formulation we mean that for every permissible pair of values of the independent variables x and y, we can find at least one number z that corresponds to this pair. If the function is single-valued, there is one and only one number z that corresponds to the pair. In order to present a geometric interpretation of the function, we would use a three-dimensional figure with x, y, and z on the three axes. The relationship among the three variables given by the function can be represented as a surface in three-dimensional space. Suppose the function is single-valued and continuous; then for one pair of values of x and y we have one and only one value of z, and this defines a point in the space. If we consider all permissible pairs of values of x and y (and the corresponding values of z), we generate a surface that is a "picture" of the functional relationship.

Now we inquire about the rate of change of z with respect to one or the other of the two independent variables. To do this, we introduce the operator "∂," which is the symbol used to designate the partial derivative. Another symbol commonly used to designate the partial derivative of the function with respect to, say, x is $f_x(x, y)$. The partial derivative of z with respect to x is defined as

$$\frac{\partial z}{\partial x} = f_x(x, y) = \lim_{\Delta x \to 0} \frac{\Delta z}{\Delta x} = \lim_{\Delta x \to 0} \frac{f(x + \Delta x, y)}{\Delta x}$$

The variable x takes on an increment or decrement, Δx, but the variable y is kept constant. The partial derivative of z with respect to x is computed by taking the derivative of z with respect to x, treating y as if it were a constant. Likewise, the partial derivative of z with respect to y is computed by taking the derivative of z with respect to y and treating x as if it were constant. The rules of differentiation presented in Chapter 8 still apply when one is computing the derivative of z with respect to either x or y; the only difference is that the other independent variable is treated like any other constant in the equation.

To make the explanation more concrete, let us find the partial derivatives of some illustrative functions. We are given an implicit function in three variables x, y, and z. Its equation is the following:

$$z - 2x^2 - 8y^3 + 14 = 0$$

We can rewrite this as an explicit function of two independent variables. Suppose we choose z as the dependent variable:

$$z = f(x, y) = 2x^2 + 8y^3 - 14$$

To find the partial derivative of z with respect to x, we treat y as a constant and take the derivative with respect to x. Using Rules 1 and 2 of Chapter 8, we have

$$\frac{\partial z}{\partial x} = 4x$$

Since $8y^3$ is a constant when y is treated as a constant, and since the derivative of a constant is zero, the variable y does not enter the formula for the partial derivative in this example. Had we taken the partial derivative of z with respect to y we would obtain

$$\frac{\partial z}{\partial y} = 24y^2$$

In this case, x is treated as a constant.

Consider, also, the implicit function given by

$$z + 2x^2y - 4xy^2 + 3x - y + 13 = 0$$

Again, let z be an explicit function of the independent variables x and y:

$$z = -2x^2y + 4xy^2 - 3x + y - 13$$

The partial derivative of z with respect to x is

$$\frac{\partial z}{\partial x} = -4yx + 4y^2 - 3$$

This derivative can be calculated for various values of x and y. For example, at the point $x = 2$ and $y = 1$, we have for the value of the partial derivative

$$f_x(2, 1) = -4(1)(2) + 4(1)^2 - 3 = -7$$

Now let us consider the partial derivative of z with respect to y. We treat x as a constant and obtain

$$\frac{\partial z}{\partial y} = -2x^2 + 8xy + 1$$

When $x = 2$ and $y = 1$, then

$$f_y(2, 1) = -2(2)^2 + 8(2)(1) + 1 = 9$$

We can say that when $x = 2$ and $y = 1$ (hence $z = -18$, from the original equation), then z is decreasing with respect to x at a rate of 7 units for each unit increase in x, and z is increasing with respect to y at a rate of 9 units for each unit increase in y.

We are, of course, not required to write z as an explicit function of x and y. We might have written y as an explicit function of x and z. Suppose we have the implicit function given by

$$x + z - xy + zy = 0$$

Let the explicit function be denoted by $y = f(x, z)$. Simplifying the equation and writing y as a function of x and z, we have

$$(x - z)y = x + z$$
$$y = \frac{x + z}{x - z}$$

We determine, first, the partial derivative of y with respect to x. We notice that this is a quotient of functions of x (when z is treated as a constant), so we use Rule 4 of Chapter 8:

$$\frac{\partial y}{\partial x} = \frac{\partial}{\partial x}\left(\frac{x + z}{x - z}\right) = \frac{(1)(x - z) - (1)(x + z)}{(x - z)^2} = -\frac{2z}{(x - z)^2}$$

To find the partial derivative of y with respect to z, we follow the same procedure. With x regarded as a constant

$$\frac{\partial y}{\partial z} = \frac{\partial}{\partial z}\left(\frac{x + z}{x - z}\right) = \frac{(1)(x - z) - (-1)(x + z)}{(x - z)^2} = \frac{2x}{(x - z)^2}$$

The geometric interpretation of the partial derivative is like that of the total derivative discussed in Chapter 7. Let the function f be given as

$$z = f(x, y)$$

We have a three-dimensional surface corresponding to the function f, and we are interested in the interpretation of the partial derivative of z with respect to x. Now if we assign some value to y (hold y constant), we obtain a relation between z and x. This relation is "pictured" in one of the many two-dimensional planes that make up the three-dimensional space (see Figure 2.11 and the discussion there). That is, for any *one* value of y the surface reduces to the special case of a curve. The partial derivative of z with respect to x measures the slope of this curve (which relates z to x) in the zx plane, defined by the given value of y. For a different assigned value of y, we would have a different plane and, in general, a curve with a different slope. We say that y is a parameter of the function $\dfrac{\partial z}{\partial x}$. By the same type of argument, if we were to calculate the partial derivative of z with respect to y, we would conceptually hold x constant and measure the slope of a curve in the zy plane. In this case, x is a parameter of the function $\dfrac{\partial z}{\partial y}$.

The same interpretation and methods of differentiation apply also to functions of more than two independent variables. Let z be written as a function of n independent variables. When we take the partial derivative of z with respect to one of the n variables, we measure the rate of change of z with respect to that one variable, and we treat the other $(n - 1)$ variables as constants. Of course, we cannot give a visual interpretation to the partial derivative in the case where n is greater than two. But we can conceive of a space of four or more dimensions with the same properties as those having two or three dimensions. We can consider the explicit function as describing a figure in $(n + 1)$ dimensional space. Then the partial derivative of z with respect to one of the n variables still measures the slope of the curve relating z to that one variable, when the other $(n - 1)$ independent variables are assumed to be constant.

B. DIFFERENTIATION OF IMPLICIT FUNCTIONS

Up to now, we have deliberately chosen as examples of implicit functions those that can easily be expressed as explicit functions. In the last example in the preceding section, for instance, the equation of the implicit function in x, y, and z was purposely designed so that y could easily be written as an explicit function of x and z. But in economics there frequently appear functions that cannot easily be expressed in this form. Consider the implicit function given by the equation

$$f(x, y, z) = 3z^4 + x^3z^3 - xy^2z + 6 = 0$$

We see immediately that z cannot be easily written as an explicit function of x and y. Consequently, it is of some importance to be able to differentiate functions in implicit form.

We shall present the rule for differentiation of implicit functions without proof. Special properties of continuity on the part of the functions are required, but such conditions are generally satisfied by the functions used in economics.

Let us assume an implicit function in three variables,

$$f(x, y, z) = 0$$

and let z be treated as an explicit function of both x and y. Then we assert the following rules:

$$\frac{\partial z}{\partial x} = \frac{-\dfrac{\partial f}{\partial x}}{\dfrac{\partial f}{\partial z}}$$

and

$$\frac{\partial z}{\partial y} = \frac{-\dfrac{\partial f}{\partial y}}{\dfrac{\partial f}{\partial z}}$$

Suppose the function f is specified by the equation

$$f(x, y, z) = 3z^4 + x^3z^3 - xy^2z + 6 = 0$$

To find the partial derivative of z with respect to x, we use the first rule given above:

$$\frac{\partial f}{\partial x} = 3z^3x^2 - y^2z \qquad \frac{\partial f}{\partial z} = 12z^3 + 3x^3z^2 - xy^2$$

Hence, by the first formula

$$\frac{\partial z}{\partial x} = \frac{-f_x}{f_z} = -\frac{3z^3x^2 - y^2z}{12z^3 + 3x^3z^2 - xy^2}$$

For the partial derivative of z with respect to y:

$$\frac{\partial f}{\partial y} = -2xyz \qquad \frac{\partial f}{\partial z} = 12z^3 + 3x^3z^2 - xy^2$$

Therefore

$$\frac{\partial z}{\partial y} = \frac{-f_y}{f_z} = \frac{2xyz}{12z^3 + 3x^3z^2 - xy^2}$$

C. HIGHER PARTIAL DERIVATIVES

Functions of one variable were shown to have second, third, and higher-order derivatives. We can define partial derivatives of order higher than one in an analogous manner. The second partial derivative of the continuous function

$$z = f(x, y)$$

with respect to x is computed by differentiating the first partial derivative $\partial z / \partial x$ partially with respect to x. That is, we take the derivative of the function $f_x(x, y)$ with respect to x, holding y constant. The symbols used to denote this second partial derivative are

$$\frac{\partial^2 z}{\partial x^2} \quad \text{or} \quad f_{xx}(x, y)$$

Similarly, the second partial derivative with respect to y is obtained by differentiating the first partial derivative $\partial z/\partial y$ partially with respect to y, holding x constant. The symbols used to denote this second partial derivative are

$$\frac{\partial^2 z}{\partial y^2} \quad \text{or} \quad f_{yy}(x, y)$$

Consider, for example, the function given by

$$z = f(x, y) = 14 + 3x^3 + x^2 - xy^2 + 2y^3 - x^2y^2$$

We take the first partial derivative of this function with respect to x:

$$\frac{\partial z}{\partial x} = f_x(x, y) = 9x^2 + 2x - y^2 - 2y^2x$$

We also take the first partial derivative with respect to y:

$$\frac{\partial z}{\partial y} = f_y(x, y) = -2xy + 6y^2 - 2x^2y$$

The second partial derivative with respect to x is obtained by differentiating $f_x(x, y)$ with respect to x:

$$\frac{\partial^2 z}{\partial x^2} = f_{xx}(x, y) = 18x + 2 - 2y^2$$

The second partial derivative with respect to y is found by differentiating $f_y(x, y)$ with respect to y:

$$\frac{\partial^2 z}{\partial y^2} = f_{yy}(x, y) = -2x + 12y - 2x^2$$

The third partial derivatives with respect to x and y are found by repeating this procedure on the second partial derivatives.

There is another important characteristic of functions of more than one variable, however. Besides these two second derivatives, there are also second-order mixed derivatives:

$$\frac{\partial^2 z}{\partial x \partial y} = f_{xy}(x, y) = \frac{\partial f_y(x, y)}{\partial x}$$

and

$$\frac{\partial^2 z}{\partial y \partial x} = f_{yx}(x, y) = \frac{\partial f_x(x, y)}{\partial y}$$

That is, we can differentiate the function f first with respect to y, and then differentiate this partial derivative with respect to x, and vice versa. In this case, the first partial derivative of the function with respect to, say, y is computed; then this partial derivative is in turn differentiated partially, but this time with respect to x.

Under certain conditions of continuity that are possessed by virtually all functions, these two mixed derivatives are equal, that is,

$$\frac{\partial^2 z}{\partial x \partial y} = \frac{\partial^2 z}{\partial y \partial x}$$

Hence, the mixed partial derivative can be computed in two ways that yield the same result. Take, for instance, the function for which the second-order partial derivatives have already been calculated:

$$z = f(x, y) = 14 + 3x^3 + x^2 - xy^2 + 2y^3 - x^2y^2$$

The first partial derivatives were found to be

$$\frac{\partial z}{\partial x} = 9x^2 + 2x - y^2 - 2y^2x$$

$$\frac{\partial z}{\partial y} = -2xy + 6y^2 - 2x^2y$$

If we differentiate the first of these with respect to y, we find

$$\frac{\partial^2 z}{\partial y \partial x} = -2y - 4xy$$

Differentiating the second with respect to x:

$$\frac{\partial^2 z}{\partial x \partial y} = -2y - 4xy$$

we see that

$$\frac{\partial^2 z}{\partial y \partial x} = \frac{\partial^2 z}{\partial x \partial y} = -2y - 4xy$$

These higher-order partial derivatives will prove useful in Chapter 11, where maxima and minima of functions of several variables are discussed.

D. ECONOMIC APPLICATIONS OF PARTIAL DERIVATIVES

1. Marginal Productivity

Generally more than one factor of production is engaged in the production of any one commodity. In Chapter 3, Section D, it was shown that the relation among the amounts of factor inputs employed by the firm, on the one hand, and the quantity of resulting product, on the other, can be expressed in functional notation. The production function can be written showing the output as an explicit function of factor inputs.

Assume we have two factor inputs—labor and capital represented by L and K respectively—engaged by the firm in the production of commodity X. We let l, k, and x signify the quantities of L, K, and X respectively (measured in appropriate units). The production function of the firm may be written

$$x = j(l, k)$$

where we assume this function j is continuous. In Chapter 3, we demonstrated how the *average productivity* of, say, L is determined from the production function, once the production function is specified by an equation. We merely divide the production function by l. We did not, however, derive the marginal productivity function. With the use of partial derivatives, we are now in a position to do this.

The *marginal productivity* of the factor L is defined as the change in total output with respect to a change in the quantity of the factor L used, given the amount of the factor K. We see, then, that it is the partial derivative of x with respect to l for the function j:

Marginal Productivity of $L = \dfrac{\partial x}{\partial l}$

Similarly, if the amount of labor is conceptually held constant and the amount of capital is variable, we obtain the marginal productivity of capital:

Marginal Productivity of $K = \dfrac{\partial x}{\partial k}$

Suppose we know the production function of a firm. Suppose, further, that the quantity of the good X produced, x, is a function of the amount of three factor inputs, L, K, and R. These symbols might represent labor, capital, and land respectively. Let their quantities be represented by l, k, and r respectively. The known production function is given by the equation

$$x = j(l, k, r) = 50l + 100k + 40r - \tfrac{1}{3}l^2 - k^2 - \tfrac{3}{4}r^2 lk.$$

To find the marginal productivity of the three factor inputs, we derive three partial derivatives:

$$\frac{\partial x}{\partial l} = 50 - \tfrac{2}{3}l - \tfrac{3}{4}r^2 k$$

$$\frac{\partial x}{\partial k} = 100 - 2k - \tfrac{3}{4}r^2 l$$

$$\frac{\partial x}{\partial r} = 40 - \tfrac{3}{2}lkr$$

For given values of r and k, we have diminishing marginal productivity for the factor L. That is, the partial derivative $\partial x/\partial l$ is a decreasing function of l. Likewise, for the given quantities l and r there is diminishing marginal productivity for the factor K, and the same is true for the factor R when l and k are held constant.

To obtain the *marginal product* (the value of the marginal productivity function) of any one of the factors, we merely substitute a value for l, k, and r in the partial derivative of x with respect to that factor. For instance, when $l = 2$, $k = 5$, and $r = 1$, we have for the marginal product of L

$$j_l(2,\, 5,\, 1) = 50 - \tfrac{2}{3}(2) - \tfrac{3}{4}(1)^2\,(5) = \frac{539}{12} = 44.9$$

Notice that the marginal product of L depends upon the amounts of K and R used, as well as upon the amount of L used.

2. Marginal Utility

Even when we are dealing in economics with nonmeasurable magnitudes, the notations of calculus are still very useful. The theory that lies behind consumer demand is the theory of utility. The negative slope of the demand curve is "rationalized" by the assumption that each consumer maximizes his total utility, given his income. We cannot observe people's utilities, or rather their scales of preference, and so we cannot measure utility. Though we cannot measure it, we can derive from the utility theory certain propositions about economic magnitudes that are measurable—particularly, about consumer response to price changes. It is demonstrated in economic theory that if consumers maximize total utility, they will consume those quantities of any two commodities X and Y such that the ratio of the marginal utility of X to the marginal utility of Y is equal to the ratio of the given price of X to the given price of Y. From this proposition, the negatively-sloped demand curve for, say, X is derived.

In terms of calculus, let us now ask what is meant by marginal utility. In general, each consumer will consume many commodities, and from this "bundle" of commodities he will derive a certain (nonmeasurable) total utility. For the sake of simplicity, let us assume that the individual consumes only two commodities, X and Y, and spends his entire income on them. Let the amounts of these two commodities be denoted by x and y respectively. Then we can write the total utility in functional notation:

$$u = f(x, y)$$

where u signifies total utility as a continuous function of the amounts of X and Y. We cannot write an equation for the utility function because it is not measurable. We can, however, give a precise meaning to marginal utility. We define the marginal utility of the commodity X as the partial derivative of the utility function with respect to x. That is,

$$\frac{\partial u}{\partial x} = f_x$$

The marginal utility of y is defined as

$$\frac{\partial u}{\partial y} = f_y$$

Let us now proceed to the conclusion that total utility is maximized when the ratio of marginal utilities is equal to the price ratios. Let p_x represent the given price of X and p_y the given price of Y. The condition for maximization of total utility, given prices and income, can be written

$$\frac{f_x}{f_y} = \frac{p_x}{p_y}$$

In nonmathematical economic theory, ratios of the marginal utilities are interpreted diagrammatically as the slopes of indifference curves. The ratio of the prices is interpreted as the slope of the budget line. At the point where the budget line is tangent to an indifference curve the above condition is satisfied, and total utility is maximized. We shall go into more detail and derive the maximization conditions in Chapter 12.

3. Partial Elasticities

Let us return for a moment to the discussion in Section A of Chapter 3. We saw that when the quantity demanded of a good is expressed as a function of one variable (usually its price), there are other economic variables that are parameters of this function. The demand curve relating quantity demanded to price is drawn for given consumer income, other prices, etc.; it will shift position in the quantity-price plane if the values of these other variables should change. We have already considered the price elasticity of demand when the quantity demanded of a commodity is expressed as a function of its price only. In other words, we have measured movements along the demand curve. But in what way, and by how much, will the quantity demanded change if the parameters of the demand curve should change? To answer this question, we must introduce these other variables explicitly into the demand equation. That is, we must take them out of the category of parameters by expanding the dimensions of the demand relation.

Let us write the market demand for commodity Q as a function of more than one independent variable. Denote by q the quantity of commodity Q demanded, and let it be a function of the price of Q, p, and consumer income, y:

$$q = f(p, y)$$

When deriving the price elasticity of demand, we do so for a given level of income—a given demand curve in the qp plane. This is another way of saying that we use a partial derivative in the elasticity formula rather than the total derivative (as we did in Section A of Chapter 9). Suppose the demand function f is specified by the equation

$$q = 50 - .8p^2 + .3y$$

The price elasticity of demand is given by the formula

$$e_p = \frac{\partial q}{\partial p} \cdot \frac{p}{q} = \frac{-1.6p^2}{q}$$

For a chosen level of income (for a given two-dimensional demand curve), and for a chosen price and quantity demanded (for a given point on the demand curve), we obtain the value of the price elasticity of demand.

We can also compute the income elasticity of demand for the commodity Q. The *income elasticity* of demand is the percentage change in the quantity demanded in response to a percentage change in income, prices remaining constant. If the income elasticity is positive, the good is called a superior good; if negative, it is called an inferior good. The income elasticity of the demand function f is

$$e_y = \frac{\partial q}{\partial y} \cdot \frac{y}{q} = \frac{.3y}{q}$$

This elasticity will be positive for all permissible levels of income, and so we say that the good Q is a superior good. When consumer income increases, the quantity demanded by consumers increases for any given set of prices.

Another elasticity concept frequently used in economic theory is the cross elasticity of demand. When two commodities are inter-related, the demand for each will depend upon the price of the other. Substitutes and complements in consumption immediately come to mind. The *cross (price) elasticity of demand* for a good is defined as the percentage change in the quantity demand of that good which occurs in response to a percentage change in the price of another good; the price of the first good (and any other variables influencing demand) remaining constant. If the two goods are substitutes in consumption, the cross elasticity will turn out to be positive, and the greater its value the greater is the degree of substitution. In case the two goods are complementary, the cross elasticity will be negative.[1]

Suppose the demand function for good Q is written so as to explicitly include the price of another good R as an independent variable. Let the price of Q be represented by p_q, and the price of R by p_r. Then we write the demand for Q as

$$q = f(p_q, p_r)$$

where q is the quantity demanded of the good Q. The cross elasticity of demand for Q is defined as

$$e_{p_r} = \frac{\partial q}{\partial p_r} \cdot \frac{p_r}{q}$$

Assume the demand for Q is given by the following equation:

$$q = \frac{10}{p_q} + .4p_r^2$$

The cross elasticity of demand for Q with respect to the price of R is

$$e_{p_r} = \frac{\partial q}{\partial p_r} \cdot \frac{p_r}{q} = \frac{.8p_r^2}{q}$$

For every permissible value of p_r and q, the elasticity is positive. Hence, we say that the good R is a substitute in consumption for the good Q, and vice versa.

PROBLEMS

GROUP I:

Find the first partial derivatives $\partial z/\partial x$ and $\partial z/\partial y$ for the following functions and the indicated values of the derivatives.

[1] The cross elasticity will turn out negative, also, if the income effect of a change in price outweighs the substitution effect.

1. $z = f(x, y) = 3x^3 - y^2 + 2x^2y - 2y^3x + y$.
   Find $f_x(1, 2), f_x(3, 4), f_y(1, 2), f_y(3, 4)$.
2. $z = f(x, y) = (x^2y + 3y^3x)^2$.
3. $z = f(x, y) = \log_e(2x + y^2)$.
   Find $f_x(2, 4), f_y(1, 0)$.
4. $z = f(x, y) = e^x + (e^y)^2$.
   Find the second partial derivatives $\partial^2z/\partial x^2$, $\partial^2z/\partial y^2$, $\partial^2z/\partial x\partial y$ and $\partial^2z/\partial y\partial x$ for the following functions and the indicated values of the derivatives.
5. $z = f(x, y) = xy$.
   Find $f_{xx}(-8, 4), f_{yy}(0, 0), f_{xy}(2, 10), f_{yx}(6, 3)$.
6. Problem 2 above: find $f_{xx}(3, 1), f_{yy}(0, 1), f_{xy}(2, 2), f_{yy}(-2, -2)$.
7. Problem 3 above.
8. You are given the production function

$$x = j(l, k, r, v) = 10l + 50k + 20r + 12v - \tfrac{1}{2}l^2 - \tfrac{1}{4}k^2 - \tfrac{1}{5}r^2 - \tfrac{1}{8}v^2$$

where x represents total output and l, k, r, and v are amounts of factor inputs, L, K, R, and V. Find the marginal productivity functions for each of the factors of production. Are there diminishing marginal returns to each of the factors? How do you know? Compute the marginal products of each of the factors for $l = 10, k = 5, r = 20$, and $v = 14$.

9. You are given the following demand function for the commodity X:
   $x = 300 - .5p_x^2 + .02p_o + .05y$, where x denotes the quantity demanded of X, p_x the price of X, p_o the price of a related commodity, and y consumer income.
   (a) Compute the price elasticity of demand when $p_x = 12, p_o = 10$, and $y = 200$.
   (b) Compute the cross elasticity of demand for X with respect to p_o when $p_x = 12, p_o = 10$, and $y = 200$.
   (c) Compute the income elasticity of demand for X when $p_x = 12$, $p_o = 10$, and $y = 200$.

10. You are given the following aggregate consumption function for the economy as a whole
    $C = 10 + .6Y + .1A^2$, where C denotes total consumption, Y national income, and A total holdings of liquid assets by households.
    (a) Find the marginal propensity to consume out of income.
    (b) Find the marginal propensity to consume out of assets.

GROUP II:

Find the first partial derivatives for the following functions.

11. $z = f(x, y) = \left(\dfrac{x^2 + 3y}{x + 2y}\right)^3$.

12. $f(x, y, z) = 2x^2z - 3xyz + 2xy^3 - .5x^2y^2z^2 = 0.$
13. $f(x, y, z) = (4x - 3x^2z + yz^3 - 7)^2 = 0.$
14. $f(x, y, z) = \sqrt{x^2 + y^2 + z^2} = 0.$
15. Find the second partial derivatives for problem 12 above.

CHAPTER 11

Maxima and Minima

The most fundamental assumption of economic theory is the assumption of maximizing behavior. It is a very fruitful assumption in the sense that it yields widespread implications that explain the behavior of practically all economic institutions in our society. Each household is assumed to maximize the total utility obtained from the goods and services which that household consumes, given its income and the prices of the goods and services. From this assumption, the law of demand for goods and services is derived. Each individual firm producing a good or service is assumed to maximize its total profits, and from this assumption the law of supply of goods and services is derived. The assumption of maximizing behavior enables the economist to make predictions about observable economic phenomena.

Since the magnitudes that are assumed to be maximized can be expressed as functions of other variables, it is important to know how a maximum or minimum value of a function can be found. In geometric terms, this is interpreted as a maximum or minimum point on a curve (in the case of an explicit function of one variable) or a surface (in the case of an explicit function of two variables). A maximum point is a point that is higher than all neighboring points on the curve or surface; a minimum point is one that is lower than all neighboring points.

A. MAXIMA AND MINIMA OF FUNCTIONS OF ONE VARIABLE

When a function is denoted by $y = f(x)$ and the value of the derivative is positive for a chosen value of x, the function is increasing at that point. That is, y increases as x increases. If the value of the derivative is negative, the function is decreasing at that point: y decreases as x increases. In the first case, the line tangent to the curve at the point has a positive slope; in the second case, it has a negative slope. See the unbroken curve in Figure 11.1, and consider all values of x less than ten. Note that the tangent lines for all of these values of x have positive slopes. Now consider all values of x greater than ten, and note that the tangent lines for all of these values of x have negative slopes. At the point at which this curve is a maximum, the point (10, 16), the line tangent to the curve is horizontal. The function is neither increasing nor decreasing at this point; the value of the derivative is zero. The equation corresponding to the unbroken curve in Figure 11.1 is

$$y = 16 - .1(x - 10)^2.$$

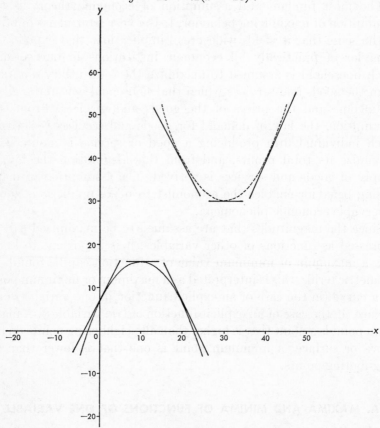

Figure 11.1

Suppose that a function had been given instead by the equation

$$y = 30 + .1(x - 30)^2$$

The curve corresponding to this equation is shown as the broken curve in Figure 11.1. The minimum point on this curve is seen to be (30, 30). The line tangent to the curve at this point is horizontal, so the function is neither increasing nor decreasing at this point. The value of the derivative is zero.

More generally, we may say that a necessary condition for either a maximum or a minimum of a function is that the value of the first derivative be equal to zero. To find the maximum or minimum value of the function given by

$$y = 16 - .1(x - 10)^2$$

we must compute the first derivative of the function:

$$\frac{dy}{dx} = -.2(x - 10)$$

$$\frac{dy}{dx} = 0$$

Setting this derivative equal to zero, and solving for x we obtain

$$-.2x + 2 = 0$$
$$x = 10$$

Hence, we know that the function is either a maximum or a minimum when $x = 10$. To find the value of the function at this point, we merely substitute $x = 10$ in the equation of the function and solve for the value of y:

$$y = 16 - .1(10 - 10)^2 = 16$$

We know that the point (10, 16) is either a maximum or minimum point on the curve.

Now let us consider the other function whose graph is shown in Figure 11.1:

$$y = 30 + .1(x - 30)^2$$

We set the first derivative equal to zero, thus

$$\frac{dy}{dx} = .2(x - 30) = 0$$

Solving for x, we have

$$.2x - 6 = 0$$
$$x = 30$$

Substituting this value for x in the original equation, yields the value of y:

$$y = 30 + .1(30 - 30)^2 = 30$$

Therefore, we know that the point (30, 30) on the curve corresponding to this equation is either a maximum or a minimum point.

In both of the preceding examples, we set the first derivative of the function equal to zero. In the first example, we know by looking at Figure 11.1 that the values of x and y so obtained yield the maximum of the function. In the second case, we also know by looking at Figure 11.1 that the values of x and y yield the minimum of the function. But if we had not drawn the curves, we would not have known this. Consequently, by setting the first derivative equal to zero we do not have enough information from this condition alone to determine whether the values of x and y so obtained definitely yield a maximum or definitely yield a minimum. So we say the condition that the first derivative be equal to zero is a necessary but not a sufficient condition to determine a maximum or minimum value of a function.

In order to determine the sufficient condition for a maximum or minimum, we must consider the second derivative of the function. In the first preceding example, the first derivative was computed as

$$\frac{dy}{dx} = -.2x + 2$$

The second derivative is

$$\frac{d^2y}{dx^2} = -.2$$

This value is negative, and we say that the extreme value of the function is a maximum. In the second preceding example, the first derivative is

$$\frac{dy}{dx} = .2x - 6$$

We compute the second derivative,

$$\frac{d^2y}{dx^2} = .2$$

which is positive. We conclude that the extreme value of this function is a minimum.

Note the criteria we have used to arrive at the necessary and sufficient conditions for a maximum or minimum in this problem. We concluded that the extreme value of the former function is a maximum because the second derivative turned out to be a negative number. The extreme value of the latter function was judged to be a minimum because the second derivative is a positive number. In both of these instances the second derivative emerged as a (positive or negative) constant number, and not another function of x. The first derivatives, however, are functions of x, and there is no reason why one will not encounter second derivatives which are also functions of x.

We must now consider this more general case in which the second derivative is a function of x. Suppose we are given the function specified by the following equation:

$$y = f(x) = e^x - 10x$$

We wish to find a maximum or minimum value of this function if one exists. To begin, we find the first derivative and set it equal to zero. Using Rules 1 and 7 of Chapter 8, we obtain

$$\frac{dy}{dx} = e^x - 10 = 0$$

We wish to solve this equation for the value of x. Since

$$e^x = 10$$

can be written[1]

$$x = \log_e 10$$

the value of x which satisfies this equation can be found in Table A at the end of the book. The value of $\log_e 10$ is seen to be 2.30, rounded to two decimal places. Hence, we have the critical value of x—the value of x which satisfies the necessary condition. The value of y is found by substitution of this value for x in the original equation (noting that $e = 2.71828$):

$$y = (2.71828)^{2.30} - 10(2.30) = 9.9742 - 23.0000 = -13.03$$

to two decimal places. If one exists, the maximum or minimum of the curve will occur at the point $(2.30, -13.03)$.

Now we are faced with the second question. Is this a maximum or is it a minimum? The second derivative is computed as

$$\frac{d^2y}{dx^2} = \frac{d}{dx}(e^x - 10) = e^x$$

For $x = 2.30$, the critical value of x which locates the extreme value of the original function, will the *value* of this second derivative be greater than zero or less than zero? Substitution of 2.30 for x in the formula for the second derivative yields

$$e^{2.30} = (2.71828)^{2.30} = 9.97$$

Since this value of the second derivative is positive, we conclude that the extreme value of the original function is a minimum. Had the value of the second derivative turned out to be negative, when the critical value of x was substituted in the equation for the second derivative, the extreme value of the function would have been a maximum.

[1] See footnote 1 in Chapter 8 on page 126.

This example serves to illustrate the general rule that gives the necessary and sufficient conditions for a maximum or minimum value of a function. Let us state the rule in general terms. Given a function denoted by $y = f(x)$, let x_o be the critical value of x—the value of x that satisfies the equation found by setting the first derivative of $f(x)$ equal to zero. Assume that the value of the second derivative when $x = x_o$ is not itself zero [2], that is, $f''(x_o) \neq 0$. Then the value $f(x_o)$:

(1) Is a *maximum* value of $f(x)$ if

$$f'(x_o) = 0 \quad \text{and} \quad f''(x_o) < 0$$

(2) Is a *minimum* value of $f(x)$ if

$$f'(x_o) = 0 \quad \text{and} \quad f''(x_o) > 0$$

The geometric interpretation of these conditions can also be given. At a maximum point on a curve, the curve is neither increasing nor decreasing (the line tangent to the curve is horizontal) and the curve is concave to the x axis (concave downward). The concavity of the curve is indicated by the negative sign of the value of the second derivative. At a minimum point on a curve, the curve is neither increasing nor decreasing (the line tangent to the curve is horizontal), and the curve is convex to the x axis (concave upward). The convexity of the curve is indicated by the positive sign of the value of the second derivative.

1. Relative Maxima and Minima

The preceding examples of maximum and minimum values of a function had certain peculiarities. In particular, the curves had either one and only one maximum point or one and only one minimum point. Many curves, however, are not of this nature. Take, for instance, the curve in Figure 11.2. This curve has four maxima and three minima within the domain of x between a and b shown in the Figure. We must therefore consider *relative* maxima and minima of a function. In order to keep the geometric interpretation identical with that presented in the preceding two cases, we will ignore the endpoints of a curve (for example, the values a and b of x in Figure 11.2), which are called *cusps*. That is, we will ignore maximum and minimum points at which the tangent line is not horizontal.

The general proposition describing maxima and minima is the

---

[2] The case in which $f''(x_o) = 0$ will be covered in the subsequent discussion on inflection points.

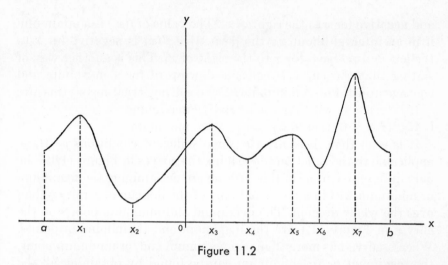

Figure 11.2

following: Let a function f be given (hence, its domain of definition is also given). If there is a number x_o in the domain of f such that

$$f(x_o) \geq f(x)$$

for all x in the domain sufficiently close to x_o, then $f(x_o)$ is said to be a *relative* maximum value of f. If, moreover, this condition holds for all x in the domain of $f(x)$, then $f(x_o)$ is said to be *the* maximum value of f. A *relative* minimum and *the* minimum of f are defined in a similar way. Somewhat less precisely, we can say that *the* maximum is the largest of the relative maxima, and *the* minimum is the smallest of the relative minima. In Figure 11.2, $f(x_7)$ is the maximum of $f(x)$ while $f(x_1)$, $f(x_3)$, $f(x_5)$, and $f(x_7)$ are all relative maxima. Likewise $f(x_2)$, $f(x_4)$, and $f(x_6)$ are all relative minima, and $f(x_2)$ is the minimum.

We state the following necessary condition for a relative maximum or minimum: Given that $a < x_o < b$, and given that $f'(x_o)$ exists, if $f(x_o)$ is a relative maximum or minimum of f, then $f'(x_o) = 0$. Given that the derivative exists, the relative maxima and minima occur only where the first derivative is zero. To find the maximum and the minimum of a function f, find all permissible values of x for which $f'(x) = 0$; substitute these values in $f(x)$, and the largest of these values of $f(x)$ is the maximum whereas the smallest value is the minimum.

What, then, about the sufficient conditions for relative maxima and minima? The value of $f(x_o)$ is a relative maximum if in an interval about x_o the derivative $f'(x)$ is positive for x to the left of x_o

and negative for x to the right of x_o. The value of $f(x_o)$ is a minimum, if in an interval about x_o, the derivative $f'(x)$ is negative for x to the left and positive for x to the right of x_o. This is another way of stating that the curve is concave downward for a maximum and concave upward for a minimum. The conditions that insure this are:

If $f''(x_o) < 0$, then $f(x_o)$ is a relative maximum.

If $f''(x_o) > 0$, then $f(x_o)$ is a relative minimum.

It is seen that these are the same sufficient conditions as those applicable to the functions describing the curves in Figure 11.1. The only difference is that in this case we are determining the maximum or minimum within a restricted part of the domain of x rather than over the whole domain. The maximum and minimum points on the curves in Figure 11.1 are the maximum and the minimum points. When a curve has more than one maximum and/or minimum point, the maximum or the minimum can be found by obtaining all the values of the function for which maxima and minima exist and choosing the largest and smallest of these respectively.

2. Points of Inflection

For any one of the values of x for which $f'(x) = 0$, we have a relative maximum if the second derivative is negative. We have a relative minimum if the second derivative is positive. But what if the second derivative turns out to be zero also? We then have what is called a *point of inflection* on the curve.

A point of inflection exists at a point where the concavity of the curve changes. Either the curve changes from concave upward to concave downward, or from concave downward to concave upward. At a point where change of concavity occurs, the second derivative must, in general, change from positive to negative or from negative to positive. Therefore, at this point the second derivative must, in general, be zero. There are some types of functions, rarely encountered in economics, for which this explanation is not appropriate. In these cases a second derivative which is equal to zero may yield a maximum or minimum point. But we shall ignore these economically unimportant exceptions and treat all second derivatives equal to zero as inflection points.

A point of inflection is shown in Figure 11.3. The equation of this curve is

$$y = f(x) = 6 + (x - 3)^3$$

The first derivative is

$$f'(x) = 3(x - 3)^2$$

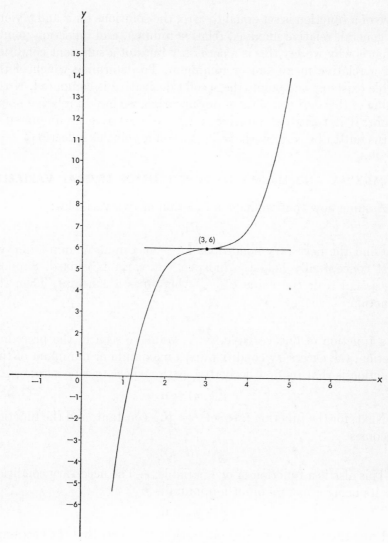

Figure 11.3

The second derivative must vanish if there exists an inflection point, so we set the second derivative equal to zero in order to see if any value of x satisfies the resulting equation:

$$f''(x) = 6(x - 3) = 6x - 18 = 0$$

The solution of this equation is $x = 3$. Substituting this value for x in the original equation, we find the value of $y = 6$; we say there is an inflection point at the point $(3, 6)$ on the curve.

From these considerations, we can see that when the first derivative of a function is set equal to zero, the solutions for x and y yield, in general, relative maxima, relative minima, and inflection points. That is why we say this is a necessary but not a sufficient condition for a relative maximum or minimum. To determine which of the three exists at one point, the second derivative is computed. If the value of this derivative turns out negative, we have a relative maximum; if it turns out positive, we have a relative minimum; if it turns out to be zero, we have in general a point of inflection.

B. MAXIMA AND MINIMA OF FUNCTIONS OF SEVERAL VARIABLES

Assume now that we have a function of two variables:

$$z = f(x, y)$$

To find the necessary conditions for a maximum or minimum, we first conceptually hold the independent variable y fixed. Suppose we assign to it the value $y = a$, where a is a constant. Then the function

$$z = f(x, a)$$

is a function of one variable, x. As we have seen in the preceding section, the necessary condition for a maximum or minimum of this function is that its first derivative with respect to x be zero:

$$f_x(x, a) = 0$$

Next, for the function f we set $x = b$, a constant, and the function becomes

$$z = f(b, y)$$

This also is a function of one variable, y. The necessary condition for its being a maximum or minimum is

$$f_y(b, y) = 0$$

From this nonrigorous demonstration, we assert that the necessary conditions for the function

$$z = f(x, y)$$

to be a maximum or minimum are

$$\frac{\partial z}{\partial x} = 0 \quad \text{and} \quad \frac{\partial z}{\partial y} = 0$$

For example, consider the function given by the equation

$$z = 8 + 4x^2 - 3x + 2y^2 - y$$

The necessary conditions for a maximum or minimum of this function are

$$\frac{\partial z}{\partial x} = 8x - 3 = 0 \qquad \text{and} \qquad \frac{\partial z}{\partial y} = 4y - 1 = 0$$

Let us now investigate the sufficient conditions for a maximum or minimum of the function f. We shall merely state them without proof. A maximum or minimum exists, in general, if the following condition involving a determinant (see Chapter 6) is satisfied:

$$\begin{vmatrix} \dfrac{\partial^2 z}{\partial x^2} & \dfrac{\partial^2 z}{\partial x \partial y} \\[2ex] \dfrac{\partial^2 z}{\partial x \partial y} & \dfrac{\partial^2 z}{\partial y^2} \end{vmatrix} = \left(\frac{\partial^2 z}{\partial x^2}\right)\left(\frac{\partial^2 z}{\partial y^2}\right) - \left(\frac{\partial^2 z}{\partial x \partial y}\right)^2 > 0$$

This determinant must be positive in order to have a maximum or minimum.[3] Furthermore, we can state the conditions that will insure our having one or the other:

$$\frac{\partial^2 z}{\partial x^2} < 0 \quad \text{negative} \quad \text{and} \quad \frac{\partial^2 z}{\partial y^2} < 0 \quad \text{negative} \quad \text{for a maximum}$$

$$\frac{\partial^2 z}{\partial x^2} > 0 \quad \text{positive} \quad \text{and} \quad \frac{\partial^2 z}{\partial y^2} > 0 \quad \text{positive} \quad \text{for a minimum}$$

Either one of these two conditions will yield a positive value for the determinant. Therefore, we know that either one produces a situation which results in an extreme value of the function. Moreover, if the first condition is the one actually obtained (the signs of both second partial derivatives are negative), we can say definitely that the extreme value is a maximum. If the signs of both partial derivatives are positive, the extreme value is definitely a minimum.

Let us return to the equation for which the necessary conditions have already been found. The solutions of those two equations yield the values $x = \frac{3}{8}$ and $y = \frac{1}{4}$, so we know that a maximum or minimum can occur only at the point for which $x = \frac{3}{8}$ and $y = \frac{1}{4}$. We do not know, however, whether there is actually a maximum or a minimum at this point. Therefore, we compute the second partial derivatives

$$\frac{\partial^2 z}{\partial x^2} = \frac{\partial}{\partial x}(8x - 3) = 8$$

$$\frac{\partial^2 z}{\partial y^2} = \frac{\partial}{\partial y}(4y - 1) = 4$$

$$\frac{\partial^2 z}{\partial x \partial y} = \frac{\partial}{\partial y}(8x - 3) = \frac{\partial}{\partial x}(4y - 1) = 0$$

[3] A maximum or a minimum may occur when the value of this determinant is zero. As in the case of explicit functions of one variable, however, we shall ignore this possibility as unimportant for our purposes.

We form the determinant from these derivatives:

$$\begin{vmatrix} \dfrac{\partial^2 z}{\partial x^2} & \dfrac{\partial^2 z}{\partial x \partial y} \\[2mm] \dfrac{\partial^2 z}{\partial x \partial y} & \dfrac{\partial^2 z}{\partial y^2} \end{vmatrix} = \begin{vmatrix} 8 & 0 \\ 0 & 4 \end{vmatrix} = (8)(4) - (0)^2 = 32$$

The value of the determinant is positive, that is, $32 > 0$. Consequently, we definitely have either a maximum or a minimum at the point for which $x = \frac{3}{8}$ and $y = \frac{1}{4}$. Which of the two is it? We notice that both second derivatives are positive:

$$\frac{\partial^2 z}{\partial x^2} = 8 > 0 \qquad \text{and} \qquad \frac{\partial^2 z}{\partial y^2} = 4 > 0$$

We come to the final conclusion that we have a *minimum* of the function $z = f(x, y)$ when $x = \frac{3}{8}$ and $y = \frac{1}{4}$. To find the value of z at this point (the minimum value of z), we merely substitute these values for x and y in the original equation, thus

$$z = 8 + 4(\tfrac{3}{8})^2 - 3(\tfrac{3}{8}) + 2(\tfrac{1}{4})^2 - \tfrac{1}{4} = \tfrac{468}{64}$$

In this particular example, the determinant formed from the second derivatives turned out to be a constant number. Had the second partial derivatives been functions of x and y, rather than constant numbers (so the determinant included functions of x and y), no basic alteration would be required. Just as in the case of explicit functions of one variable, the critical values of the independent variables can be substituted in the equations included in the determinant to find the value of the determinant. For example, in our illustration, the critical values are $x = \frac{3}{8}$ and $y = \frac{1}{4}$. If the determinant had consisted of equations in x and y, these critical values would be substituted for x and y in the equations. Then the determinant is reduced to some numerical value. If that value is positive, we definitely have either a maximum or a minimum. To find which exists, the critical values are substituted for x and y in the equations given by the second partial derivatives. If the *values* of both partial derivatives are positive, the extreme value of the function is a minimum. If, on the other hand, the *values* of both partial derivatives are negative, the extreme value is a maximum. In other words, the procedure is exactly like that followed for explicit functions of one variable: if an equation rather than a constant number emerges in the second derivatives, the critical values of the independent variables are substituted in the equations to reduce them to constant numbers. The only difference in this case is that we are dealing with two independent variables instead of one.

This demonstration has been carried out for an explicit function of *two* independent variables, but we can extend the conclusion to include a function of any number of independent variables. The necessary condition for the existence of a maximum or minimum of an explicit function of several variables is that all the first partial derivatives be equal to zero. For the function

$$y = f(x_1, x_2, x_3, \ldots, x_n)$$

where the subscripts on the x's refer to different variables, we can write the necessary condition for a maximum or minimum as

$$\frac{\partial y}{\partial x_r} = 0 \quad r = 1, 2, 3, \ldots, n$$

The partial derivative of y with respect to each independent variable must be equal to zero. The sufficient conditions for a maximum or minimum of a function of several variables involve mathematical techniques that are beyond the scope of this book.

PROBLEMS

Find the maxima and/or minima, if any, of the following functions for the ranges of the independent variables specified.

1. $y = f(x) = x^2$.
2. $y = f(x) = 14 - 2x + 3x^3$.
   $-3 < x < 3$.
3. $y = f(x) = 20 + .2(x - 10)^2$.
4. $y = f(x) = 14 - 2x^2 + .4x^3$.
   $-10 < x < 10$.
5. $y = f(x) = \sqrt{x} - 10x$.
   $0 < x < 5$.
6. $y = f(x) = 200 + 2x - .01x^2 + .007x^3$.
   $0 < x < 40$.
7. $z = f(x, y) = 10 + 3x^2 - x + 2y^3 - y$.
   $-3 < x < 3$.
   $-3 < y < 3$.
8. $z = f(x, y) = x^2 y$.
   $-10 < x < 10$.
   $-10 < y < 10$.
9. $z = f(x, y) = 5 + 12x + 9y - x^2 y$.
   $-5 < x < 5$.
   $-5 < y < 5$.
10. $z = f(x, y) = 2 + x^2 + y^2$.
    $-3 < x < 3$.
    $-3 < y < 3$.

CHAPTER 12

Economic Applications of Maxima and Minima

The concept of maximization runs through the entire literature of economic theory. Behind the conditions of market equilibrium can be found the assumption that firms, consumers, and factor owners maximize some magnitude. Consequently, the mathematical methods for obtaining the maximum value of a function are of vital importance in econometric theory.

A. PROFIT MAXIMIZATION OF THE FIRM

It is from the theory of the individual firm that the economist derives the market supply schedule under conditions of pure competition. Each firm in the industry is assumed to maximize its total profit, where total profit is defined as the difference between total revenue from sale of the product and total cost of production. Under a monopolistic market structure, where there is but one seller of the product, the monopolist is also assumed to maximize his total profit. From this condition, the total amount of the product offered for sale on the market is determined. We, therefore, turn our attention to the theory of the firm. We shall show how the methods of the preceding chapter can be used to find the output that maximizes total profit. This is called the equilibrium output of the firm, and we shall compute this equilibrium output under some alternative assumptions about the structure of the market.

1. Pure Competition

A firm that produces a commodity in a purely competitive market cannot, by its own behavior alone, influence the market price of that commodity. The price is determined by market forces outside the control of the individual firm. Since the price is unaffected by the firm's output, it is taken as given—a constant. Let p represent the given price of the product X. Then the total revenue of the firm is defined as

$$R(x) = px$$

where R is total revenue and x is the quantity of the commodity X produced (and sold) by the firm. Since p is a constant, total revenue is proportional to output.

Let the total cost of production for the firm be denoted by $C(x)$. We are already familiar with this procedure of expressing total cost as a function of output. Total profit, P, is defined as the difference between total revenue and total cost:

$$P(x) = R(x) - C(x)$$

We assume that these functions are all continuous, so that their derivatives exist at all points.

The necessary condition for profit to be a maximum is

$$\frac{dP}{dx} = 0$$

But this can be written

$$\frac{dP}{dx} = \frac{dR}{dx} - \frac{dC}{dx} = 0$$

and therefore,

$$\frac{dR}{dx} = \frac{dC}{dx}$$

This last expression is an alternative way of stating the necessary condition for profit to be a maximum. Notice, now, that $\frac{dR}{dx}$ is by definition marginal revenue, and $\frac{dC}{dx}$ is by definition marginal cost. Consequently, this last expression states the familiar theoretical proposition that in equilibrium for the firm marginal cost must equal marginal revenue. Moreover, in the special case of pure competition

$$\frac{dR}{dx} = \frac{d}{dx}(px) = p$$

That is, marginal revenue of the firm equals the price of the product (for all permissible values of x). Hence, we can say that in equilibrium for the firm under conditions of pure competition marginal cost must equal the price of the product.

The sufficient condition for total profit to be a maximum is

$$\frac{d^2P}{dx^2} = \frac{d^2R}{dx^2} - \frac{d^2C}{dx^2} < 0$$

and this condition implies

$$\frac{d^2R}{dx^2} < \frac{d^2C}{dx^2}$$

The slope of the tangent to the marginal revenue curve must be less than the slope of the tangent to the marginal cost curve at that output for which total profit is a maximum. Since

$$\frac{d^2R}{dx^2} = \frac{d}{dx}(p) = 0$$

we say that the marginal revenue curve is in this case a horizontal line, that is, it has slope equal to zero at all points and lies at a distance of p units above the x axis. Furthermore, the sufficient condition states: for profit to be a maximum, the marginal cost curve must have a tangent line with a slope greater than the slope of the tangent to the marginal revenue curve. Since the marginal revenue curve is a horizontal line, the marginal cost curve must be increasing with output. This is another way of saying that the second derivative of the total cost function must be greater than zero.

This last condition insures the stability of the equilibrium, which can be seen by considering what would happen if this condition did not hold. If the marginal cost curve were a horizontal line (if $\frac{d^2C}{dx^2} = 0$), it would (1) lie above the marginal revenue curve for all amounts of output, or (2) lie below the marginal revenue curve for all amounts of output, or (3) be equal to marginal revenue for all amounts of output. In the first case, no amount of production would be profitable, so the firm would go out of business. In the second, there would be no conceivable limit to the size of the firm—it could always increase total profits by expanding output. But this is inconsistent with the assumption of pure competition, for the firm would eventually become a monopolist. In the third case, there are an infinite number of outputs (including zero output) that maximize total profit. We may interpret this for our purpose as meaning that the firm would produce nothing. There remains one other possibility, namely that the marginal cost curve is decreasing with output ($d^2C/dx^2 < 0$). In this case there would again be no limit to the size of the firm, for it could always increase total profits by expanding output. In none of these four cases do we have a stable equilibrium for the firm. Consequently, the sufficient condition for profit maximization must be satisfied if we are to have a stable situation.

To find the output that maximizes total profit, we would solve for the value of x in the equation that defines the necessary condition for profit maximization. To be insured that this is indeed the level of output for which the firm's total profit is maximized, we would then test to see if the second derivative of the profit function is negative for this value of x.

Let us take a concrete example. Suppose that the price of the product is given to the firm as $20. The total revenue function is then

$$R = 20x$$

Suppose, further, that the total cost of production is given by the equation

$$C = 5,000 + .00002x^3 - .018x^2 + 7.4x$$

where total cost, C, is expressed in dollars. The first term on the right ($5,000) is total fixed cost (constant with respect to output). The remaining terms show the behavior of total variable cost as output is varied. We have for total profit

$$P = R - C = 20x - 5000 - .00002x^3 + .018x^2 - 7.4x$$

The necessary condition for total profit to be a maximum is

$$\frac{dP}{dx} = 20 - .00006x^2 + .036x - 7.4 = 0$$

We solve this equation for the value of x by rewriting it as

$$-.00006x^2 + .036x + 12.6 = 0$$

This is seen to be in the form of the general quadratic

$$ax^2 + bx + c = 0$$

where $a = -.00006$, $b = .036$, and $c = 12.6$. We have already found in Chapter 4 that the solutions of the general quadratic are given by the formula

$$x = \frac{-b \pm \sqrt{b^2 - 4ac}}{2a}$$

Substitution of the values of a, b, and c in this formula leads to the solutions

$$x = 850 \quad \text{and} \quad x = -250$$

rounded to the nearest integer. These two values of x give a maximum of P, a minimum of P, or an inflection point. For practical reasons, we would reject the negative solution because output of the firm cannot be less than zero, but we are not yet sure that when $x = 850$, profit is truly a maximum.

In order to determine whether this output is such as to maximize profit, we consider the sufficient condition

$$\frac{d^2P}{dx^2} < 0$$

and ask, "Is this condition also satisfied?" We compute the second derivative:

$$\frac{d^2P}{dx^2} = -.00012x + .036$$

Substituting $x = 850$ into this equation yields

$$-.00012(850) + .036 = -.066 < 0$$

Since this value is negative, we may conclude that an output of 850 units per unit of time maximizes total profit. Incidentally, substitution of the value $x = -250$ makes the second derivative positive, which means that this output (if it could be produced) would make total profit a minimum.

The final step is to calculate the maximum profit of the firm. We merely substitute the value $x = 850$ in the profit equation, thus

$$P = 20(850) - 5,000 - .00002(850)^3 + .018(850)^2 - 7.4(850) = \$6,432.$$

We might have taken the alternative course of setting marginal cost equal to the price, from our knowledge of the principles of economic theory. This gives

$$.00006x^2 - .036x + 7.4 = 20$$

But this is seen to be the same quadratic equation as that yielded by taking the first derivative of the profit function and setting it equal to zero. This formulation is merely another way of stating the same condition and, of course, leads to the same solution for x.

To clearly establish the connection between the analytic solution and the geometric solution usually presented in economics textbooks, it is instructive to plot on graph paper the total revenue and total cost functions, and on another graph the marginal cost and marginal revenue functions. These curves will be seen to have the usual shapes assumed in economic theory. It is interesting to note that the geometric solution for the equilibrium output of the firm is the same as that derived here analytically.

2. Monopoly

The general proposition, "Total profit of a firm is maximized at that output for which marginal cost is equal to marginal revenue" holds also for a monopolist. The only difference between this case and the case of the firm under pure competition is that marginal revenue is not equal to the price of the product. Since the monopolist can affect the market price by varying output, the price will differ from marginal revenue.

We again define total profit as total revenue minus total cost:

$$P = R - C$$

The necessary and sufficient conditions for profit maximization are

$$\frac{dP}{dx} = \frac{dR}{dx} - \frac{dC}{dx} = 0$$

and

$$\frac{d^2P}{dx^2} = \frac{d^2R}{dx^2} - \frac{d^2C}{dx^2} < 0$$

However, we do not now have $d^2R/dx^2 = 0$.

The market demand function for the product is the average revenue function of the monopolist since he is the only seller. Assume the market demand function is given as

$$x = 2000 - 20p$$

Where x is the quantity demanded of the product X per unit of time and p is its price (in, say, dollars). It is convenient for our purposes to write the inverse of this function:

$$p = 100 - .05x$$

This is the average revenue function (price function) of the monopolist. Now total revenue is defined to be price times quantity sold:

$$R = x \cdot p = x(100 - .05x) = 100x - .05x^2$$

To obtain marginal revenue, we take the first derivative of R; hence,

$$\frac{dR}{dx} = 100 - .10x$$

It is worth pausing at this point to compare the average revenue curve with the marginal revenue curve. When output is zero, both are equal to 100. The slope of the average revenue curve is $-.05$, while the slope of the marginal revenue curve is $-.10$. That is, the marginal revenue curve lies below the average revenue curve for all positive levels of output and declines at a faster rate than the average revenue curve. Thus, we have again stated analytically certain propositions that are usually stated geometrically in textbooks on economic theory.

We turn next to the costs of the monopolist. Assume his total cost function is given by

$$C = 5x + .0125x^2$$

where C is measured in dollars. Marginal cost is given by

$$\frac{dC}{dx} = 5 + .025x$$

The total profit of the monopolist is

$$P = R - C = 100x - .05x^2 - 5x - .0125x^2$$

The necessary condition for profit maximization is therefore

$$\frac{dP}{dx} = \frac{dR}{dx} - \frac{dC}{dx} = 100 - .10x - 5 - .025x$$

$$= 95 - .125x = 0$$

Solving this equation for x gives

$$x = 760 \text{ units}$$

The sufficient condition for profit maximization is

$$\frac{d^2P}{dx^2} = -.125 < 0$$

Therefore, we are assured that total profit is a maximum when output is 760 units per unit of time. Maximum total profit is computed as

$$P = 100(760) - .05(760)^2 - 5(760) - .0125(760)^2 = \$36,100$$

Again, it is enlightening to plot the average revenue, marginal revenue, and average and marginal costs on graph paper. The equilibrium output of the monopolist can then be shown geometrically as that output for which the marginal cost curve intersects the marginal revenue curve. The average profit (difference between average revenue and average cost) and the total profit can also be indicated.

B. THE PRODUCTION FUNCTION

In Chapter 10, we saw that when we assume two factor inputs are used in the production of a commodity, the output is expressed as a function of these two inputs. We can write the production function as

$$x = j(l, k)$$

where x designates the quantity of the commodity X produced and l and k represent the amounts of the factors L and K used in the production of X. We saw, furthermore, that the marginal productivities of the two factor inputs are

$$\frac{\partial x}{\partial l} \quad \text{and} \quad \frac{\partial x}{\partial k}$$

Now suppose that we are interested in knowing what amounts of the factor inputs L and K result in the maximum total production of X. We have the necessary conditions for x to be a maximum from Section B of Chapter 11, namely

$$\frac{\partial x}{\partial l} = 0 \quad \text{and} \quad \frac{\partial x}{\partial k} = 0$$

This condition states that both marginal products must be zero. The sufficient conditions for a maximum of x are

$$\begin{vmatrix} \dfrac{\partial^2 x}{\partial l^2} & \dfrac{\partial^2 x}{\partial l \partial k} \\[2ex] \dfrac{\partial^2 x}{\partial l \partial k} & \dfrac{\partial^2 x}{\partial k^2} \end{vmatrix} > 0$$

and

$$\frac{\partial^2 x}{\partial l^2} < 0 \quad \text{and} \quad \frac{\partial^2 x}{\partial k^2} < 0$$

If all of these conditions are satisfied, we have determined the amounts of L and K that give the maximum amount of X.

Let the continuous production function be given by

$$x = j(l, \ k) = -.02l^3 + .5l^2 - .01k^3 + .3k^2$$

where x, l, and k are measured in some appropriately defined units. The necessary conditions for x to be a maximum are

$$\frac{\partial x}{\partial l} = -.06l^2 + l = 0$$

$$\frac{\partial x}{\partial k} = -.03k^2 + .6k = 0$$

We solve these equations for the values of l and k. These equations are seen to be quadratic equations of the general form $ax^2 + bx + c = 0$.

Therefore, we use the same method of solution as we did in the example of profit maximization for the firm under pure competition. In the first equation $a = -.06$, $b = 1$, and $c = 0$; in the second equation $a = -.03$, $b = .6$, and $c = 0$. Using the formula for solving the general quadratic with these values, and substituting for a, b, and c, we obtain $l = 0$ or $l = 17$, rounded to the nearest integer. For the values of k, we have $k = 0$ or $k = 20$.

In order to determine which pair of these values, if any, yields a maximum of x, we consider the sufficient conditions for a maximum or a minimum of x. Thus, we compute the higher partial derivatives

$$\frac{\partial^2 x}{\partial l^2} = -.12l + 1$$

$$\frac{\partial^2 x}{\partial k^2} = -.06k + .6$$

$$\frac{\partial^2 x}{\partial l \partial k} = \frac{\partial^2 x}{\partial k \partial l} = 0$$

We then form the determinant

$$\begin{vmatrix} \dfrac{\partial^2 x}{\partial l^2} & \dfrac{\partial^2 x}{\partial l \partial k} \\[2ex] \dfrac{\partial^2 x}{\partial l \partial k} & \dfrac{\partial^2 x}{\partial k^2} \end{vmatrix} = \begin{vmatrix} (-.12l + 1) & 0 \\[2ex] 0 & (-.06k + .6) \end{vmatrix}$$

$$= (-.12l + 1)(-.06k + .6) - (0)^2$$
$$= .0072lk - .06k - .072l + .6$$

The value of this determinant must be greater than zero in order to have either a maximum or a minimum of x. Let us see what the value of the determinant turns out to be when we substitute our solutions for l and k in the determinant equation. If we substitute the pair $l = 0$, $k = 0$, the determinant equals .6, which is greater than zero. Consequently, this pair yields either a maximum or a minimum of x. If we set $l = 0$ and $k = 20$, the determinant equals $-.6$; for $l = 17$ and $k = 0$, the determinant equals $-.62$. In both of these cases, we have neither a maximum nor a minimum of x. Finally, for $l = 17$ and $k = 20$, we have .62 for the value of the determinant, so these values of l and k give either a maximum or a minimum. We conclude that the pairs $l = 0$, $k = 0$ and $l = 17$, $k = 20$ each yields either a maximum or a minimum of x.

The final conditions for a definite maximum of x are

$$\frac{\partial^2 x}{\partial l^2} = -.12l + 1 < 0$$

$$\frac{\partial^2 x}{\partial k^2} = -.06k + .6 < 0$$

Substituting $l = 17$ and $k = 20$ in these conditions, we have

$$\frac{\partial^2 x}{\partial l^2} = -.12(17) + 1 = -2.04 + 1 = -1.04 < 0$$

and $$\frac{\partial^2 x}{\partial k^2} = -.06(20) + .6 = -.1.2 + .6 = -.6 < 0$$

So the values $l = 17$, $k = 20$ definitely yield a maximum of x. Clearly, when $l = 0$, $k = 0$, the values of the second partial derivatives are positive. We conclude that total output is a maximum when 17 units of L and 20 units of K are used in the productive process.

To find the maximum output, we merely substitute these values for l and k in the production function:

$x = -.02(17)^3 + .5(17)^2 - .01(20)^3 + .3(20)^2 = 86.24$ units of output per unit of time

The advantage of this analytical procedure over the geometric is evident. To represent the production function geometrically would require a production surface in three-dimensional space with x, l, and k measured on the three axes. This is a cumbersome procedure. Furthermore, locating the maximum point on the surface may involve physical errors in measurement, and perhaps some rough estimating. Such difficulties are avoided by use of the differential calculus.

C. UTILITY MAXIMIZATION

In economics, we frequently encounter problems in which certain functions have to be maximized or minimized under what are called side conditions. Such problems are called problems of constrained maxima and minima, or maxima and minima subject to side conditions. A complete treatment of these types of problems is beyond the scope of this book, but we will indicate here how such problems are approached. We can combine this procedure with a demonstration of how the purely formal apparatus of partial derivatives can be used to great advantage even when the variables involved are not measurable economic magnitudes like cost, profit, and output.

We turn to the economic theory of utility. In economics each consumer is assumed to maximize the total utility he derives from the goods he consumes, subject to his budget constraint (that is, given his income and the prices of the goods). For the sake of simplicity we shall assume that the individuals consume only two goods, X and Y. Let the quantities of these goods be denoted by x and y, respectively. We assume, in addition, that the consumer spends his entire (given) income on these two goods. The unobservable and nonmeasurable utility function is given symbolically as

$$u = f(x, y)$$

where u designates total utility. The budget equation of the consumer is given as

$$p_x \cdot x + p_y \cdot y = I$$

where p_x is the given price of good X, p_y is the given price of good Y, and I is his given income. p_x, p_y, and I are constants in this equation. The budget equation states that all income is spent on X and Y, since $p_x \cdot x$ is the money value of x purchased and $p_y \cdot y$ is the money value of y purchased.

The basic assumption of utility theory is that the consumer will maximize u subject to the side condition of the budget equation. The individual will maximize u by choosing appropriate amounts of X and Y, taking into consideration the market prices of X and Y and his income. This is a problem of constrained maxima.

We write the utility function

$$u = f(x, y)$$

We can express the budget equation as a function in x and y, since the other values in the equation are constants:

$$g(x, y) = p_x \cdot x + p_y \cdot y - I = 0$$

The consumer maximizes u subject to

$$g(x, y) = 0$$

To find the necessary condition for maximized u, we form the new function

$$h(x, y) = f(x, y) + \lambda g(x, y) = u + \lambda g$$

The symbol λ is an unknown constant called the *Lagrange multiplier*. It can be shown that the necessary conditions for the maximization of u are

$$\frac{\partial h}{\partial x} = \frac{\partial u}{\partial x} + \lambda \frac{\partial g}{\partial x} = 0$$

$$\frac{\partial h}{\partial y} = \frac{\partial u}{\partial y} + \lambda \frac{\partial g}{\partial y} = 0$$

But

$$\frac{\partial g}{\partial x} = \frac{\partial}{\partial x}(p_x \cdot x + p_y \cdot y - I) = p_x$$

and

$$\frac{\partial g}{\partial y} = \frac{\partial}{\partial y}(p_x \cdot x + p_y \cdot y - I) = p_y$$

Consequently, we can rewrite the necessary conditions for a maximum of u as

$$\frac{\partial u}{\partial x} + \lambda p_x = 0$$

$$\frac{\partial u}{\partial y} + \lambda p_y = 0$$

These can, in turn, be expressed as

$$\frac{\frac{\partial u}{\partial x}}{p_x} = -\lambda$$

$$\frac{\frac{\partial u}{\partial y}}{p_y} = -\lambda$$

Therefore, it is clear that

$$\frac{\frac{\partial u}{\partial x}}{p_x} = \frac{\frac{\partial u}{\partial y}}{p_y}$$

or

$$\frac{\frac{\partial u}{\partial x}}{\frac{\partial u}{\partial y}} = \frac{p_x}{p_y}$$

We now have the necessary conditions for a maximum of u written in a different form. The first partial derivatives of u with respect to x and y are the marginal utilities of x and y respectively. Hence, we can conclude that when total utility is maximized, it is necessary that the marginal utility of each commodity be proportional to its price. An alternative way of stating this is that the ratios of the marginal utilities must equal the ratios of the market prices. This condition of equilibrium for the consumer enables us to relate his behavior to the behavior of market prices, which are observable and measurable. It is this condition from which the law of consumer demand is derived. For if p_x falls with p_y constant, the marginal utility of X must be reduced relative to the marginal utility of Y. Under the usual assumptions, this implies increased consumption of X. Through the use of mathematical symbols, we translate the subjective theory of utility into an "objective" law of economics. The law is objective in the sense that it relates two observable and measurable magnitudes—quantity consumed and price.

PROBLEMS

1. For a firm in a purely competitive industry the price of the product is given as \$25. The total cost of production is
$$c = 3,000 + 10x - .03x^2 + .00005x^3$$
where c denotes total cost and x denotes the quantity produced.
   (a) Graph the total revenue, total cost, and total profit functions on the same diagram from $x = 0$ to $x = 800$.
   (b) Compute the marginal revenue, marginal cost, average revenue, and average cost functions.
   (c) Graph the marginal revenue, average revenue, marginal cost, and average cost functions on the same diagram from $x = 0$ to $x = 800$.
   (d) Find the equilibrium output of the firm and illustrate it graphically on the diagrams corresponding to parts (a) and (c).
   (e) Find the total profit of the firm and illustrate it on the diagrams corresponding to parts (a) and (c).

2. The market demand function for a commodity X is given as
$$x = 500 - 5p$$
The commodity X is produced by a monopolist whose total cost of production function is given as
$$c = 4000 + 10x + .00046x^3$$
   (a) Find the equilibrium output for the monopoly.
   (b) Find the total profit for the monopoly.
   (c) Find the price of the commodity X.
   (d) Graph on the same diagram the average revenue, the marginal revenue, the average cost, and the marginal cost curves of the monopoly. Indicate the equilibrium output, the price of the product, and the total profit of the monopoly.

3. The production function of a firm is given as
$$x = j(l, k) = .3l^2 - .01l^3 + .4k^2 - .02k^3$$
where x denotes the amount of the commodity X produced and l and k represent the amounts of the factors of production L and K. Find the values of l and k which maximize x and the value of maximum x.

4. Assume the total net investment function for the economy as a whole is given as
$$I = f(i, Y) = 50 + 8i - 40i^2 + .6Y - .003Y^2$$
where I denotes total investment, i denotes the interest rate, and Y denotes national income. Find the values of i and Y that maximize I and the value of maximum I.

CHAPTER 13

Elements of Integral Calculus

The concept of an "integral" is used widely in mathematical analysis. It has two different characteristics and two corresponding distinct applications. We may look at this concept from these two different angles. From one viewpoint, an integral is the limit of a certain summation or addition process. In geometric terms, this interpretation corresponds to the area enclosed by a curve or by a set of curves. Regarded in this way, the integral is called a *definite integral*.

From another viewpoint, an integral is the result of reversing the process of differentiation. When y is a function of x and its derivative exists, then the derivative of y is also a function of x. The reverse problem is that of finding, from a given function, a second function that has the given function as its derivative. If it can be found, this second function is called the *indefinite integral* of the given function. Let us consider each of these viewpoints separately, and then see what relevance they have to economic theory.

A. THE DEFINITE INTEGRAL

Suppose we have a curve given by the equation

$$y = f(x) = 10 + 2x$$

and suppose that we wish to find the area under this curve and above the x axis from $x = 3$ to $x = 7$. We can obtain an approximation to the total area under the curve by first considering the approximate area of one part of the total area. We can next consider another part of the total area, and so on until we have considered all parts. For example, we can first consider the part from $x = 3$ to $x = 4$. The approximate area under this section of the curve is the area of the rectangle given by $f(4)$ times one. That is, the area of a rectangle is given by the length times the width. In this case the width of the rectangle is $4 - 3 = 1$ and the length is $f(4) = 18$. The curve corresponding to $y = 10 + 2x$ and the rectangle described above are shown in Figure 13.1.

The area of this rectangle is $18 \cdot 1 = 18$. We say the area of this rectangle is an approximation to the area under the curve (and above the x axis) between $x = 3$ and $x = 4$, because it involves an error equal to the shaded portion of the rectangle.

Next, we treat the area under the curve between $x = 4$ and $x = 5$. This area is approximated by the area of the rectangle whose width is $5 - 4 = 1$ and whose length is $f(5) = 20$. This rectangle also involves an error equal to the portion that lies above the curve.

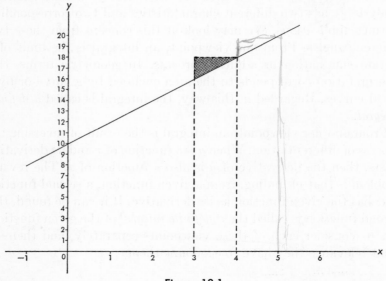

Figure 13.1

Proceeding in this way, we compute the areas of the rectangles up to and including $x = 7$. From $x = 5$ to $x = 6$ and from $x = 6$ to $x = 7$, we do the same thing. Now the approximate total area under the curve and above the x axis from $x = 3$ to $x = 7$ is the sum of the areas of the four rectangles so computed. Figure 13.2 shows the curve and the four rectangles. The total error committed in estimating the area under the curve is equal to the sum of the four shaded portions of the rectangles.

We can calculate the sum of the areas of the four rectangles; it is

$$f(4) \cdot 1 + f(5) \cdot 1 + f(6) \cdot 1 + f(7) \cdot 1 = 18 + 20 + 22 + 24 = 84$$

We conclude that 84 is the approximate area under the curve and above the x axis from $x = 3$ to $x = 7$. To write this more conven-

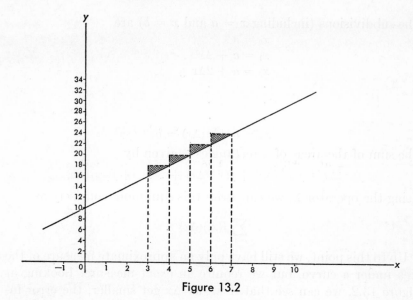

Figure 13.2

iently, we introduce the operator Σ. This Greek letter, sigma, means "the summation of." Hence we write

$$\sum_{x=4}^{7} f(x)(\Delta x) = 84$$

The symbol

$$\sum_{x=4}^{7}$$

means that we let x increase by finite increments from $x = 4$ to $x = 7$. Since in our example $\Delta x = 1$, we would expand the preceding expression as follows:

$$\sum_{x=4}^{7} f(x)(\Delta x) = f(4) \cdot 1 + f(5) \cdot 1 + f(6) \cdot 1 + f(7) \cdot 1 = 84$$

as we have already seen.

It is easy to generalize this procedure for obtaining an approximation to the area under a curve. Assume we know the equation of a curve,

$$y = f(x)$$

and we wish to find the approximate area under this curve and above the x axis between the limits $x = a$ and $x = b$. We first divide the interval from a to b into n parts of equal width:

$$\Delta x = \frac{b - a}{n}$$

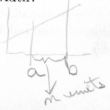

The subdivisions (including $x = a$ and $x = b$) are

$$x_0 = a$$
$$x_1 = a + \Delta x$$
$$x_2 = a + 2\Delta x$$

$$\vdots \qquad \vdots$$

$$x_n = a + n(\Delta x) = b$$

The sum of the areas of n rectangles is given by

$$f(x_1)\Delta x + f(x_2)(\Delta x) + f(x_3)(\Delta x) + \ldots + f(x_n)(\Delta x)$$

Using the operator Σ, we can write this sum more concisely as

$$\sum_{i=1}^{n} f(x_i)(\Delta x)$$

Up to this point, we still have only an approximate measure of the area under a curve, but we require an exact measure. Looking at Figure 13.2, we can see that if we let Δx get smaller, the error involved in using the sum of areas of rectangles also becomes smaller. For instance, if we let $\Delta x = \frac{1}{2}$ instead of one, we get twice as many rectangles from $x = 3$ to $x = 7$, and the sum of the shaded triangles becomes smaller. If we set $\Delta x = \frac{1}{4}$, the sum of the shaded triangles would become even smaller. Finally, if we let Δx approach zero, the sum of the errors also approaches zero. Stating this another way, if we let n approach infinity (let the number of rectangles approach infinity), the error disappears. Hence, we have as the exact measure of the area under a curve given by $f(x)$ and above the x axis between the limits $x = a$ and $x = b$

$$\lim_{n \to \infty} \sum_{i=1}^{n} f(x_i)(\Delta x) = \lim_{\Delta x \to 0} f(x_i)(\Delta x) = \int_a^b f(x)\, dx$$

This last expression is called the *definite integral*, and the symbol $\int$ is an operator meaning "sum" just as Σ is an operator. The definite integral is a limiting sum that gives the area under the curve. It is a limit, just as the derivative is a limit, except in this case it is the limit of a sum.

So much for the meaning of the definite integral. The process of computing the integral is called *integration*. But how do we compute it? Are there any rules similar to those presented for the differentiation of a function? Before answering this question, let us turn our attention to the other viewpoint from which the integral may be considered—the indefinite integral. We shall see that discussion of the indefinite integral will greatly facilitate the computation of the definite integral.

B. THE INDEFINITE INTEGRAL

Indefinite integration is the reverse of differentiation. It consists in finding a function whose derivative is given. If $f(x)$ is a given function and $F(x)$ is a function not given and if $F'(x) = f(x)$, we write for the indefinite integral

$$\int f(x)\, dx = F(x) + k$$

where k is an arbitrary constant. The constant k is added to $F(x)$ purely for the purpose of generality. Since the derivative of a constant is zero, the result of differentiation is not affected if an arbitrary constant is added to the function $F(x)$. Both the derivative of $F(x)$ and the derivative of $F(x) + k$ are equal to $f(x)$.

Suppose we are given a function,

$$\frac{dy}{dx} = x^2$$

This is a "differential equation" involving the derivative $\dfrac{dy}{dx}$ of a function y, so far unknown. Can we find this function from the equation? We know

$$\frac{d}{dx}\left(\frac{1}{3}x^3\right) = x^2$$

Therefore, one possible form of the function we seek is

$$y = \tfrac{1}{3}x^3$$

But if we were to add any constant whatsoever to this function, we would get the same derivative. Consequently, this is not a unique solution of the differential equation. If we were to add an arbitrary constant k (where k may also be zero), then

$$y = \tfrac{1}{3}x^3 + k$$

is the form of the function required. Furthermore, we can expect no other form of y to have the derivative x^2. We may write this result as follows:

$$\int (x^2)\, dx = \tfrac{1}{3}x^3 + k$$

Notice that the additive constant, which disappears on differentiation, reappears in the reverse process.

This basic relationship between differentiation and integration can be summarized in the following expression:

$$\frac{d}{dx} [\int f(x) \, dx] = f(x)$$

Assuming $f(x)$ is a continuous function, the derivative of the indefinite integral of $f(x)$ is the function $f(x)$ itself.

There are rules for indefinite integration that are similar to those for differentiation; for example:

(1) The integral of a sum is the sum of the integrals.
(2) The integral of a difference is the difference of the integrals.
(3) The integral of a constant times a function is the constant times the integral of the function.

Let us consider two examples that illustrate the rules for indefinite integration. We perform the indicated integration:

$$\int (10x^4 - x^3 + 6x^2 - 4x + 13)dx$$
$$= 10\int(x^4)dx - \int(x^3)dx + 6\int(x^2)dx - 4\int(x)dx + \int 13dx$$
$$= 10(\tfrac{1}{5}x^5) - \tfrac{1}{4}x^4 + 6(\tfrac{1}{3}x^3) - 4(\tfrac{1}{2}x^2) + 13x + k$$
$$= 2x^5 - \tfrac{1}{4}x^4 + 2x^3 - 2x^2 + 13x + k$$

For our second example, we have

$$\int \frac{1}{x} \, dx = \log_e x + k$$

$$\text{since } \frac{d}{dx} \, (\log_e x) = \frac{1}{x}$$

Textbooks on the calculus customarily give tables of indefinite integrals for more complicated functions, and this greatly facilitates the procedure of integration.

Computation of the Definite Integral

With knowledge of indefinite integration as the reverse of differentiation, we can answer the question posed at the end of Section A: How does one compute the definite integral? The answer is given in what is known as the fundamental theorem of the integral calculus. We merely assert it here without proof.

If f is a given continuous function, if a and b are numbers, and if F is any function such that $F'(x) = f(x)$, then

$$\int_a^b f(x)dx = F(b) - F(a)$$

Let us see how this theorem is used to obtain the definite integral illustrated in Section A. We were given there that

$$y = f(x) = 10 + 2x$$

and we wish to find the definite integral from $x = 3$ to $x = 7$. From our knowledge of indefinite integration, we know

$$F(x) = \int (10 + 2x)dx = 10x + x^2 + k$$

Therefore, by the fundamental theorem

$$\int_3^7 (10 + 2x)dx = F(7) - F(3) = [10(7) + (7)^2 + k]$$

$$- [10(3) + (3)^2 + k] = 119 - 39 = 80$$

We interpret this geometrically in the following way. The area under the curve given by $y = 10 + 2x$ and above the x axis from $x = 3$ to $x = 7$ is 80. Recall that our approximation to this area in Section A was 84. The total error involved in using the sum of the areas of the rectangles with $\Delta x = 1$ amounts to 4. This is the total area of the shaded portions of the rectangles in Figure 13.2.

Suppose our problem is to find the area under the curve

$$y = f(x) = 8x^3 - 2x + \frac{1}{x}$$

from $x = 1$ to $x = 4$. The indefinite integral is

$$F(x) = \int \left(8x^3 - 2x + \frac{1}{x} \right) dx = \int 8x^3\, dx - \int 2x\, dx + \int \frac{1}{x} dx$$

$$= 2x^4 - x^2 + \log_e x + k$$

We can check this by seeing if the reverse process of differentiation on the function $F(x)$ gives $f(x)$:

$$\frac{d}{dx} F(x) = \frac{d}{dx} (2x^4) - \frac{d}{dx} (x^2) + \frac{d}{dx} (\log_e x) + \frac{d}{dx} (k)$$

$$= 8x^3 - 2x + \frac{1}{x} = f(x)$$

The definite integral is evaluated as

$$\int_1^4 \left(8x^3 - 2x + \frac{1}{x} \right) dx = F(4) - F(1)$$

$$= [2(4)^4 - (4)^2 + \log_e 4 + k] - [2(1)^4 - (1)^2 + \log_e 1 + k]$$

$$= 512 - 16 + 1.3863 - 2 + 1 - 0 + k - k = 496.3863$$

The values of $\log_e 4$ and $\log_e 1$ were obtained from the table of natural logarithms at the end of the book. The area under the curve corresponding to

$$y = 8x^3 - 2x + \frac{1}{x}$$

and above the x axis from $x = 1$ to $x = 4$ is 496.3863.

C. APPLICATIONS OF INTEGRATION

The most important applications of integration to economic problems must await discussion of probability theory in a later part of the book. We will mention but a few applications at this time. These applications are designed to emphasize the relationship of integration to differentiation and should be sufficient to familiarize the reader with the basic value of integral calculus.

1. Marginal and Average Cost

Obviously if the marginal cost function is the first derivative of the total cost function, then the total cost function is the integral of the marginal cost function. Now suppose we do not know the average cost function, but we do know the marginal cost function. In order to find the average cost, we must first compute the total cost, since average cost is defined to be total cost divided by output.

Let C represent the total cost of production of a firm. Since marginal cost is given as

$$C' = \frac{dC}{dx}$$

where x denotes the amount of good X produced, we have

$$C = \int C' dx$$

Average cost is C/x. The integration introduces an arbitrary constant; however, if we know the value of C for any *one* value of x, we can determine the total cost function completely.

Assume the marginal cost is known to be

$$C' = .03x^2 - .10x + 4$$

where C' is measured in dollars. Assume, also, that we know the total fixed cost is \$1,000. Then we know $C(0) = 1,000$. To find the total cost function, we integrate the marginal cost function:

$$C = \int (.03x^2 - .10x + 4)\ dx$$
$$= .01x^3 - .05x^2 + 4x + k$$

where k is, again, an arbitrary constant. From the additional information that fixed cost is \$1,000, we know

$$C(0) = .01(0)^3 - .05(0)^2 + 4(0) + k = 1,000$$

Hence $k = 1,000$ and

$$C = .01x^3 - .05x^2 + 4x + 1,000$$

We merely divide total cost by output to obtain the average cost, denoted by A:

$$A = .01x^2 - .05x + 4 + \frac{1,000}{x}$$

The same type of argument applies to the revenue of the firm. If the marginal revenue is given, the total revenue is found by integrating the marginal revenue function. Average revenue is then calculated by dividing total revenue by output.

2. Maximum Profits

An interesting problem is that of finding the maximum profit for a firm when the information given is in terms of marginals only. We are given the marginal cost of production:

$$\frac{dC}{dx} = 2 + .08x$$

where C and x again refer to total cost (in dollars) and output respectively. We also know the marginal revenue. Assume that the firm is operating under pure competition, and that the price is given to the firm as $10. Then marginal revenue is

$$\frac{dR}{dx} = 10$$

where R signifies total revenue.

Since marginal cost is an increasing function of output (its derivative is positive), we know profit is a maximum when marginal cost is equal to marginal revenue (equals price). So we can calculate the output that yields maximum total profit by setting marginal cost equal to marginal revenue and solving for x:

$$2 + .08x = 10$$
$$x = 100$$

Can we find the total profit at this output? We know that total profit is defined as total revenue minus total cost, so

$$\frac{dR}{dx} - \frac{dC}{dx} = \frac{dP}{dx}$$

where P designates total profit. Therefore,

$$P = \int\left(\frac{dP}{dx}\right) dx = \int\left(\frac{dR}{dx}\right) dx - \int\left(\frac{dC}{dx}\right) dx = R - C$$

We treat the integral of marginal revenue first:

$$\left(\frac{dR}{dx}\right) dx = \int (10)\, dx = 10x + k_1$$

Since we have assumed pure competition, we know that k_1 must be zero in this case, that is, total revenue equals the given price of $10 times the output. We turn next to the integral of marginal cost:

$$\left(\frac{dC}{dx}\right) dx = \int (2 + .08x)\, dx = 2x + .04x^2 + k_2$$

But we cannot assume that $k_2 = 0$. k_2 equals the total fixed cost of the firm. Consequently, if we know the fixed cost, we can determine total profit.

Suppose fixed cost is $100, $(k_2 = 100)$. Then the total profit function is given as

$$P = 10x - 2x - .04x^2 - 100$$

and total profit when output is 100 is

$$10(100) - 2(100) - .04(100)^2 - 100 = 300$$

We conclude that maximum total profit of the firm is $300.

PROBLEMS

Find the indefinite integrals, $f(x)$, of the following functions.

1. $f'(x) = 4 + 3x$.

2. $f'(x) = 2x^3 - 4x^2 + 6x - 1$.

3. $f'(x) = x^{-2} + 6x + 4$.

4. $f'(x) = \sqrt{x}$.

5. $f'(x) = \dfrac{1}{x^3} - \dfrac{1}{x} + \tfrac{1}{4}$.

6. $f'(x) = a + bx + cx^2$.

7. $f'(x) = \sqrt{a + bx}$.

8. $f'(x) = e^x$.

Find the following definite integrals.

9. $\displaystyle\int_1^6 (2x + 3)\, dx$.

10. $\displaystyle\int_1^4 \frac{1}{x}\, dx$.

11. $\displaystyle\int_3^7 (x^3 - 4x^2 + 2x - 3)\, dx$.

12. $\displaystyle\int_{-3}^3 (\frac{1}{x^2} + x^2 - \tfrac{1}{5}x)\, dx$.

13. $\int_{10}^{20} (10) \, dx.$

14. $\int_{0}^{4} (2x^4 - 4x^3 + 3x^2 - x + 1)^3 \, dx.$

15. The marginal cost of production function of a firm is given as
$$C'(x) = 10 - .12x + .006x^2$$
where C' denotes marginal cost and x denotes the quantity produced. Find the total cost function if total fixed cost is known to be $1,000.

16. The marginal revenue function of a monopolist is given as
$$R'(x) = 50 - .0002x^2$$
where R' denotes marginal revenue and x denotes the quantity produced and sold. It is known that total revenue is zero when $x = 0$. Find the market demand function for the commodity.

17. The market demand function for a commodity X is given as
$$x = \frac{100}{p}$$
where x denotes the quantity demanded per unit of time and p denotes the price of X. Find the area under the demand curve and above the quantity axis from $x = 2$ to $x = 10$.

18. The marginal propensity to consume out of income for the economy as a whole is given as $\frac{3}{4}$. It is known that when income is zero, consumption equals $12 billion. Find the function relating aggregate consumption to national income. Find aggregate saving as a function of income.

PART **III**

Econometric Models

CHAPTER 14

Static Models

We have now reached a point where we can bring together the various topics discussed in Parts I and II. These aspects of mathematical formulation are combined in a model, which is the starting point for any econometric study. In Part I, we saw that relationships among economic magnitudes can be formulated in mathematical terms. A set of economic relationships can be expressed by a set of simultaneous equations, such as a demand equation and a supply equation. In Part II, we have examined certain operations that can be performed on equations in order to achieve results stipulated in advance from considerations of economic theory. These operations come under the heading of differential and integral calculus. We now turn our attention to econometric models, which utilize the preceding mathematical methods.

An *econometric model* is an econometric theory. It is an abstract representation of the operation of economic forces in the "real world," similar to an architect's blueprint as an abstract representation of a real building. From the viewpoint of the model, we regard economic life as explainable by a set of simultaneous equations, and the model is a complete system or set of such equations. A model is constructed for the ultimate purpose of solving the equations simultaneously, thereby obtaining the values of the variables that are contained in the equations. If the equations can be solved for the values of the variables, we shall have made a prediction. For example, we might solve simultaneously a demand equation and a supply equation in order to determine the equilibrium values of market price and quantity traded. That is, we make a prediction about the price and quantity from knowledge of the demand and supply equations.

There is more than one way to classify types of econometric models. For our purposes we distinguish two basic types: static models and dynamic models. Dynamic models involve considerations of time, and we shall discuss them in the following chapter. In this chapter, we treat static models only. A model is said to be static when it abstracts from time. Another way of saying this is that we view the economic relationships as of an instant of time. It is as if time stood still and we took a photograph of the economic relationships (equations) at that one single moment.

How then do we account for changes? When we are working with this type of a model, we allow for changes in the values of the variables, but we do not concern ourselves with the fact that adjustments to change take time to work themselves out. All adjustments are assumed to be instantaneous. For instance, if there is a shift in the demand curve, suppliers adjust their output "in a flash" as it were! They move along the supply curve, but we ignore the fact that this movement takes time. Or again, take the case of the adjustment of households' aggregate consumption to a change in national income. If consumers receive more income, they are assumed to increase their consumption at the very same moment in which they receive the additional income.

When viewing the economic world through a static model, we are concerned only with the equilibrium values of the economic variables. Furthermore, the equilibrium values are instantaneous. In diagrammatic terms this means that any one demand curve is drawn for a moment of time. Likewise, the supply curve is drawn for one moment of time. Consequently, the equilibrium price and quantity (given by the intersection of the two curves) exist at this moment only. The same interpretation is put upon cost curves, revenue curves, liquidity preference curves, savings curves, etc.

Now suppose that one of these curves should shift (a parameter of one of the equations changes). We have a change in the equilibrium values. But this change is also assumed to be instantaneous. We concern ourselves only with the old equilibrium and the new equilibrium—not with the path through time of the movement from one equilibrium point to another. For that reason, the term comparative statics has been introduced to describe this way of viewing change. Strictly speaking, we might say that statics proper concerns itself with the equilibrium that exists at a moment. *Comparative statics* deals with changes from one equilibrium to another equilibrium, and this change is assumed to be timeless. If a change in the parameter of one static equation occurs, the system of equations is resolved for the new equilibrium values. No heed is taken of the "time dimension" in which we live.

The static view of economic activity may seem to be a great distortion of "reality." It involves a timeless world. The gains in convenience and simplicity, however, must be taken into account. Every theory (mathematical or not) requires "distortion" of reality in the sense that it must simplify to discover important relationships among complex events. If we keep in mind the purpose of a model, namely prediction, we cannot judge the adequacy of the model without reference to the accuracy of its predictions. The problem of time lags in adjustment may be very important in some problems. For the solution of these problems, a static model may not be adequate. For other problems or other purposes, the time lags may be small enough to be ignored without seriously hampering predictions.

A. THE EQUATIONS OF THE MODEL

Before actually demonstrating the construction of static models, we must first examine more closely the equations that go to make up the system; not all of the equations in an econometric model are of the same nature. The equations of a model are called *structural equations*, because they show the basic structure of the firm, industry, economy, etc., that is being studied. Depending upon the complexity of the problem and the particular interests of the economist, the number of structural equations will vary: the "size" of the model will vary. A simple model designed to predict United States national income may contain only three structural equations with reference to the commodity market. On the other hand, it may contain several equations to describe behavior in the commodity market, several others to describe behavior in the money market, and several more to describe behavior in the employment market. In the latter case, the number of structural equations may run into any number that is manageable. The number of equations in the model will depend in part on the number of variables the econometrician is trying to explain. It will also depend upon the number of other variables required to explain changes in any one variable in which the econometrician is interested. It is one of the problems of model construction to insure that all of the variables the econometrician seeks to explain are indeed explained by the theoretical model. Hence, the aspirations of a model may be narrow—as in the case in which we seek to explain the supply of a given type of labor in a geographic region. On the other hand, the aspirations may be much broader—as when we seek to explain the supply of all types of labor in all geographic regions within the economy. In general, the model with broader aspirations will require a greater number of structural equations.

1. Behavioral Equations

In general, the structural equations of a model are of two kinds: *behavioral equations* and *definitional equations*. Let us treat behavioral equations first. These equations describe the behavior of individuals or groups in the economy, as the case may be. They contain theoretical statements of functional relationships rather than identities or definitions. The behavioral equations may describe the behavior of domestic households, domestic firms, foreign firms or households, the government, or any relevant institution. Demand equations, supply equations, cost equations, liquidity preference equations, consumption equations, etc., are all examples of behavioral equations.

A behavioral equation may express a function of one independent variable or several independent variables. The equation, which states that the quantity of a commodity demanded depends upon the price of that commodity only, is a behavioral equation. It describes the response of households (in terms of quantities purchased) to various prices of the commodity. The equation, which states that the quantity demanded depends upon the price of the commodity, consumer income, and the prices of two other commodities is, likewise, a behavioral equation. The latter equation defines a function of four independent variables. The first "explains" the behavior of households with only one variable: the price of the commodity. The second differs only in that explicit account is taken of other variables that influence the decisions of households with respect to the quantity of the commodity purchased. Yet both are behavioral equations.

One type of behavioral equation deserves special mention. This is the behavioral equation that states that some economic magnitude is given. For instance, our supply equation may state that the quantity supplied is equal to one million units. We are then saying that this quantity does not vary when, say, price varies. The supply has zero price elasticity, and the supply curve is a vertical straight line. It must be remembered that this is as genuine and important a behavioral equation as one which states that the quantity supplied varies with price. For example, consider an analogy that describes the behavior of a person's movements. If we describe him as running at a certain speed in a northeast direction, we describe his behavior.

But if we were to describe him as standing still in a given location, we would also be describing his behavior. Our supply equation, which asserts that the quantity supplied is fixed at one million units, states that firms on the whole do not vary output in response to price. It is a behavioral equation that fixes the quantity supplied for the purpose of this particular model. As we shall see in a moment, such types of behavioral equations involve what are called exogenous variables.

2. Definitional Equations

Definitions require little elaboration. As the name implies, such equations introduce into the model certain relevant definitions. The following equation is a definition: $Y = C + S$, where Y denotes current income, C designates current consumption, and S signifies current savings. The equation states the fact that out of any current income the only possibilities open to households are consumption and saving. *Saving* is defined as current income not consumed; hence, a household may consume all or part of its income and, therefore, must save the remainder (which may be zero or negative). Such an equation really tells us nothing about how consumption and saving vary when income varies. It does not tell us whether consumption increases, decreases, or remains constant when income increases. We say that it is not a behavioral equation; it is merely a definition of the income disposal alternatives open to the household.

Another example of a definitional equation is the mathematical statement that the price of a commodity times the quantity purchased is equal to total expenditures on the commodity. Obviously, this equation does not describe the behavior of any unit or group in the economy. It merely states an apparent mathematical necessity. It actually does not explain anything about the workings of the economic system, but it may be necessary for the econometrician to state it explicitly for purposes of logical completeness.

Included also in the category of definitional equations are statements of equilibrium conditions. The mathematical assertion that quantity demanded equals quantity supplied is a definition of market equilibrium, and it is an essential part of the complete model. Likewise, in an aggregate model for the economy as a whole, the statement that national income equals total consumption plus total investment is a definition of equilibrium. It simply states that all expenditures are received as income by some people in the economy.

But again, this equilibrium condition should be stated explicitly in order that the model be complete.

Summarizing the role of equations in the theoretical structure, we say that a model is a complete system or set of structural equations. These equations are of two types: behavioral equations (those which describe behavior of units or groups in the economic system) and definitional equations (those which are identities or equilibrium conditions). Next let us turn our attention to the variables that make up the equations.

B. VARIABLES OF THE MODEL

An equation is a statement of equality between two quantities. In general, each quantity consists of a constant number and one or more variables, together with the coefficients of the variables. Consequently, we shall want to examine the variables that comprise the structural equations in an econometric model. The variables may be divided into two kinds: endogenous and exogenous variables. *Endogenous variables* are those that are explained by the model; *exogenous variables* are not explained by the model, but rather are determined by some forces outside the scope of the model. How comprehensive or broad the model is depends on how many economic variables one wishes to include in the category of endogenous variables. The more variables that are endogenous to the model—the more variables that are explained by the model—the greater is the scope or inclusiveness of the model.

In the study of any economic problem, it is unavoidable that some factors be taken as given for the purpose of the analysis. It is utterly impossible to take into account and explain all of the forces that influence the variable or variables being studied. Because of the limitations of the human mind, some simplification is absolutely required. It is the recognition of this fact that has led economists to classify economic variables as endogenous or exogenous.

1. Endogenous Variables

Endogenous variables determine other variables in the model and are, in turn, determined by other variables. They are those variables that are explained by the model. Their values are not assumed to be known beforehand, but rather their values are obtained by the solution of the simultaneous equations that comprise the model. For example, in a simple national income model we might write consumption as a function of income. Here consumption is determined by income, another variable in the model. But income may also be determined by the introduction of additional functional relationships, particularly by an investment function and the equilibrium condition that consumption plus investment equals income. In this model, then, both consumption and income are endogenous variables. Consumption is determined by income in the consumption function. Furthermore, income is determined by consumption (and investment) in the equilibrium condition. Theirs is a mutual dependence. Both play the role of determinants and the role of being determined.

Consider a model that consists of three structural equations: a demand equation, a supply equation, and the equilibrium equation that states that quantity demanded equals quantity supplied. Let the quantity demanded be a function of the price of the commodity only; also let the quantity supplied be a function of the price only. In this model quantity demanded, quantity supplied, and price are all endogenous variables. Quantity demanded is determined by price, another variable in the model. The same is true of quantity supplied. Price is determined by the equilibrium condition. Consequently, the values of all three variables are determined by the model as a whole. Each one plays the role of determining others in the system also. It is this *mutual dependence* that characterizes the endogenous variables.

2. Exogenous Variables

We have already mentioned that exogenous variables are those whose values are not determined by the model; their values are taken as given for the particular model being used. This is not to say that the value of an exogenous variable is not explainable. We merely say that it is not explained or determined by this model. Its value can, in principle, be determined by a different model of broader scope. In this particular model, the exogenous variable determines the value of at least one endogenous variable, but its value is not determined by other variables in the model.

In the previous example of a national income model, it was demonstrated that both consumption and income were endogenous variables. We did not say anything about investment. Suppose we assume that investment is exogenous. Then it is assumed equal to some known quantity. The level of investment (assumed known) was determined by something outside of this model. Investment determines income (in the equilibrium equation), but it is influenced by neither income nor consumption. It determines other variables in the model, but it is not determined by them.

As an alternative to this formulation, we might express investment as a function of the interest rate. Then investment becomes an endogenous variable; it is determined by another variable in the system, namely, the interest rate. But we must now make a decision about how we shall handle the interest rate. We might assume that it is exogenous. If we do not assume it is exogenous, we must introduce an additional variable to determine it. Then we may assume that this additional variable is exogenous. If not, we must introduce another variable to explain the variable that determines the interest rate, and so on.

There must, of course, be some stopping place. If we continue to push back the frontiers of the exogenous variables, we eventually come to the boundary between economics and other disciplines. We come to a point where the exogenous variables are noneconomic in nature. Exogenous variables are determined ultimately by technological, political, natural, or institutional forces. There are few, if any, econometric models that aspire to explain the entire economy in so many of its aspects as to get into the area of noneconomic exogenous variables. Perhaps the nearest that one comes to this in practice is the handling of government expenditures and taxes as exogenous variables. The determinants of the levels of expenditures and taxes are often noneconomic. They depend partly upon national defense considerations, political pressure groups, etc. Consequently, these variables are treated as exogenous for econometric models.

C. SOLUTION OF THE MODEL

In solving systems of simultaneous mathematical equations, it is required for the existence of a solution that the number of equations be equal to the number of the unknowns. The model, which is a system of structural equations, is complete when the number of equations in the entire set of structural equations is just enough to determine all the endogenous variables, given the exogenous variables. Suppose we have a model consisting of five variables. Suppose, further, that one of these variables is assumed to be exogenous. Then we have one behavioral equation that states that this variable is equal to some known constant. We must now develop four additional structural equations (behavioral or definitional) that permit us to determine the values of the four endogenous variables. When we have done this, the model is complete and has a solution.

We say that the system has been solved when the values of the endogenous variables have been obtained. Since the values of the exogenous variables are known beforehand, the values of all the variables in the model are determined. These are the equilibrium values of the variables.

D. ILLUSTRATIONS OF STATIC MODELS

1. Market Equilibrium for One Commodity

Let us take as our first illustration, a simple demand-supply model for a particular commodity. We shall first present the model in purely formal notation, without specifying the forms of the functions involved. Then we shall present the model in terms of the equations that represent the functions. Let x_d signify the quantity demanded of the commodity X. It may be measured in, say, pounds per unit of time. Depending upon the nature of the commodity, we would use whatever units are convenient, for example, yards, tons, or single items. Let x_s designate the quantity supplied of the commodity X, measured in the same units as quantity demanded. Finally, let p represent the price of the commodity X measured in, say, dollars per pound. We write the demand and supply functions as

$$(1) \qquad x_d = f(p)$$
$$(2) \qquad x_s = g(p)$$

Let us pause for a moment to ask whether the model at this point has a solution. The two functional notations, (1) and (2), imply two equations. Both of these equations, incidentally, will be behavioral equations. But we also note that there are three variables in the model: x_d, x_s, and p. We, therefore, need a third equation to make the model complete. The third equation needed is a definition—the equilibrium condition:

$$(3) \qquad x_d = x_s$$

We now know that the system has a solution, without having yet written the equations for the model.

Let us now proceed to solve the system. To do this we rewrite the model in equation form. Assume we know the equations; they are

$$(1) \qquad x_d = 100 - 10p$$
$$(2) \qquad x_s = 25 + 15p$$
$$(3) \qquad x_d = x_s$$

We have three variables, each of which is an endogenous variable. x_d is determined by p in equation (1); x_s is determined by p in equation (2); p is determined by x_d and x_s together in equation (3). We have three equations (two of which are behavioral and one of which is definitional), so the model is complete.

To solve this system of equations, we substitute (1) and (2) into (3). This gives

$$100 - 10p = 25 + 15p$$

Solving for p,

$$25p = 75$$
$$p = 3$$

This is the price at which the quantity demanded equals the quantity supplied—the equilibrium price. To obtain the equilibrium quantity demanded and supplied, we merely substitute this value for p into either (1) or (2). Substituting in (1) yields

$$(1) \qquad x_d = 100 - 10(3) = 70$$

Incidentally, by substitution in (2) we necessarily get the same answer:

$$(2) \qquad x_s = 25 + 15(3) = 70$$

The equilibrium price predicted by the model is \$3. The equilibrium quantity traded predicted by the model is 70 pounds per unit of time.

To illustrate the way in which exogenous variables are treated, let us now consider a variation on this theme. We present the following model in formal notation:

$$(1) \qquad x_d = f(p_x, p_o, y)$$
$$(2) \qquad x_s = g(p_x)$$
$$(3) \qquad p_o = \bar{p}_o$$
$$(4) \qquad y = \bar{y}$$
$$(5) \qquad x_d = x_s$$

Again, x_d represents the quantity demanded of commodity X, and x_s the quantity supplied. p_x denotes the price of X, and p_o the price of another commodity (say a close substitute for X in consumption). Finally, y designates consumer income. The symbol $\bar{p}_o$ indicates a constant—the known value of p_o. Likewise, $\bar{y}$ designates the known value of y.

At this formal stage, we can already tell whether the model has a solution. We note that there are five variables in the model: x_d, x_s, p_x, p_o, and y. There are five equations consisting of the five variables. Hence, the model has a solution. Equations (1) through (4) are behavioral; equation (5) is definitional.

We next consider the variables. Three are endogenous variables; two are exogenous. The values of the exogenous variables, p_o and y, are given by equations (3) and (4) respectively. That is, (3) and (4) already determine the values of p_o and y. What about the rest of the variables? There remain three endogenous variables and three structural equations, so we can determine the values of the three endogenous variables.

Assume again that we know the equations that correspond to the functions in the model, and we rewrite the model as follows:

(1) $\qquad\qquad x_d = 109 - 5p_x + 2p_o + .6y$
(2) $\qquad\qquad x_s = 25 + 10p_x$
(3) $\qquad\qquad p_o = 3$
(4) $\qquad\qquad y = 200$
(5) $\qquad\qquad x_d = x_s$

Suppose that p_x and p_o are measured in dollars per unit, y in billions of dollars, and x_d and x_s in millions of units per year. Equations (3) and (4) give us the values of p_o and y. We solve the system of equations by first substituting (3) and (4) into (1). This reduces the model to

(1') $\qquad\qquad x_d = 109 - 5p_x + 6 + 120 = 235 - 5p_x$
(2) $\qquad\qquad x_s = 25 + 10p_x$
(5) $\qquad\qquad x_d = x_s$

We have three endogenous variables and three equations. Substitute (1') and (2) into (5) to obtain the equilibrium value of p_x:

(5) $\qquad\qquad\qquad 235 - 5p_x = 25 + 10p_x$
$\qquad\qquad\qquad\qquad 15p_x = 210$
$\qquad\qquad\qquad\qquad\quad p_x = 14$

The values of the variables x_d and x_s are obtained by substitution of this value for p_x into either (1') or (2); thereby we find

$$x_d = x_s = 25 + 10(14) = 165$$

The equilibrium price of x is \$14, and the equilibrium quantity traded is 165 million units per year.

2. Theory of the Firm

Since a model is a mathematical formulation of an economic theory, we can present the theory of the individual firm in terms of a model. We assume pure competition, so that the individual firm takes the price of the product as given. The principal problem is to determine the equilibrium output, that is, the output that maximizes total profit. Our model consists of five structural equations:

(1)	$C = 80 + 2x + .04x^2$
(2)	$R = px$
(3)	$p = 10$
(4)	$P = R - C$
(5)	$P = \text{Max.} [P]$

There are five variables in the model. Equation (1) shows the total cost function of the firm, where C denotes total cost (in dollars) and x represents total output (in millions of units per year). Equation (2) gives the total revenue of the firm, where R designates total revenue and p the price of the product (in dollars per unit). Equation (3) indicates that the market is purely competitive; the price of the product is given to the firm as \$10. Therefore, p is an exogenous variable in this model. Equation (4) is the definition of total profit, and P is consequently measured in dollars. Equation (5) states the equilibrium condition for the firm, namely that total profit must be a maximum.

We solve the system of equations for the value of x that maximizes P. From this condition we can also determine the values of C, P, and R, given that p is already known. We first substitute (3) into (2) to get the total revenue function. Then we substitute (1) and (2) into (4) to obtain total profit as a function of output. Finally, we maximize P with respect to x. The total profit function is given by the equation

(4') $$P = 10x - 80 - 2x - .04x^2$$

Equation (5) states that P must be a maximum. Now it is known from our discussion in Chapter 12 that the necessary condition for maximum P is $\dfrac{dP}{dx} = 0$. We perform this operation on (4'), and solve the resulting equation for the value of x:

$$\frac{dP}{dx} = 10 - 2 - .08x = 0$$

$$x = \frac{8}{.08} = 100$$

We can check to see whether this value of x does indeed yield a maximum P by considering the sufficient condition for P to be a maximum. It will be recalled that this condition is $\dfrac{d^2P}{dx^2} < 0$.

Thus

$$\frac{d^2P}{dx^2} = \frac{d}{dx}(10 - 2 - .08x) = -.08$$

This value is less than zero, so we conclude that total profit is a maximum when output is 100 million units per year. This is the equilibrium output of the firm. With the value of x now known, the values of C, R, and P can also be determined:

(1) $C = 80 + 2(100) + .04(100)^2 = 80 + 200 + 400 = 680$
(2) $R = 10(100) = 1,000$
(4) $P = 1,000 - 680 = 320$

Since the value of p is known exogenously, the five structural equations have determined the values of the five variables in the model. The entire system is determined.

3. National Income Model

Let us next examine the following national income model, presented first in formal notation:

(1) $C = f(Y)$
(2) $I = \bar{I}$
(3) $Y = C + I$

In this model, C designates total consumption, Y total national income, and I total net investment (all measured in, say, billions of dollars). There are three variables: C and Y are endogenous and I is exogenous. There are also three equations. In equation (1), C is determined by Y; in (2) I is given as some known value $\bar{I}$; in (3) Y is determined by C and I. Note that C and Y are determining and determined, while I is determining but not determined in the model. The model is complete since there are sufficient equations to determine the values of all three of the variables.

Let us now present the three equations, all assumed known to us:

(1) $C = 10 + \tfrac{3}{4}Y$
(2) $I = 30$
(3) $Y = C + I$

Equations (1) and (2) are behavioral equations, and equation (3) is a definition (of equilibrium). To solve the system, we substitute (1) and (2) into (3) and solve for the value of Y:

(3')
$$Y = 10 + \tfrac{3}{4}Y + 30$$
$$(1 - \tfrac{3}{4})Y = 40$$
$$Y = \frac{40}{\frac{1}{4}} = 160$$

Substituting this value for Y in (1) yields the value of C, thus

(1') $C = 10 + \tfrac{3}{4}(160) = 10 + 120 = 130$

The value of I is known, so the entire system is determined.

Our assumption that investment is exogenous was a convenient simplification. Suppose now we wish to explain the value of I, also. We thereby make investment an endogenous variable. Assume that the level of investment depends upon the interest rate, and rewrite the model as

(1) $C = 10 + \tfrac{3}{4}Y$
(2) $I = 90 - 1200r$
(3) $Y = C + I$

where r denotes the interest rate. Now I is determined as well as determining. But our model is seen to be incomplete; we have four variables and only three equations. For a complete model, we need another equation, and this equation must involve the interest rate, r. If we assume the interest rate is exogenous and known to be equal to five per cent, our model becomes

(1) $C = 10 + \tfrac{3}{4}Y$
(2) $I = 90 - 1200r$
(3) $r = .05$
(4) $Y = C + I$

Equations (1), (2), and (3) are behavioral equations and (4) is a definition. To solve the system, we substitute (3) into (2) to get the value of I:

(2') $I = 90 - 1200(.05) = 30$

Substituting this value for I along with (1) into (4) gives

(4') $Y = 10 + \tfrac{3}{4}Y + 30$
$$Y = 160$$

Note that we have the same values of I, C, and Y in this model that we had in the previous one. The difference is that in this model we have explained why investment is equal to \$30 billion. In the previous model, we merely assumed that this value was given without attempting to explain what determined the level of investment.

We could also make the interest rate endogenous to our model. To do this, however, we would need additional variables to explain the interest rate. In turn, we would then need one or more equations to describe the behavior of these determinants of the interest rate. In particular, we would need a theory of the money market, which might be the liquidity-preference theory. It can readily be seen, therefore, that the model can be as broad or as narrow as the number of variables we seek to explain.

E. COMPARATIVE STATICS

Every economic phenomenon is characterized by change. How shall we account for change in our static view of the economy? Comparative statics is the term used to describe change within the context of a static model. Essentially, it amounts to tracing through the consequences of changes in the parameters of the structural equations. Each equation contains parameters or constant numbers. But we have seen in Section E, of Chapter 2, that parameters are "variable" constants—constant for the purpose of a solution but permitted to vary as the conditions of the model change. When any one or more of the parameters of a system change, the equilibrium values of the variables in the model will change. The problem of comparative statics is that of finding the new equilibrium values of the variables when the parameters of the model change.

As we have already pointed out, our interest centers on the old equilibrium and the new equilibrium, not on the time required for the change or the path of movement through time to the new equilibrium. Suppose we consider our first illustrative static model presented in Section D. It is a model of behavior in the market for a single commodity:

(1) $$x_d = 100 - 10p$$
(2) $$x_s = 25 + 15p$$
(3) $$x_d = x_s$$

As we have seen, the solution of this model is $p = 3$, $x_d = x_s = 70$. Now suppose we have a change in a parameter of the demand function. Let us assume the quantity intercept, 100, changes to 125. In diagrammatic terms, this is equivalent to a shift to the right in the demand curve. What is the new equilibrium? In terms of the diagram, what is the new point of intersection of the demand and supply curves? Our new model is written:

(1) $$x_d = 125 - 10p$$
(2) $$x_s = 25 + 15p$$
(3) $$x_d = x_s$$

We now solve this system in the same way, which gives $p = 4$, $x_d = x_s = 85$. Price rises by \$1, and total output of the industry expands by 15 pounds per unit of time. The static model predicts new equilibrium values of the variables.

This model does not stipulate what made the demand curve shift. The model might indicate this also if we had more variables in the demand equation. Consider our alternative model of the market for one good (also presented in Section D):

(1) $$x_d = 109 - 5p_x + 2p_o + .6y$$
(2) $$x_s = 25 + 10p_x$$
(3) $$p_o = 3$$
(4) $$y = 200$$
(5) $$x_d = x_s$$

The exogenous variables, p_o and y, are parameters of the demand equation. If the price of the substitute good, p_o, should rise (because of a change in supply in that market), one condition of the model changes. Equation (3) becomes

(3′) $$p_o = 6$$

if the price of the substitute doubles. Then equation (1′) for this model becomes

(1′) $$\begin{aligned} x_d &= 109 - 5p_x + 2(6) + .6(200) \\ &= 241 - 5p_x \end{aligned}$$

In the former case, we had

(1′) $$x_d = 235 - 5p_x$$

Solving this new system of equations yields the solution $p_x = 14.4$, $x_d = x_s = 169$. The former solution gave $p_x = 14$ and $x_d = x_s = 165$.

In the theory of the firm (the second illustration of Section D), we have a problem of comparative statics if a parameter of the cost function or a parameter of the revenue function should change. For example, a rise in the prices of factors of production will raise total cost of production for each level of output. A shift to the right in the market demand curve will raise the price of the product (taken as given by the firm) and so raise total revenue for each level of output. In the comparative statics of the firm we attempt to answer the question, "What will be the new equilibrium output of the firm and new equilibrium levels of total cost, revenue, and profit if a change occurs in a parameter of the system?"

Illustrations of this problem are left to the student as an exercise. Referring to the second illustration of Section D, assume the price of the product rises from $10 to $15 and find the new equilibrium values of the endogenous variables. Then assume that the price of the product does not change, but rather that the total cost function, equation (1), changes to

(1') $$C = 80 + 3x + .08x^2$$

Again, solve the system for the new values of the variables.

Finally, let us turn to the comparative statics of the simple national income model:

(1) $$C = 10 + \tfrac{3}{4}Y$$
(2) $$I = 30$$
(3) $$Y = C + I$$

Assume there is a given change in the level of investment: I increases from $30 billion to $40 billion, a $10 billion increase. Equation (2) becomes

(2') $$I = 40$$

We solve the system in the same way that we did in Section D and obtain the values $Y = 200$, $C = 160$, and $I = 40$. The former level of income was $160 billion. A $10 billion increase in investment produces a $40 billion increase in income. This is the familiar principle of the investment multiplier. The investment multiplier is defined as

$$k = \frac{\Delta Y}{\Delta I}$$

In this case, we have

$$k = \frac{40}{10} = 4$$

A given increment in investment increases income by an amount equal to four times the increase in investment.

The investment multiplier operates through "rounds" of expenditure. The investment expenditure is paid to the factors of production as income. Part of this income is spent on consumption and the remainder is saved. Some persons receive these consumption expenditures as income and they, in turn, consume part of it and save part of it in the second "round." This process is continued until all of the original increase in investment has gone into savings. At the end of the process, income has risen by some multiple of the increase in investment. Now these "rounds" of expenditure obviously take time to work themselves out, and the new equilibrium level of income does not occur immediately. In the static model, however, we do not concern ourselves with the time required to achieve the new, higher level of income. We are interested in the final result only, and this is all that the static model shows.

F. CONCLUSION

Before passing on to the examination of other types of models, it is essential to emphasize the flexibility of model construction. The model should not be regarded as a rigid set of theories or conclusions. It is a tool of analysis, and alternative assumptions or conditions are compatible with it. Models are similar to a set of wrenches used by a mechanic. The wrench appropriate for tightening one bolt is not necessarily appropriate for another. Furthermore, a wrench can be varied in size or manipulated in usage so as best to solve any given mechanical problem. The conditions of the problem and the objectives desired will largely determine what wrench shall be used and the way in which it shall be used.

The same is true of econometric models. They can be altered, revised, and manipulated to serve the purposes of the research worker. They are a matrix by means of which various ideas can be systematically expressed. Consequently, the success of a model depends partly upon the ingenuity of its user.

PROBLEMS

You are given the following behavioral equations and values of the exogenous variables. Complete the models and find the equilibrium solutions for the values of the endogenous variables.

1. $$x_d = 310 - 20p \qquad \text{market demand equation}$$
$$x_s = 10 + 10p \qquad \text{market supply equation}$$

where x_d and x_s are the quantities demanded and supplied of the commodity X respectively and p denotes its price.

2. $$x_d = 310 - 20p_x - 2p_o + .2y \qquad \text{market demand equation}$$
$$x_s = 25 + 10p_x - .1w \qquad \text{market supply equation}$$

where x_d and x_s are the quantities demanded and supplied of X, p_x is the price of X, p_o is the price of another commodity, y is consumer income, and w is the wage rate of labor used to produce the commodity X. You are given that $w = 10$, $y = 200$ and $p_o = 4$.

3. $$C = 15 + .6Y + .1A \qquad \text{consumption function}$$
$$I = 80 - 1000r \qquad \text{investment function}$$

where C denotes consumption, Y is income, A is total assets of households, I is investment, and r is the interest rate. You are given that $A = 100$ and $r = .04$.

4. $$c = 100 + 1.5x + .03x^2 \qquad \text{total cost function of a firm}$$

where c denotes the total cost and x denotes the output of the commodity X produced by the firm, which operates in a purely competitive market. You are given that the price of the commodity X is 20.

5. Suppose the level of consumer income in Problem 2 decreases from 200 to 100. Find the new equilibrium values of the endogenous variables.

6. Suppose the interest rate in Problem 3 changes from .04 to .06, and consumer asset holdings increase from 100 to 150. Find the new equilibrium values of the endogenous variables.

7. Suppose the price of the product in Problem 4 increases from 20 to 30. Find the new equilibrium values of the endogenous variables. Suppose the total cost function changes to

$$c = 200 + 2x + .05x^2$$

Find the new equilibrium values of the endogenous variables.

CHAPTER 15

Dynamic Models

Time plays no explicit or essential part in the static models of the preceding chapter. It is true that time enters into the definitions of the variables in the sense that we defined a period relevant to the quantities measured. For example, output was measured as so much per unit of time (per year or per month); national income was taken to mean income per unit of time, and so on. It is impossible to define such flows (as opposed to stocks) without reference to a time unit. What does it mean to say that a firm's output is one million tons? This could mean one million tons per week, per month, per year, etc. Therefore, static models do not completely escape from considerations of time. Though necessary, time is implicitly contained in these models. But it is not a distinguishing mark; it is merely necessary in order that we may speak sensibly about any flow. The concept of time durations is not a peculiar or an essential characteristic.

Dynamic models, on the other hand, are those in which time does enter explicitly. The variables are understood as existing at some point in time or during some interval of time. In the static national income model, we simply wrote consumption as a function of income. In a dynamic model, the time at which these variables enter the functional relationship must be explicitly asserted. Consumption in year t may be written as a function of income in year t. Or consumption in year t may be expressed as a function of income in year t-1, that is, current consumption depends upon the income of the previous year.

This latter relationship is called a lagged relationship, because the independent variable is lagged behind the dependent variable with respect to time. As a result of the explicit role played by time, the information imparted by the model is greater than that given by the static model. Comparative statics dealt only with the attainment of a new equilibrium, once a parameter of the system had changed. It contained no information about the movement of the variables over time or the rate at which the variables approached their new equilibrium values. Dynamics is a theory that determines the behavior through time of all variables in the system. If a parameter of the system changes, it tells us the rate at which the variables approach their new equilibrium values, if at all.

The classification of structural equations as behavioral or definitional applies also to dynamic models; so does the classification of variables as endogenous or exogenous. With reference to the variables, only one modification is required. In a dynamic model, it is possible to have lagged endogenous variables. The values of these variables, like the values of exogenous variables, are known in the current time period, and their role in model building is similar. Sometimes a distinction is made between exogenous variables and lagged values of the endogenous variables. The general term used to describe both is predetermined variables. Neither is determined within the system itself, and both are determinants of other variables. For our purposes, we shall treat lagged endogenous variables in the same way that we treat exogenous variables.

There are, in general, two types of dynamic models. In one type we deal with quantities that are relevant to specified time periods or time intervals. For instance, quantity demanded is interpreted to mean the quantity demanded during one year or one month. The units of time are viewed as discrete, and the models involve finite difference equations (see Chapter 3, Section I). In the second type, the variables are viewed as changing continuously through time rather than in finite steps or jumps from one period to the next. Each value of a variable exists at a point in time. These dynamic models involve what are called differential equations. Some dynamic models may be a mixture of these two types. Hence, they will include both discrete and continuous time descriptions.

A. DISCRETE DYNAMIC MODELS

The best way to understand the difference between static and dynamic models is to work out some specific examples. For purposes of comparison, we shall consider dynamic illustrations in which the economic problems are similar to those covered in Chapter 14.

1. The Cobweb Model

The famous cobweb theorem is a relatively simple model of the market for a particular commodity. It is an excellent example of a dynamic model involving discrete time units, and it may be used to analyze the market for a perishable farm crop. Furthermore, it lends itself readily to diagrammatic representation.

Let the quantity demanded of the perishable good X be denoted by x_{dt} (measured in millions of bushels per year), and let its price be denoted by p_t (in dollars per bushel). The quantity demanded during any period of time is assumed to depend upon the current price. Thus, if we know the demand equation, we can write

$$(1) \qquad x_{dt} = 200 - 5p_t$$

The subscript t on the variables refers to the time period. In general, the time period may be measured in any convenient units; we assume that it is a year, so t refers to year t. The demand equation is interpreted as follows: the quantity demanded of the good X during year t is a decreasing linear function of the price of X in year t.

In the cobweb model, it is assumed that the quantity supplied in year t is a function of the price in the previous year. There are plausible grounds for this assumption. The crop must be planted well before the date of harvest and sale. It follows that the output decisions of farmers are based upon the prevailing market price at the time of planting. Again, assuming that the supply equation is known, this hypothesis leads to the lagged supply formulation

$$(2) \qquad x_{st} = 10 + 2p_{t-1}$$

where x and p are measured in millions of bushels per year and dollars per bushel respectively. The subscript t on x signifies the quantity supplied in year t, and the subscript t-1 on p denotes the price in the previous year. The lagged variable, p_{t-1}, is predetermined and so is treated like an exogenous variable—it is known in year t.

If this were a static model, we would have no lagged prices. More exactly, the question of lags would not arise at all. One would abstract from time by omitting time subscripts on all of the variables. In the static model, we would add another equation: the definition of equilibrium, $x_d = x_s$, and the model would be determinate. The equilibrium values of all the variables would be determined by the simultaneous solution of the three equations.

Can we do the same in this dynamic model? The time subscripts force us to use a somewhat different procedure. Since the price in the supply equation is predetermined, we can assign some value to it. Suppose we know the initial value of the lagged price, and we call our first relevant period year one. Then $t = 1$ and p_{t-1} is labeled p_o. Assume this initial lagged price is $10.00 per bushel. From the supply equation, we know that 30 million bushels are supplied in year one. However, we do not have an equilibrium because demanders are willing to pay $34.00 per bushel for this quantity—as seen from the demand equation. This means that forces are in operation to change output, for when the market price is $34.00 in year one, suppliers will produce 78 million bushels in year two. Now when suppliers produce 78 million bushels, the market price in year two drops to $24.40 per bushel (again obtained from the demand equation). Hence, once more suppliers will change their output for year three, and so on. When for any given values of the variables in the model there exist forces that change those values, we do not by definition have an equilibrium.

Table 15-A shows what happens to output and price as we proceed through time. With a known initial price, $p_o = 10$, the initial quantity traded in year one is 30 million bushels. In general, the quantity traded each year is read off the supply equation, and the price in each year is obtained from the demand equation by substitution of the quantity produced for x_{dt}.

Table 15–A

t	x_t	p_t	$p_o = 10$
1	30.00	34.00	
2	78.00	24.40	
3	58.80	28.24	
4	66.48	26.70	
5	63.40	27.32	
6	64.64	27.07	
7	64.14	27.17	
.	.	.	
.	.	.	
.	.	.	
∞	64.28	27.14	

We see in this particular example that the quantity traded on the market approaches 64.3 million bushels. The price approaches $27.14 per bushel. We could obtain this same result by solving the equations as if all the variables referred to the same point of time (as in the static model). By removing the time subscripts the price variable is the same variable in both the demand and supply equations. By adding the equilibrium definition we can simultaneously solve the equations. The solution turns out to be $p = 27.14$ and $x_d = x_s = 64.3$.

It would seem, then, that the dynamic model has not given us more information than the static one. We must remember, however, that in addition to the equilibrium solution we have also determined the movement of the variables over time. We have, furthermore, determined the rate at which they approach their equilibrium levels. Such information is not imparted by the static model! This fact is clearly demonstrated in Figures 15.1, 15.2, and 15.3. In Figure 15.1, the demand and supply curves are depicted. Notice that the figure drops the time subscripts on the variables. This is necessary in order to relate both quantity supplied and demanded to one and the same variable, the price. This is a procedure comparable to the analytic solution when the model is treated as if it were static. The broken line in the figure traces the movement to the equilibrium point (64.3, 27.14).

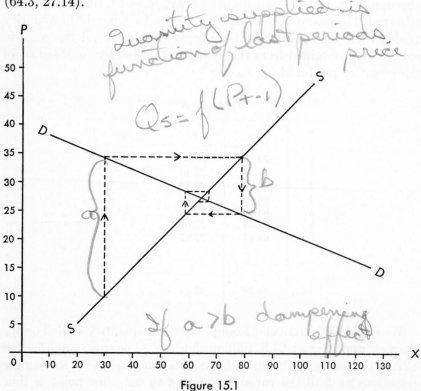

Figure 15.1

Figures 15.2 and 15.3 show the movements of the market price and the quantity exchanged through time; this is called the time path of the variables. The observations are plotted in the center of each time period and are assumed to remain unchanged during that

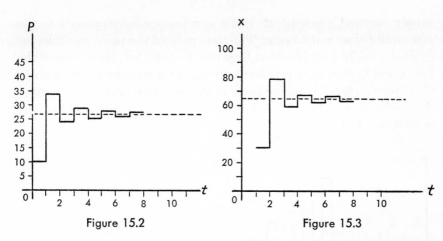

Figure 15.2   Figure 15.3

period. The variables move by steps from one year to the next, which is a necessary consequence of defining them in discrete terms. It is seen that these two variables approach the equilibrium solution: $p = 27.14$, $x = 64.3$. These values are the equilibrium values because once obtained no tendency exists to move elsewhere as long as the demand and/or supply curves do not shift. The variables oscillate around their equilibrium values, but these oscillations are *damped*, that is, they get smaller and smaller through time and approach the equilibrium. For this reason, the model is called a *stable equilibrium model*. The equilibrium is said to be stable because regardless of where one starts, the system approaches the equilibrium solution.

The complete dynamic model contains equations (1) and (2). Equation (3) gives the initial value of the lagged price:

(3) $p_o = 10$

The stable equilibrium is given by equation (4):

(4) $x_{dt} = x_{st}$

This model is complete. For different values of p_o, we would obtain different approaches to the same equilibrium, but in any case the system does approach the equilibrium. These approaches through time distinguish the stable dynamic model from the static model.

There is little new that need be said about the effects of changes in the parameters of the model. If, as the system approaches equilibrium, a change in one or more of the parameters should occur, a disturbance is injected into the approach. Then a new approach is started to a new equilibrium. This is easily visualized by assuming a shift in the demand curve for the product. It will intersect the supply curve at a new point. But a new broken-line approach to the new equilibrium must begin. The time path of the price variable, for example, might look like that shown in Figure 15.4. Here each of the horizontal broken lines represents an equilibrium solution for a given set of parameters. As one or more of the parameters changes, so does the equilibrium. The actual time path of the price is depicted by the unbroken curve.

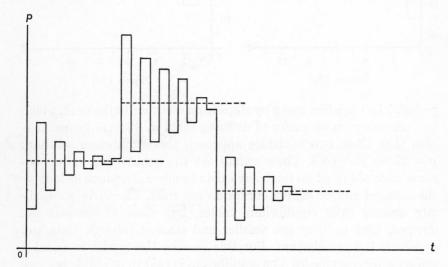

Figure 15.4

a. *The Explosive Cobweb.* The foregoing case illustrates a stable cobweb model. In terms of Figure 15.1, the stability results from the fact that the supply curve is steeper in slope than the demand curve. The slope of the supply curve with respect to the quantity axis is $\frac{1}{2}$, while the slope of the demand curve is $\frac{1}{5}$ (the negative sign is ignored). The outcome would be quite different if the situation were reversed, that is, if the demand curve had a greater slope—in absolute value—than the supply curve. If this were the case, the price and quantity exchanged would diverge farther and farther from the intersection point, starting from any point other than the point of intersection. The system does not approach equilibrium, and the model is said to be explosive.

Consider the following demand and supply equations:

(1) $x_{dt} = 200 - 3p_t$
(2) $x_{st} = -10 + 4p_{t-1}$

The lines corresponding to these equations are plotted in Figure 15.5, where the intersection is shown to be at the point (110,30). That is, if the system is solved as if it were static, the solution is $p = 30$, $x_d = x_s = 110$.

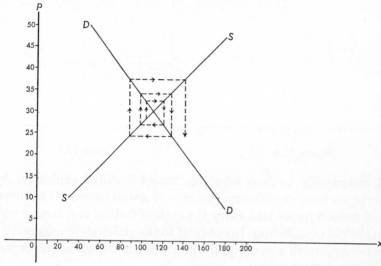

Figure 15.5

Let us now repeat the process of choosing a lagged price less than or greater than the equilibrium price. Assume $p_o = 28$. We get the behavior of price and quantity traded over time shown in Table 15-B. The time paths of the variables are shown in Figures 15.6 and 15.7.

Table 15–B

t	x_t	p_t	$p_o = 28$
1	102.00	32.67	
2	120.68	26.44	
3	95.76	34.75	
4	129.00	23.67	
5	84.68	38.44	
6	143.76	18.75	
7	65.00	45.00	
8	170.00	10.00	
9	30.00	56.67	
.	.	.	
.	.	.	
.	.	.	
.	.	.	

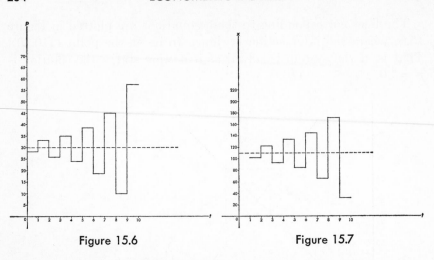

Figure 15.6   Figure 15.7

It can readily be seen why this model is called explosive. Any disturbance from equilibrium (because of a shift in one of the curves) sets in motion forces that carry the system farther and farther away from the old equilibrium. In contrast to the stable dynamic model, it does not approach a new equilibrium when a change in one or more of the parameters occurs.

b. *The Nondamped Oscillating Cobweb.* In the stable model, the oscillations depicting the time paths were damped. Over time the variables approached their equilibrium values. In the explosive case, the oscillations grew larger and the variables moved farther away from equilibrium. There remains the case in which the system neither approaches nor diverges from the equilibrium. The time paths show that price and quantity continue indefinitely to oscillate between two fixed values. This result is shown in Figure 15.8 for the price of the commodity. The quantity traded behaves in exactly the same way.

This phenomenon can be illustrated in terms of the demand and supply curves by constructing linear curves with identical slopes. Starting from any point on one of the curves except the equilibrium point, the broken curve forms a rectangle. One moves on the broken line continuously among four points and traverses the same route again and again.

These three variations on the cobweb theorem strikingly illustrate the purpose and use of dynamic analysis. Variations in the model lead to different results with respect to the course of the variables over time. This is knowledge that could not be acquired from a

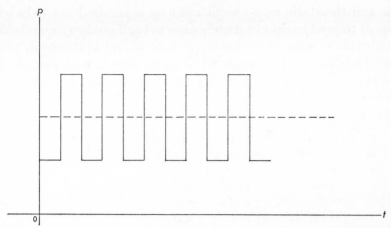

Figure 15.8

static model, as useful as a static model may be for the analysis of many important economic problems.

2. The Theory of the Firm

Let us turn now to a somewhat different type of problem in which dynamics is a useful tool. Multidate decisions by individual firms provide an informative application of the dynamic technique. In the static model of the single firm, there was no question of planning over time. Such a model is not well suited for problems of inventory management. Inventory decisions cannot ignore the element of time. The question of "how long" as well as "how much" to hold must be answered. The professional literature on inventory problems is vast and complex. We shall merely attempt to illustrate the nature of such problems with a highly simplified and artificial dynamic model. Further reading on inventory decision processes is contained in the bibliography at the end of the book.

We make two basic assumptions: (1) that the firm produces and sells in a purely competitive market and (2) that there are only two time periods the firm considers in making its inventory decision: call these year one and year two. The firm must decide not only the amount to produce but also the amount to sell in each year (these were assumed identical in the static case). If the firm decides that sales are to be less than production in the first year, then the firm will carry part of its production over into the second year as inventories. The firm's decision with respect to production and sales (hence, inventories) is based upon the usual assumption that the firm maximizes total profit. There is a primary distinction between this and the static case—profit must be maximized not only with respect to production but with respect to both production and sales. Furthermore, since more than one time period is involved, profit must be maximized with respect to production in both periods and sales in both periods. For convenience, all sales are assumed to be made at the end of each year.

We first define the following variables:

p_t = price of the commodity at the end of year t

x_t = production during year t

s_t = sales at the end of year t

y_t = inventories in stock at the end of year t

$c(x_t)$ = total cost of production function, that is, the total cost of producing the amount x during year t

ky_t = total cost of storage function per year, where k is a constant, that is, the total cost of storing the amount y for one year. Since k is assumed to be a constant, the cost of storage function is linear.

To simplify the problem, we introduce two conditions:

(1) $$y_1 = x_1 - s_1 \geq 0$$
(2) $$y_2 = (x_1 + x_2) - (s_1 + s_2) = 0$$

The first condition merely states that inventories at the end of the first year may be zero but cannot be negative. The firm cannot carry less than no inventories. Equation (2) states that inventories at the end of the second year are zero—none are carried over into a third year.

We define total profit, P, as

(3) $$P = p_1 s_1 + p_2 s_2 - c(x_1) - c(x_2) - ky_1$$

Since we have assumed pure competition, p_1 and p_2 are constants —market prices are given to the firm and are unaffected by its behavior; k is also a known constant. The first two terms on the right side of the equation are total revenue from sales in years one and two. The second two terms are the cost of production for the amounts produced in years one and two. The last term is the total cost of storing inventories from the end of year one to the end of year two. Hence, total profit is total revenue from all sales minus total costs of both production and storage.

Profit is to be maximized with respect to x_1, x_2, s_1, s_2, and y_1. But by substituting equation (1) for y_1 in the last term and equation (2) for s_2 in the second term, we can simplify the expression for profit. In particular, we can eliminate s_2 and y_1. Then we have to maximize

(4) $$P = p_1 s_1 + p_2(x_1 + x_2 - s_1) - c(x_1) - c(x_2) - k(x_1 - s_1)$$

with respect to only three variables: x_1, x_2, and s_1. Rewrite the expression for P so as to separate the terms in these variables:

(5) $P = [s_1(p_1 - p_2 + k) + x_1(p_2 - k) - c(x_1)] + [x_2p_2 - c(x_2)]$

Note that if $(p_1 - p_2 + k)$ is negative, then P is largest for $s_1 = 0$, that is, store all that is produced. For s_1 cannot be negative, and any positive nonzero value for s_1 makes the first term negative. If, on the other hand, $(p_1 - p_2 + k)$ is positive, then P is largest for s_1 made as large as possible. That is, $s_1 = x_1$ by equation (1); all production is sold in year one, so $y_1 = 0$.

The common sense of this result is clear. If the price next year, p_2, exceeds the price this year plus the cost of storage per unit, $p_1 + k$, then store all you can and sell it in year two. If the reverse is true, don't store at all. Finally, if the price this year plus storage cost per unit just equals the price next year, that is, if $p_1 - p_2 + k = 0$, the size of s_1 does not affect profit, so it does not matter which decision is made.

Let us take each of these three cases separately, compute the profit, and then maximize it.

Case 1: $p_2 < p_1 + k$
Therefore $s_1 = x_1$ so $y_1 = 0$
And $s_2 = x_2$ by equation (2)
$P = x_1(p_1 - p_2 + k + p_2 - k) - c(x_1) + x_2p_2 - c(x_2)$
$\ \ = x_1p_1 - c(x_1) + x_2p_2 - c(x_2)$

For maximum P we have

$$\frac{\partial P}{\partial x_1} = p_1 - c'(x_1) = 0 \qquad \frac{\partial P}{\partial x_2} = p_2 - c'(x_2) = 0$$

With $c(x_1)$ and $c(x_2)$ known, these equations can be solved for the values of x_1 and x_2 (see Chapters 11 and 12). In this case, we have the familiar condition that the amount of production in each year is chosen so as to equate the marginal cost of production to the price in that year.

Case 2: $p_2 > p_1 + k$
Therefore $s_1 = 0$ so $y_1 = x_1$
And $s_2 = x_1 + x_2$ by equation (2)
$P = x_1(p_2 - k) - c(x_1) + x_2p_2 - c(x_2)$

For maximum P:

$$\frac{\partial P}{\partial x_1} = p_2 - k - c'(x_1) = 0 \qquad \frac{\partial P}{\partial x_2} = p_2 - c'(x_2) = 0$$

Production in the first year, x_1, is chosen so as to make the marginal cost of production equal to the price in the second year minus the marginal storage cost. Production in the second year, x_2, is chosen as in Case 1.

Case 3: $p_2 = p_1 + k$

Therefore, s_1 is arbitrary; P and, therefore, the solution for x_1 and x_2 is the same as in Case 1.

In actual applications, one most often deals with more than two time periods, and the decisions of firms are rarely, if ever, of the type derived here, namely, store all production or sell all of it. More developed inventory models lead to decisions with respect to how much shall be produced in each of several years and what proportion of this production shall be stored. They also derive a rule for determining how long, on the average, each unit of the product shall be stored. Nevertheless, this oversimplified model serves to illustrate the general nature of the inventory problem and the way in which dynamic models can be used to solve the problem.

3. National Income Models

Dynamic theory has proved itself valuable in the study of national income and business cycles of prosperity and depression. There exist many theoretical formulations that have as their core the solution of difference equations. Let us consider a variation on a national income model presented by R. F. Harrod.[1] It clearly demonstrates how difference equations comprise an integral part of the solution of a dynamic system. The theory is presented in terms of saving and investment. This, of course, is an alternative to stating the theory in terms of consumption and investment (as in the static model of Section D, Chapter 14). If consumption is a function of income, then saving is a function of income, and in equilibrium saving equals investment.

Assuming the structural equations are known, we have the following complete model:

(1) $$S_t = .1Y_t$$
(2) $$I_t = .5(Y_t - Y_{t-1})$$
(3) $$Y_0 = 200$$
(4) $$S_t = I_t$$

The symbols S, I, and Y designate saving, investment, and income respectively (all measured in billions of dollars per year). Y_0 denotes the value of income in the initial year, that is, when $t = 0$. Equation

[1] R. F. Harrod, "An Essay in Dynamic Theory," *Economic Journal*, Vol. XLIX (1939), pp. 14–33.

(2) is a *difference equation:* an equation that involves finite differences in one or more of the variables. General solutions for finite difference equations were discussed in Chapter 3.

We combine equations (1), (2), and (4) to get

$$.1Y_t = .5Y_t - .5Y_{t-1}$$
(5)
$$Y_t = 1.25Y_{t-1}$$

Since (5) holds, we could also write

$$Y_{t-1} = 1.25Y_{t-2}$$
$$Y_{t-2} = 1.25Y_{t-3}$$

and so on. Hence, this equation cannot be regarded as the solution of the model.

To obtain the general solution, we must find the solution of the difference equation (5). This general solution will express Y_t in terms of the parameter and the initial value of Y given by equation (3)—refer to Chapter 3, Section I, first example. The general solution is seen to be

(6)
$$Y_t = (1.25)^t Y_0$$

Equation (6) describes the time path of national income, which is shown in Figure 15.9.

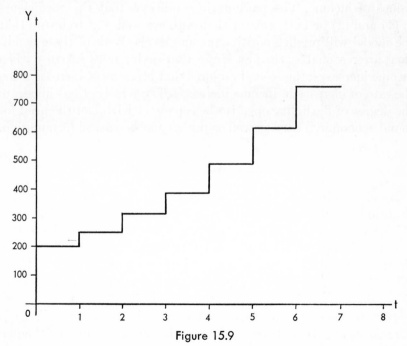

Figure 15.9

The model leads to a nonoscillating increase in national income over time for the given coefficient of 1.25. This increase is due to the fact that the coefficient in (6) is greater than one. It is interesting to note that if this coefficient had been positive but less than one, national income would show a nonoscillating decrease over time. If it had been equal to one, then income would remain constant at $200 billion, and the graph in Figure 15.9 would be a horizontal line.

For purposes of comparison, it is worth noting that if the co-efficient in (6) were negative, the model would predict an oscillating time path of income. With a coefficient of less than minus one (say -2), the oscillation would be explosive; for values between minus one and zero, the oscillation would be damped. Finally, if the coefficient in (6) were zero, income would always be zero (except in the initial year when $t = 0$), and if equal to minus one, income would be nondamped but oscillate between the fixed values of 200 and -200. In all of these cases, the model predicts either negative income or zero income in at least some years, which is not plausible. Consequently, restrictions on the coefficients in equations (1) and (2) must be introduced to insure that the model predicts only positive values of income. The parametric conditions that the coefficients in (1) and (2) be both greater than zero are sufficient to insure that the model will predict positive income levels. Both of these conditions are reasonable: the first states that saving must increase when income increases; the second requires that investment increase when the rate of increase in income increases. These restrictions illustrate the degree of flexibility open to the econometrician and the need for sound economic theory as well as precise mathematical formulation.

B. CONTINUOUS DYNAMIC MODELS

By shortening the length of the time period, we approach the situation of continuous models. In a continuous model, the variables are regarded as changing continuously through time instead of moving in steps from one period to the next. Changes in income in the discrete model, for example, were denoted by $(Y_t - Y_{t-1})$. When the income variable is treated as continuous with respect to time, changes are indicated by the first derivative of income with respect to time, dY/dt. Such models contain what are called *differential equations*. It is convenient to think of the differential equation as a difference equation in which the differences are infinitesimal—expressed as derivatives rather than finite differences. The solution of a continuous model involves the process of integration discussed in Chapter 13.

1. The Market for One Commodity

The following dynamic model is given for a particular commodity X:[2]

(1) $$x_d(t) = 100 - 10p(t)$$
(2) $$x_s(t) = 25 + 15p(t)$$
(3) $$\frac{dp}{dt} = .10(x_d - x_s)$$

where x_d, x_s, and p denote the quantity of X demanded, the quantity supplied, and the price of X respectively. Each of these variables is assumed to be a continuous function of time, denoted by t. In place of the equilibrium condition of the static model, we have equation (3) which states that the rate of change of price over time depends upon the difference between the quantity demanded and the quantity supplied. The change in price is proportional to excess demand. When the quantity demanded exceeds the quantity supplied, the price rises. The price falls whenever the quantity supplied exceeds the quantity demanded. Only when equilibrium is disturbed is there a price change, for in equilibrium $x_d - x_s = 0$ so that $dp/dt = 0$. Given a change in a parameter of either the demand or supply equation or both, equation (3) tells us in what direction price will move. Furthermore, it tells us the *rate* at which the price will approach its new equilibrium value, if at all.

Substitution of equations (1) and (2) into equation (3) yields

(4) $$\frac{dp}{dt} = .10[75 - 25p]$$

Let us pause here to note the equilibrium price. Solving the system *as if* it were static gives $\bar{p} = 3$, where $\bar{p}$ designates the equilibrium price. Now returning to equation (4) we see that it may be written

(4') $$\frac{dp}{dt} = .10[25\bar{p} - 25p] = -2.5(p - \bar{p})$$

Since the coefficient in this differential equation is negative, the price will tend over time to approach its equilibrium value. For if

[2] *See* A. Marshall, *Principles of Economics* (8th ed.; London: Macmillan and Co., Ltd., 1930), p. 374, and G. C. Evans, *Mathematical Introduction to Economics* (New York: McGraw-Hill Book Company, Inc., 1930), p. 48.

p is less than $\bar{p}$, then the derivative dp/dt is positive, so that p rises toward $\bar{p}$. Conversely, if p is greater than $\bar{p}$, $\dfrac{dp}{dt}$ is negative so that p falls toward $\bar{p}$ over time. When $p = \bar{p}$, then dp/dt is zero and there is no further change in p.

By the solution of the differential equation (4'), moreover, we can find the time path of price and the rate at which it approaches $\bar{p}$. The solution is given in the footnote below.[3] Had the coefficient of (4') been positive, which is inconsistent with the usual assumptions of economic theory with regard to the slopes of the demand and supply curves, the price would not have approached its equilibrium for any values of the variables other than the equilibrium values. In this case, a disturbance would not lead to a new equilibrium.

2. National Income Models

The discrete national income model of Section A can be formulated also as a continuous model. Let us rewrite that model in terms of continuous variables:

$$(1) \qquad\qquad S(t) = .1Y(t)$$

$$(2) \qquad\qquad I(t) = .5\frac{dY}{dt}$$

$$(3) \qquad\qquad S(t) = I(t)$$

where saving, investment, and income represented by S, I, and Y

---

[3] We have $\dfrac{dp}{dt} = -2.5(p - \bar{p})$, where $\bar{p}$ is a known constant. Introduce a new variable which is also a function of time:

$$(1) \qquad\qquad y(t) = p(t) - \bar{p}$$

Differentiating this expression gives

$$(2) \qquad\qquad \frac{dy}{dt} = \frac{dp}{dt} - 0 = -2.5\,[p(t) - \bar{p}]$$

Dividing by y, we obtain

$$(3) \qquad\qquad \frac{y'(t)}{y(t)} = \frac{-2.5\,[p(t) - \bar{p}]}{p(t) - \bar{p}} = -2.5$$

This can be written as the differential equation

$$(4) \qquad\qquad \frac{1}{u}\frac{dy}{dt} = -2.5$$

The integral of (4) by the methods of Chapter 13 is

$$(5) \qquad\qquad \int \frac{1}{y}\frac{dy}{dt} = ae^{-2.5t} = y(t)$$

Hence from (1) we have

$$(6) \qquad\qquad p(t) = y(t) + \bar{p} = ae^{-2.5t} + \bar{p}$$

When $t = 0$, then $a = p_0 - \bar{p}$, where p_0 is the price at time zero. Therefore

$$(7) \qquad\qquad p(t) = \bar{p} + (p_0 - \bar{p})e^{-2.5t}$$

For known p_0, this equation gives the time path of the price of the commodity.

are all expressed as continuous functions of time, t. Equation (2) is a differential equation.

As the first step in the solution, we follow the same procedure as that used in the discrete case. Equations (1) and (2) are substituted into equation (3). This substitution yields

$$.1Y(t) = .5\frac{dY}{dt}$$

or

(4) $$\frac{dY}{dt} - .2Y(t) = 0$$

The problem then becomes one of finding the solution of this differential equation for the behavior of income over time. After both sides of the equation have been multiplied by $1/Y$, the equation may be written

(5) $$\frac{1}{Y}\frac{dY}{dt} = .2$$

To find Y as a function of time, we must integrate. Integration of both sides of equation (5) yields

(6) $$\int \frac{1}{Y}\frac{dY}{dt}\,dt = \int \frac{dY}{Y} = \int .2dt$$

We know from Rule 6 of Section F, in Chapter 8, that the left side of (6) can be written as log Y, since the derivative of log Y is $1/Y$. Considering the right side, we know from Chapter 13 that the indefinite integration indicated gives $.2t + K$, where K is an arbitrary constant. Hence, we rewrite (6) as

(7) $$\log_e Y = .2t + K$$

To find the solution that gives Y as a function of t, we merely translate the logarithmic expression into an exponential one (see Section G, Chapter 8):

(8) $$Y(t) = e^{(.2t+K)} = e^{.2t} \cdot e^K = Ae^{.2t}$$

where $A = e^K$. Now we have an arbitrary constant in the solution. But we may specify a value for A by stating the initial value of Y. The value of Y at time zero will be designated by Y_0. That is, the value of the function $Y(t)$ when $t = 0$ is denoted by Y_0. Then

$$Y(0) = Ae^{.2(0)} = Ae^0 = A$$

Therefore, the final solution becomes

(9) $$Y(t) = Y_o e^{.2t}$$

Under the assumption that $Y_0 = \$200$ billion, the time path of national income is shown in Figure 15.10. Note the continuity of the time path as opposed to those shown for discrete dynamic models.

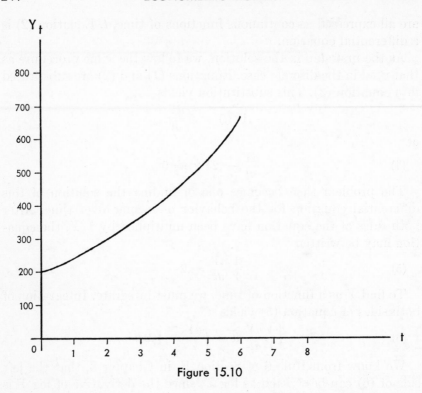

Figure 15.10

The solutions for S and I can also be found. Their time paths can be plotted from equations (1) and (2) when the value of Y at each time point is known.

C. CONCLUSION

It is not the purpose of this chapter to present an exhaustive set of examples of dynamic models. The foregoing illustrations are designed to show the kind of knowledge given to economists by dynamic models, and how these differ from static models. A careful scrutiny of the illustrations should permit a grasp of the import of other applications that may be encountered. Many variations of dynamic models appear in the professional literature. For a complete understanding of some of these, extensive and intensive knowledge of mathematics is required. Often simple differential equations are not encountered. Then more sophisticated mathematical techniques must be used to find the solution, if one exists.

Be this as it may, enough can be gained from the illustrations of this chapter to indicate the importance that dynamic models have for dealing with problems of economic fluctuations. Though not regular in amplitude or duration, the so-called business cycles are a kind of economic oscillation with respect to time. Seasonal cycles in production, inventories, and consumption can be better understood with the aid of dynamic analysis. Again it should be emphasized that dynamics, like statics, is a useful tool of analysis rather than a codified body of substantive principles. Its success for theoretical analysis and prediction depends in part upon the ingenuity that is shown in its application to diverse problems. It is a powerful tool, but even powerful tools will not do the job by themselves. They must be used wisely.

PROBLEMS

1. You are given the following dynamic national income model:

(1) $S_t = aY_t$ (3) $Y_0 = 300$
(2) $I_t = b(Y_t - Y_{t-1})$ (4) $S_t = I_t$

where S denotes saving, Y income, I investment, and a and b are constants. The subscripts refer to time. Compute and plot the time path of national income from $t = 0$ to $t = 5$, inclusive, for the following values of a and b:

(1) $a = .1$ $b = .2$
(2) $a = .6$ $b = -.2$
(3) $a = 0$ $b = 2$

2. Construct a cobweb model which results in time paths for the endogenous variables which are nondamped oscillations.

3. Plot the time paths from $t = 0$ to $t = 4$, inclusive, for saving and investment corresponding to the continuous dynamic model presented in Section B.2.

4. You are given the following continuous dynamic model:

(1) $S(t) = .1Y(t)$
(2) $I(t) = -1\dfrac{dY}{dt}$
(3) $S(t) = I(t)$

where S denotes saving, I investment, and Y income, all as continuous functions of time. Assume income in period zero is 300 and find the general solution for income as a function of time. Plot the time path of income from $t = 0$ to $t = 5$, inclusive.

CHAPTER 16

The Problem of Uncertainty

No doubt there has been a bothersome question running through the reader's mind throughout our discussion of econometric models. Up to now, we have assumed that we know with complete certainty the economic relationships that we are studying. Not only do we assume knowledge of which variables to include in the structural equations, but also the values of the parameters. For instance, in our linear demand equations for a commodity X, we assigned definite and known values to the price coefficient and the quantity intercept. The significance of this assumption can be seen when one asks himself whether he could, just by thinking about it, tell what the demand equation is for steel in the United States today. Could one tell merely from economic theory what the aggregate consumption equation is for the United States today or for any past period? Obviously not! We come, then, to the really crucial problem of econometrics—the problem of measurement. More exactly, this is the problem of estimating from empirical data the values of the parameters in the structural equations.

In general, we do not know beforehand the values of the parameters of any model. True, economic theory can tell us which variables are relevant to a structural equation. We know that we can write the quantity demanded and the quantity supplied as dependent upon the price of a commodity. We also know the direction in which income, other prices, etc., influence the demand for that commodity. And we know the direction in which factor prices and technological conditions influence the quantity supplied. Furthermore, our theoretical reasoning can tell us that the demand curve is in general negatively sloped (more exactly that the partial derivative of quantity demanded with respect to price cannot be positive). Likewise, the supply curve is in general positively sloped (the partial derivative of quantity supplied with respect to price cannot be negative). In a linear demand or supply equation, this means that the price coefficient cannot be positive for the demand equation and cannot be negative for the supply equation. Now these are all questions of deductive logical consistency; the stated conclusions follow necessarily from the basic assumptions of utility maximization by households and profit maximization by firms.

This theoretical reasoning, however, does not tell us what the *values* of the price coefficients will be. The coefficient of the price variable in a linear demand equation, for example, can range from zero to minus infinity; any of these values is consistent with the theoretical requirement that the coefficient be nonpositive. Likewise, the law of aggregate consumption states that consumption increases when income increases but by less than the increase in income. That is, the first derivative of consumption with respect to income is positive but less than one. Again, economic reasoning does not tell us whether that first derivative is $+.001$ or $+.999$ or any one value that is positive but less than one. These are important problems, and their solution does not depend upon deductive logic. Rather, it is a question of inductive logic, or reasoning from particular empirical observations to universal laws of behavior.

If economic theory cannot tell us more than the forms of the structural equations, we must turn to the facts in the case to derive approximate values of the parameters of the model. We must use empirical observations on prices, quantities produced and consumed, income, saving, or whatever economic magnitudes are relevant to the model. In other words, we use empirical observations of the values of the variables; these are our data from which the parameters of the model are to be estimated. It is in this way that econometrics differs from mathematical economic theory. The econometrician uses statistics to arrive at quantitative estimates of the parameters in the model, and he does this in a systematic way. Assuming that we can be successful in estimating the parameters, quantitative predictions can be made about the values of the endogenous variables, given the values of the exogenous variables. We can go beyond essentially qualitative theoretical conclusions such as "the price will rise," and tell approximately by how much the price will rise in response to some given change.

A. STATISTICAL MEASUREMENT

We may conveniently regard the problem of statistical measurement in the following way: there exists one "true" economic relationship, say the "true" demand equation for tennis shoes in the

United States today. If we could get a complete and perfectly exact count of all potential and actual customers and a perfectly exact measure of the quantity they would buy at all possible prices, all incomes, all prices of other goods, etc., we could have a perfect measure of the "true" demand equation. But because of human and technological limitations, we obviously cannot do this. One must be satisfied with something less than perfection. We, therefore, take a sample of observations on price, quantity consumed, income, and other such economic magnitudes. From this sample, we attempt to estimate the parameters of the "true" demand equation. Because we must work with a sample of observations instead of all possible observations, our estimates of the "true" parameters will contain some error. If the error is relatively large, the estimate will be a poor one. But if the error is small (in terms of criteria established by statistical analysis), our estimate may be considered reliable.

Let us consider the problem of statistical measurement in more general terms. Theoretical models consist of general equations or laws of economics that refer to the entire economic body being studied. The consumption function, for example, implies that a relationship holds between consumption and, say, income for all consumers as a whole. This entire body being studied is called the *population* in statistics. The population is an abstract term and refers to all conceivable observations of some stated kind, such as all conceivable observations of consumption and income by American households. It must be emphasized that it is not the households that are the observations; it is rather the amounts of consumption and income. Similarly, in the case of a supply function it is the combination of a price and the corresponding quantity offered for sale that comprises one observation.

Now if it were at all practical, we could obtain the desired statistical measurement by recording all of the conceivable observations on the economic magnitudes in question. But in almost all cases complete enumerations of the population are impossible or impractical. Imagine the cost of interviewing every cotton farmer in the United States every year to find out how much he will produce at given prices! In addition to the prohibitive costs of observing the population directly, there are social customs, time limitations, etc., that result in further barriers to complete enumerations of the population in most cases. Consequently, we must work with a sample of observations drawn from the population, for example, the consumption and income of 1,000 households in the United States. From a "parameter" of the sample, called a statistic, we attempt to infer the value of a parameter of the population. The parameter of the population is regarded as the "true" parameter, and the statistic of the sample is interpreted as a (good or poor) estimate of the unknown "true" parameter.

The statistical theory of random sampling describes the relationship between samples and the population. There will not be exact correspondence between the population and any one sample that we might draw from that population, because what we get in the sample depends partly on chance. The errors due to chance make it impossible to draw inferences about the population with certainty. These inferences can be made only with probabilities. It is this idea of randomness (and the related theory of probability) on which modern statistical measurement is based.

B. RANDOM VARIABLES

We have called our lack of knowledge about the values of parameters the problem of uncertainty. How shall we handle this uncertainty within the framework of the econometric model? It has already been pointed out that we use statistical inference, but how do we alter the theoretical formulation so as to make the model amenable to statistical measurements based on the calculation of probabilities? To answer this question, we introduce a new type of variable into the model: the so-called random variable. In econometric terminology, all the variables dealt with in the structural equation up to this point are called *systematic variables*. Thus, we have endogenous and exogenous systematic variables. We call them systematic because definite values can be assigned to these variables with certainty.

They are related one to another in an orderly and predictable way. Knowledge of economic theory enables us to conclude that they behave according to specified directional laws, for example, that, for given other conditions, the price of a commodity and the quantity demanded always move in opposite directions (quantity demanded is a monotonic decreasing function of price). The same general types of directional specifications can be made for cost functions, investment functions, production functions, etc.

Because we don't get this exact and orderly variability in our empirical observations—because all other things are not in fact constant—we must have some means for explaining the deviations from the exact theoretical predictions of the model. For this reason, we introduce into the behavioral equations (but not the definitions, per se) random variables.

When we think of the word "random," we think of something erratic or "hit-or-miss." There is a certain amount of accuracy in such a conception. More exactly, we may think of a *random variable* as one such that any value it may assume is as likely as any other. More exactly still, we may define it as a variable that can assume values with definite probabilities. A random variable is one which is subject to the laws of probability.

Random variables are sometimes called random errors. They are errors in the sense that when we come to apply the model to empirical data, we find that our systematic relationships do not predict without error. Suppose we have a demand-supply model for a commodity X, and suppose that we have estimated the parameters of the equations. In repeated predictions of the market price of X, we would in general find that the predictions are not always 100 per cent correct. The actual market prices will differ, by more or less, from the predicted prices. Are these errors random in nature, or is there a systematic "bias" in the model that is unaccounted for by the systematic variables? If they are random, then we can account for their influence on the variable to be explained by adding to the explanatory systematic variables of the equations other variables that are random variables. There are in general two sources of these random errors: (1) errors of observation and (2) errors of omission.

1. Errors of Observation

We have seen that when an econometrician attempts to estimate the parameters of a model, he makes the estimate from a sample of observations on the values of the systematic variables. Assume he has a series of published tables on market prices of X and quantities traded on the market. This is the sample. Can he be assured that these are the actual or "true" prices and quantities? No! The data in the sample are never, except by accident, exactly identical with the population data. Someone had to go out into the "field" and collect this information. First, the information may not have been accurately received by the data collector. Questions asked of traders in the market may have been misunderstood; firms may be unwilling to relinquish certain exact cost or output data; families may have to make rough guesses as to their consumption, especially if the answer depends on memory. Secondly, there may be clerical errors in aggregating, recording, or averaging the figures. Sometimes adequate data are not available to the data collector and interpolations based upon other data must be made. These chance phenomena cause some unavoidable deviation in the sample from the actual or "true" values of the economic magnitudes.

These errors in the observation of the values of the systematic variables will lead to errors in the predictions of the model. If a theoretical relationship is stated between aggregate United States consumption and national income, the several observations on pairs of values of consumption and income will not exactly satisfy the theoretical consumption equation. If these pairs of values are plotted as points in a diagram, the points will not all lie on the consumption curve. The deviations of the observed values from those expected from the equation can, under certain circumstances, be treated as random.

2. Errors of Omission

When writing a demand equation for a particular commodity X, for example, we may write the quantity demanded as a function of the price of X only. Now we know from economic theory that other variables influence the quantity demanded: income, other prices, population, tastes, etc. The question arises as to whether these other variables ought to be included as additional systematic variables in the demand equation. If so, how many and which other prices ought to be included? How shall we measure tastes as a variable? Should income be divided into two distinct variables: permanent income and transitory income? Clearly we do not want to include a thousand independent variables in the demand equation, even if we know that each one of those variables exercises some influence upon the quantity demanded. The result would be a gigantic model, and it probably would be unmanageable. Even if it were manageable, we still could not be sure that we have not overlooked some factor that is influential to some degree. There must be some stopping point!

Because of these practical considerations, we shall have errors that result from the omission of some determining variables. These errors would exist even if there were no errors of observation. Errors of omission arise because we cannot possibly take into account all of the determining factors separately. Furthermore, it would be folly to attempt to do so, since we have available to us a means for including them as a group. We can treat them collectively as a random variable.

At their present stage of development, our statistical tools are not capable of handling both types of error simultaneously. Therefore, we assume that all of the error in an equation is due entirely to either one or the other source. If our judgment suggests that we have included all of the important determining variables, we attribute the error to imperfections in our observations. If we have a high degree of confidence in the reliability of the data, we attribute all of the error to the omission of variables.

Any disturbances in the variables we seek to explain that cannot be explained by changes in the values of the systematic variables are assumed to be random. We have seen that the errors or disturbances assumed to be random may actually contain systematic components. But it is permissible to regard them as random if the components are (1) many in number, (2) individually small in influence, and (3) independent of each other. If these three requirements are met, then the sum of the components will behave as if it were random.

Suppose that we theoretically relate aggregate United States consumption to national income and a random variable. Then suppose we find that our "random" variable is not really random (there are statistical tests available to judge this). This means that there are other strong systematic influences operating on consumption. After examination, we might find that this strong influence is the interest rate. We may then reformulate our model, making consumption a function of income and the interest rate and a random variable. If then the residual amount of consumption that is not explained by both income and the interest rate behaves as if it were random, we have a statistically reliable structural equation. Consequently, there is continual interaction between the theoretical and empirical stages of economic research. Any given equation may require repeated empirical and theoretical re-examination before it is accepted as a valid structural equation.

C. RESTATEMENT OF ECONOMETRIC MODELS

The feature of uncertainty may be said to exist in two senses. First, there is the assumption of uncertainty on the part of the economic body being studied. In the case of the individual firm or a government planner, the uncertainty exists on the part of the decision-maker. For example, the firm will not be certain of the demand for the commodity. It may not be certain of the costs of its competitors or the future prices of some factors of production. This is especially true in dynamic models of the firm dealing with planning for the future, such as the inventory model of Chapter 15. In an uncertain world, decisions may be based upon expected prices, costs, outputs, etc. We cannot adequately treat such decision rules at this point. They must await consideration of probability theory, which we shall discuss in the next part of the book.

The second sense in which we may speak about uncertainty is the uncertainty of the research worker. It is this type of uncertainty that we have emphasized in the preceding sections of this chapter—uncertainty about the "true" values of the parameters in a market or social relationship. Though the two kinds of uncertainty are not completely separate, the second type is the more important for economists. Economics is a social science that uses individual behavior primarily as a steppingstone to understand group behavior. It is ultimately interested in equations that describe the behavior of such social groups as consumers, industries, speculators, laborers, and government.

The econometrician's choice between a static and a dynamic model is governed by theoretical factors and the kind of information that he desires to know. The characteristic of uncertainty may be appended to either static or dynamic models. Indeed, it must be included if the econometrician is to have meaningful and testable empirical predictions. A model cannot strictly be said to be an econometric model unless it is formulated with a view to its statistical properties. We shall illustrate the formulation of a static and a dynamic econometric model. The characteristics of deductive logical consistency and completeness (discussed in Chapters 14 and 15) are not to be disregarded, but we shall emphasize the preparation of the model for statistical analysis.

1. Static Models

One of the first steps in an econometric investigation is the formulation of the theory. As we have seen, economic theory can tell us the general forms of the functional relationships. It can tell us, for instance, that the quantity demanded is a decreasing function of price, but it cannot tell us whether the demand equation is linear, quadratic, cubic, etc. Consequently, the second step is a general review of the data to determine approximately whether the equation is linear or of another type. We shall say more about this in a later chapter.

Let us assume that we have a static model designed to explain the price and quantity traded of the commodity X. Furthermore, suppose a preliminary look at the data suggests the equations are linear in two variables, price and quantity. We write our model as follows:

$$(1) \qquad x_d = a + bp + u \qquad b \leq 0$$
$$(2) \qquad x_s = c + dp + v \qquad d \geq 0$$
$$(3) \qquad x_d = x_s$$

where x_d and x_s denote the quantity demanded and quantity supplied respectively, p denotes the price of X, and a, b, c, and d are constants. Note that this model differs from our previous static models. In the first place, we have not assumed that we know the values of the parameters beforehand. We have used the symbols a, b, c, and d for the parameters. We know from economic theory that the quantity demanded is in general a decreasing function of price, so we can stipulate in advance that the price coefficient, b, in the demand equation cannot be positive. Likewise, we can restrain the value of the price coefficient, d, in the supply equation to be nonnegative. But this is as far as economic theory can carry us. The problem remaining is a statistical one, namely to estimate the values of the unknown parameters a, b, c, and d.

The second main characteristic, which distinguishes this model from previous static models, is the inclusion of random variables. The variable u is assumed to be a random variable in the demand equation and v a random variable, different from u, in the supply equation. These variables orient the model toward the statistical analysis that will be applied to it in order to estimate the values of the parameters from a sample. These random terms are subject to the laws of probability upon which modern statistical estimation is based. The quantities demanded and supplied are linear functions of the random variables, so they too may be treated as random variables. We shall not go into the actual statistical analysis at this point. Before discussing the statistical techniques, it is important that we understand the proper formulation of the model.

2. Dynamic Models

As an illustration of an uncertain dynamic model, let us reconsider the continuous national income model presented in Chapter 15. We add the random variables, thus

(1) $$S(t) = aY(t) + u \qquad a > 0$$

(2) $$I(t) = b\frac{dY}{dt} + v \qquad b > 0$$

(3) $$S(t) = I(t)$$

Here again S, I, and Y represent saving, investment, and income respectively. The variables u and v are assumed random, while a and b are positive constants. The parameters are unknown. Assuming we do successfully estimate the values of a and b, the systematic relation will predict a steadily increasing level of income over time (see Figure 15.10). The actual values of income over that same period of time will in general differ somewhat from the predicted values. If these errors of measurement are small and in fact random (according to the proper statistical test), the model may be considered a good dynamic predictor of income.

We can see clearly from these two illustrations what the role of random variables is in econometrics. Since random variables are subject to the laws of probability, they put the model into a form that permits the estimation of parameters by statistical inference. It is to these statistical procedures that we now turn our attention. Part IV is an exposition of elementary probability theory and statistical inference. After having become familiar with the meaning and techniques of statistical analysis, we shall reconsider econometric models from a more comprehensive viewpoint in Part V.

Statistical Inference

CHAPTER 17

Elements of Probability Theory

Statistical analysis is an integral part of econometrics. Before we can say much more about econometrics, it is necessary to explore the statistical theory upon which economic measurement is based. This statistical theory, in turn, rests upon the laws of probability. In this chapter, we shall define probability and discuss the characteristics of some of the laws of probability. Since our interest is to be centered upon the practical application of statistics to economics, rather than upon the theory of statistics itself, this chapter and the next are in the nature of a summary. Nevertheless, we shall want to investigate enough details about probability theory to understand and interpret the general implications of econometric research.

An analogy may be made between a laboratory experiment in the physical sciences and statistical measurement in economics. In both cases, one seeks to find predictable relationships between some events and the causes of those events. In a laboratory one can control, to a greater or less degree, the exterior conditions that surround an event and the imputed causes of the event. The physical scientist can then vary the assigned causes and test to see if the event behaves in the way predicted under the controlled conditions. Even after all the assignable causes have been controlled, however, the outcome of any one experiment is still subject to variation from causes that the scientist cannot control or does not even know about. It is these unassignable disturbances or influences—these "accidental" errors—or, as they are more often called, random errors that create the need for a concept of probability.

Similarly, in economics we assign certain social phenomena as determinants or causes of other social phenomena. For example, aggregate national consumption is assumed to be determined or "caused" by national income. When dealing with social phenomena as we do in econometrics, we cannot conduct an experiment in the strict sense of that term, because we cannot control the causes and conditions that surround any given event. We can, however, assign causes to the event—such as national income assigned as a "cause" of consumption. Just as in an experiment, when we come to measure or test the relation between the assigned cause (which varies, but not by control) and the result, we find that the result is influenced by unassignable causes. Hence, random errors and the notion of probability will play an important part in econometrics also.

A. THE CONCEPT OF PROBABILITY

A random variable may be called a probability variable. Although we can assign values to a systematic variable with certainty, we can assign values to a random variable only with a specified degree of probability. What exactly does this probability mean? The modern analysis of probability is essentially a branch of pure mathematics. The foundations of probability theory are found in the mathematical theory of sets.[1] But we shall not find it necessary to enter into this axiomatic interpretation because a less rigorous treatment will be adequate for purposes of application.

The statistical definition of probability begins with the idea of a relative frequency. To take a classic example, suppose we were to toss a coin one hundred times. We exercise no special care in the tosses (such as a design to import a particular type of spin) and no other control over the sources of variation. It is not possible to predict whether the coin will definitely turn up heads or tails on any particular toss. Random forces or "errors" due to unassigned causes will decide whether the coin shall fall with heads or tails showing. Now suppose that out of one hundred trials (tosses of the coin) heads turns up 45 times. We say the relative frequency of heads in this experiment is 45/100. More generally, the *relative frequency* of an event (in this case, the occurrence of heads) is the number of times the event happens divided by the number of trials in the experiment (in this case, the number of tosses of the coin).

Let us take another example more closely related to the social sciences. In population studies, a research worker may be interested in the relative frequency of male births. First, what is the experiment? We do not have an experiment in the sense of actually tossing a coin. But we may regard each birth as a trial, and the total number

---

[1] See H. Cramer, *The Elements of Probability Theory and Some of Its Applications* (New York: John Wiley & Sons, Inc., 1955), Chapters 1 and 2.

of recorded births as an experiment. Suppose a set of published data shows that n births have occurred during a specified period of time. The data also show that x of these are male births; we say the event is the birth of a male and there are x of these. Consequently, the relative frequency of male births in this "experiment" is x/n.

Probability is the limiting value of the relative frequency as the series of trials approaches infinity, and if the series of trials is a random series. When a series of many trials is made, and the ratio of the number of times the event occurred to the total number of trials is nearly a number p, and this ratio is generally nearer to p when a larger number of trials is made, we define the probability of the event as p. In symbolic notation we may designate the probability of an event E as $P_r(E)$ and write

$$P_r(E) = \lim_{n \to \infty} \frac{x}{n} = p \tag{17.1}$$

where n denotes the number of *random* trials and x signifies the number of occurrences of the event E.

The concept of probability requires that the series of trials must be a random series. By a random series, we mean that any arbitrary selection from the n trials gives the same value for p as the original n trials. For, suppose we make the following quite arbitrary selection: we choose every third trial out of the total of n trials. Assume this gives us n_3 trials (n_3 is, of course, less than n). We observe that the event in question occurs x_3 times in the n_3 trials. If the original series of n trials is indeed random, then we must find

$$P_r(E) = \lim_{n_3 \to \infty} \frac{x_3}{n_3} = p \tag{17.2}$$

where p has the same value as p in formula (17.1). Next, suppose that we choose every seventh trial and this gives us n_7 trials in which the event E occurs x_7 times. We must have

$$P_r(E) = \lim_{n_7 \to \infty} \frac{x_7}{n_7} = p \tag{17.3}$$

if the original series is a random series. We could repeat this process for any number of different arbitrary selections. In general, we say a series of n trials showing x occurrences of the event E is a random series if when we choose n' of these trials out of the original series of n trials by any arbitrary method and obtain x' occurrences of E, then

$$P_r(E) = \lim_{n' \to \infty} \frac{x'}{n'} = \lim_{n \to \infty} \frac{x}{n} = p \tag{17.4}$$

It is useful to present the notion of probability in a slightly different way. The event is to be denoted by E, and we have n observations (trials) on E. Let the variable x_i be defined as $x_i = 1$ if the event E happens on the ith observation, $x_i = 0$ if the event E does not happen on the ith observation. Designate the probability of the event E as $P_r(E)$, so that

$$P_r(E) = \lim_{n \to \infty} \frac{1}{n} \sum_{i=1}^{n} x_i = p \qquad (17.5)$$

The symbol Σ means summation (see Chapter 13, Section A). In this case, we have $\dfrac{x_1}{n} + \dfrac{x_2}{n} + \dfrac{x_3}{n} + \ldots + \dfrac{x_n}{n}$, where n approaches infinity. It is seen after a little reflection that this is merely an alternative way of stating the formula (17.1). Since $x = 1$ if the event occurs and $x = 0$ if it does not, the summation gives the relative frequency of the event as the number of observations gets larger and approaches infinity.

Probability is an abstract concept; but since it involves the notion of a relative frequency that is empirically observable, we estimate probabilities from experimental results. Let us consider again the example of the unbiased coin. We define the event as the occurrence of a "head" and ask, "What is the probability of the occurrence of a 'head' when a coin is tossed at random?" We then conduct an experiment of n tosses and estimate the probability from a relative frequency. We define a random variable x_i for which $x_i = 1$ on the ith toss if heads turns up and $x_i = 0$ on the ith toss if tails turns up. Suppose we decide that the number of trials is to be thirty. The results of the experiment might be those shown in the table, where **H** designates the occurrence of heads and **T** the occurrence of tails. The relative frequency of heads in thirty trials is seen to be $\frac{16}{30}$.

Trial	Outcome	x_i	Trial	Outcome	x_i	Trial	Outcome	x_i
1	H	1	11	H	1	21	H	1
2	H	1	12	T	0	22	T	0
3	T	0	13	H	1	23	H	1
4	H	1	14	T	0	24	T	0
5	T	0	15	H	1	25	H	1
6	T	0	16	H	1	26	T	0
7	T	0	17	T	0	27	H	1
8	H	1	18	H	1	28	T	0
9	T	0	19	T	0	29	H	1
10	H	1	20	H	1	30	T	0

We test the randomness of the series by choosing only the even-numbered trials: 2, 4, 6, . . . , 30. We then have fifteen trials, and the relative frequency of heads is $\frac{7}{15}$. This is very close to the relative frequency of the original series. Choice of the odd-numbered trials only yields a relative frequency of heads of $\frac{9}{15}$, which is also not too different from the relative frequency of the original series considering that the total number of trials is small. Experience has indicated that if the number of trials were extended more and more, say to 30,000 rather than 30, the relative frequency would converge toward the number $\frac{1}{2}$. We say that the probability of the occurrence of heads is

$$P_r(H) \ = \ \lim_{n \to \infty} \ \frac{x}{n} = \frac{1}{2} \qquad (17.6)$$

In any short series of observations, such as the thirty used here, heads could occur much more than half of the time or much less. This is never the case, however, in thousands of observations that are drawn at random for the experiment. In general, moreover, the larger the number of observations the closer will the relative frequency be to the probability.

We might also consider again the occurrence of male births in the population. What is the probability that a birth will be the birth of a male? Every year thousands of births are recorded—these are the trials or observations. The relative frequency of male births turns out to be slightly greater than $\frac{1}{2}$. From the viewpoint of the statistician the probability of a male birth is $\frac{1}{2}$. This is not to say that in any ten births there will be five male births. Since the probability is a limiting value as the number of observations approaches infinity, one can only say that in a large number of observations the relative frequency of male births will be close to $\frac{1}{2}$, and the larger the number of trials or observations, in general the closer will the relative frequency be to the probability.

The probability of an event can vary between zero and one. Usually it will be some fraction between these extremes. In the example of the coin, we cannot observe more heads than there are trials, nor can we have less than zero occurrences of heads. Likewise, in the case of male births, we cannot observe more male births than there are total births. Neither can we have less than no male births. If the relative frequency of an event is equal to one, the event always happens in n trials; if it is equal to zero, the event does not happen even once in n trials. Consequently, a probability of one corresponds to *certainty*, and a probability of zero corresponds to *impossibility*. Any probability between zero and one corresponds to *uncertainty*.

From this fact, another relationship clearly appears. If the probability of an event happening is $P_r(E)$, then the probability that it does not happen is $1 - P_r(E)$. Given that the probability of heads is $\frac{1}{2}$, the probability of tails is $1 - \frac{1}{2} = \frac{1}{2}$. When the probability of an event happening is $P_r(E) = \frac{1}{5}$, the probability that it does not happen is $P_r(\text{not } E) = 1 - \frac{1}{5} = \frac{4}{5}$.

B. CALCULATION OF PROBABILITIES

In the previous section, we have spoken of the probability p of an event happening, and we implied that this meant the probability of its happening in one trial chosen at random. Another problem that has widespread implications for statistical analysis is the following. Assume that the probability of an event happening is p. The probability that it does not happen is $q = 1 - p$. We have a total of n trials, in each of which we observe either the occurrence of the event or its nonoccurrence. What is the probability that the event will happen x times in n independent trials?

To answer this question, we must first introduce the notion of *combinations*. We may regard the problem as one in which we have n distinct objects and we wish to choose x from them without paying any attention to the arrangement of the x objects chosen. The number of ways of doing this is given by a rule. Given n distinct objects, the number of possible ways of selecting x objects out of the n objects is determined by the formula

$$C_x^n = \frac{n!}{x!\,(n-x)!}$$

C_x^n is called the number of combinations of x objects out of n objects. The symbol $n!$ is read "n factorial"; $x!$ is read "x factorial," etc. $n!$ is a convenient short-hand way of writing the product of all integers from n to 1; thus

$$n! = n(n-1)(n-2)(n-3) \ \ldots \ (4)(3)(2)(1)$$

The same is true of $x!$ and $(n-x)!$

To obtain the probability that the event E will happen x times in n trials, we multiply this so-called binomial coefficient by the probabilities p and q raised to the powers x and $(n-x)$ respectively:

one event $$P_r(E_x) = C_x^n \cdot p^x \cdot q^{(n-x)}$$ no rank or order

where E_x signifies the happening of the event E x times out of n trials.

Suppose a true (unbiased) coin is tossed five times. What is the probability that heads will occur three times in five trials? Here we have $n = 5$ and $x = 3$. The probability of heads is $p = \frac{1}{2}$, and the probability of nonheads (tails) is $q = 1 - \frac{1}{2} = \frac{1}{2}$. Applying the above formula, we have

$$P_r(E_3) = C_3^5 p^3 q^2 = \left(\frac{5!}{3!\,2!}\right)\left(\frac{1}{2}\right)^3\left(\frac{1}{2}\right)^2$$

$$= \left[\frac{5 \cdot 4 \cdot 3 \cdot 2 \cdot 1}{(3 \cdot 2 \cdot 1)(2 \cdot 1)}\right]\left(\frac{1}{8}\right)\left(\frac{1}{4}\right) = \frac{80}{8} \cdot \frac{1}{8} \cdot \frac{2}{8}$$

$$= \frac{5}{16}$$

As a second example, consider the casting of one true die. Since the occurrence of any one given number turning up is a chance phenomenon, we might ask, "What is the probability of obtaining two 'fives' in three rolls of the die?" We have $n = 3$ and $x = 2$. There are six sides to the die, so we say the probability of a "five" is $\frac{1}{6}$. The probability of the nonoccurrence of a "five" is $q = 1 - \frac{1}{6} = \frac{5}{6}$. Hence

$$P_r(E_2) = C_2^3 p^2 q^1 = \left[\frac{3 \cdot 2 \cdot 1}{(2 \cdot 1)(1)}\right]\left(\frac{1}{6}\right)^2\left(\frac{5}{6}\right) = \frac{30}{432} = .069$$

C. THE LAWS OF PROBABILITY

Sometimes a probability problem may be a bit more complicated. For instance, we may wish to know not only the probability of the occurrence of an event E but perhaps the probability of the occurrence of two events E and F, or the occurrence of three events E, F, and G. There are several simple rules for the calculation of such probabilities.

1. Addition Rule: Mutually Exclusive Events

If two events E and F are mutually exclusive (cannot occur together), then the probability of either E or F is the sum of their separate probabilities:

$$P_r(E \text{ or } F) = P_r(E) + P_r(F)$$

Assume a card is drawn at random from a deck of playing cards. What is the probability that it is either a jack of clubs (call this event E) or a queen of diamonds (call this event F)? The two events are mutually exclusive since a jack of clubs cannot also be a queen of diamonds. There is one jack of clubs in the fifty-two cards, so we have

$$P_r(E) = \tfrac{1}{52}$$

There is, likewise, one queen of diamonds:

$$P_r(F) = \tfrac{1}{52}$$

For the probability of either a jack of clubs or a queen of diamonds, we find

$$P_r(E \text{ or } F) = \tfrac{1}{52} + \tfrac{1}{52} = \tfrac{1}{26}$$

The same rule applies to the occurrence of three or more mutually exclusive events. The probability of either E or F or G is

$$P_r(E \text{ or } F \text{ or } G) = P_r(E) + P_r(F) + P_r(G)$$

2. Multiplication Rule: Independent Events

Let two events be designated by E and F; the occurrence of F does not depend on whether E has occurred or not. With E and F independent, the probability of both E and F occurring is the product of their probabilities:

$$P_r(E \text{ and } F) = P_r(E) \cdot P_r(F)$$

Out of a deck of playing cards two cards are successively drawn at random, the first being replaced before the second is drawn. What is the probability that one is an ace (event E) and the other is a spade (event F)? Since the first card is to be replaced before the second is drawn, the second card does not depend upon whether the first is an ace or not—the two events are independent. There are four aces in the deck and thirteen spades, so we have

$$P_r(E) = \tfrac{4}{52} \quad \text{and} \quad P_r(F) = \tfrac{13}{52}$$

By the rule for multiplication of independent events

$$P_r(E \text{ and } F) = \tfrac{4}{52} \cdot \tfrac{13}{52} = \tfrac{52}{2704} = \tfrac{1}{52}$$

is the probability of obtaining *both* an ace and a spade. There is one chance in fifty-two that both events will occur.

This rule also applies to the occurrence of three or more independent events. For the three independent events E, F, and G:

$$P_r(E \text{ and } F \text{ and } G) = P_r(E) \cdot P_r(F) \cdot P_r(G)$$

3. Multiplication Rule: Dependent Events

In the preceding example, the occurrence of F did not depend upon whether E had happened or not. But suppose the occurrence of F does depend upon the occurrence of E. Then the joint occurrence of E and F is the probability of one multiplied by the probability of the other, given that the first event has occurred:

$$P_r(E \text{ and } F) = P_r(E) \cdot P_r(F|E)$$

The symbol $P_r(F|E)$ designates the *conditional probability* of F and is interpreted as the probability of F, given the occurrence of E.

An urn contains seven balls, of which three are red and four are white. The probability of drawing a red ball at random (event E) is

$$P_r(E) = \tfrac{3}{7}$$

After a red ball has been drawn and not replaced, the probability of drawing a white ball at random (event F given E) is

$$P_r(F|E) = \tfrac{4}{6}$$

When one red ball has been drawn, six remain of which four are white. What is the probability of drawing both a red ball and a white ball, the red ball not being replaced? We apply the formula for the joint occurrence of dependent events:

$$P_r(E \text{ and } F) = (\tfrac{3}{7})(\tfrac{4}{6}) = \tfrac{2}{7}$$

For the joint occurrence of three or more dependent events, we merely expand the rule. The probability of the occurrence of E and F and G, all of which are dependent is given as

$$P_r(E \text{ and } F \text{ and } G) = P_r(E) \cdot P_r(F|E) \cdot P_r(G|E \text{ and } F)$$

4. Addition Rule: Events Not Mutually Exclusive

If E and F are not mutually exclusive, the occurrence of either E or F means the occurrence of either E or F or both E and F. The probability of either E or F (or both) is given by the formula

$$P_r(E \text{ or } F) = P_r(E) + P_r(F) - P_r(E \text{ and } F)$$

In cards dealt from a deck of playing cards, let E designate the occurrence of a "heart" and let F designate the occurrence of a "king." What is the probability that a card chosen at random will be either a heart or a king? Note that these events are not mutually exclusive since a king can be a king of hearts. We, therefore, utilize the formula for events that are not mutually exclusive, noting that

$$P_r(E) = \tfrac{13}{52} \quad \text{and} \quad P_r(F) = \tfrac{4}{52}$$

Also,

$$P_r(E \text{ and } F) = P_r(E) \cdot P_r(F) = \tfrac{13}{52} \cdot \tfrac{4}{52} = \tfrac{1}{52}$$

Finally, we have

$$P_r(E \text{ or } F) = \tfrac{13}{52} + \tfrac{4}{52} - \tfrac{1}{52} = \tfrac{16}{52} = \tfrac{4}{13}$$

For three events E, F, and G that are not mutually exclusive, the probability of either E or F or G is obtained from the formula

$$P_r(E \text{ or } F \text{ or } G) = P_r(E) + P_r(F) + P_r(G) - P_r(E \text{ and } F)$$
$$- P_r(E \text{ and } G) - P_r(F \text{ and } G) + P_r(E \text{ and } F \text{ and } G)$$

In each of the foregoing illustrations, we were concerned with the probability of drawing a type of playing card or ball in one trial. For Rules 1 and 4, we calculated the probability of obtaining either E or F in one trial. For Rules 2 and 3, we computed the probability of obtaining E in one trial and F in the other. If the probability problem were one in which we wanted to calculate the probability of x occurrences of E in n trials (rather than one occurrence in one trial), we would merely employ the formula for combinations presented in Section B. Using the notation introduced in that section, we would have $P_r(E_x)$ rather than $P_r(E)$. The rules for addition and multiplication of probabilities still hold. For $P_r(E)$ and $P_r(F)$ in the formulas, we would substitute $P_r(E_x)$ and $P_r(F_y)$ for the probability of x occurrences of E in n trials and y occurrences of F in n trials. Each of these probabilities would then be calculated by the formula for combinations.

Suppose we have two dependent events such that

$$P_r(E_x) = C_x^n \, p^x \, q^{n-x}$$

and

$$P_r(F|E_x) = \tfrac{1}{10}$$

Then their joint probability is given by Rule 3:

$$P_r(E_x \text{ and } F) = P_r(E_x) \cdot P_r(F|E_x) = (C_x^n \, p^x \, q^{n-x})(\tfrac{1}{10})$$

D. PROBABILITY DISTRIBUTIONS

We are now in a position to alter our terminology to conform to that used in Part III on econometric models. We have spoken of the probability of an event, but we may regard the event as the value of a variable. For instance, let the event be the occurrence of a "one" in the casting of a die. We can interpret this "one" as the value of some variable. In this case, the variable may assume the values of all integers from one to six inclusive. But we know that the event is not certain; it has a definite probability. Similarly, the value "one" of the variable has a definite probability of occurring. There is another probability that a "two" will occur, a third probability that a "three" will occur, and so on.

Consequently, we say that the variable in question is a random variable. It is defined as a variable that can assume a number of values with given probabilities. A random variable is sometimes called a *chance variable* or a *stochastic variable*. The outcome of the throws of a die is a random variable, because it can assume the values 1, 2, 3, 4, 5, 6 with definite probabilities. Furthermore, this variable is a *discrete random variable*, since it can assume only the values of the integers one through six.

1. Discrete Random Variables

Let us define a random variable u that can assume the values u_i. With each value u_i, we associate a probability p_i. In the die casting example of a discrete random variable, we find

$$P_r(E = 1) = \tfrac{1}{6} = p_1$$
$$P_r(E = 2) = \tfrac{1}{6} = p_2$$
$$\cdot \qquad \cdot \qquad \cdot$$
$$\cdot \qquad \cdot \qquad \cdot$$
$$\cdot \qquad \cdot \qquad \cdot$$
$$P_r(E = 6) = \tfrac{1}{6} = p_6$$

In general, we write

$$P_r(E = u_i) = p_i$$

Now this entire array of the values the random variable can assume together with the corresponding probabilities of each of these values is called the *probability distribution* of the variable. Notice the difference between a random variable and a systematic variable. We speak only about the values of the systematic variable. Given any relation between two systematic variables, their values are known with certainty $(p = 1)$. The random variable, on the other hand, must have a probability associated with each possible value since it is uncertain which value it may assume, even in a controlled experiment.

The sum of the probabilities in a probability distribution must add up to unity. This follows from the addition rule for probabilities. In the example of die throwing, we have

$$p_1 + p_2 + \ldots + p_6 = 6(\tfrac{1}{6}) = 1$$

or in general

$$\sum_i p_i = 1$$

Let us draw the so-called histogram of this probability distribution, which is its graphical representation. It is depicted in Figure 17.1. Notice that each rectangle is drawn so that its center is at the value of the variable u. The point is plotted directly over each value

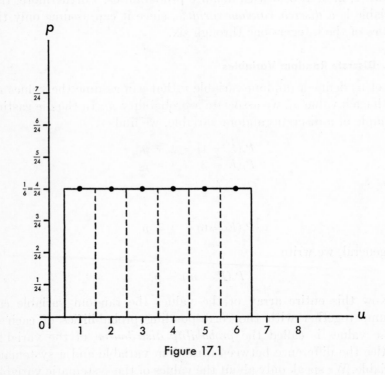

Figure 17.1

of u, and the height of each rectangle is equal to the probability corresponding to that value of u. Since each value of u has the same probability, $\frac{1}{6}$, the histogram in this case is rectangular. The total area of the histogram is equal to one, because the sum of the probabilities is equal to one.

Consider another case of a random variable u, which is also discrete. Suppose the probability distribution is given by the following table. The second column lists the probability associated with each given value of u. The histogram is shown in Figure 17.2.

u_i	p_i	P_i
-4	.05	$= .05$
-3	.08	$= .05 + .08 = .13$
-2	.12	$= .05 + .08 + .12 = .25$
-1	.15	$= .05 + .08 + .12 + .15 = .40$
0	.20	.
1	.15	.
2	.12	.
3	.08	.
4	.05	$= 1$

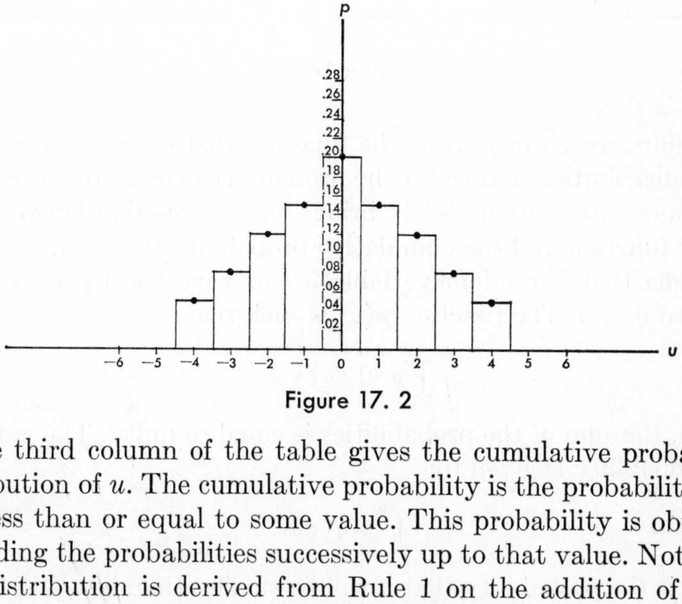

Figure 17. 2

The third column of the table gives the cumulative probability distribution of u. The cumulative probability is the probability that u is less than or equal to some value. This probability is obtained by adding the probabilities successively up to that value. Note that this distribution is derived from Rule 1 on the addition of probabilities in Section C. The probability that u is less than or equal to -2, for example, is the probability that u is equal to -4 or -3 or -2, which is the sum of their probabilities. This cumulative probability distribution can also be represented graphically and is shown in Figure 17.3. Since we are successively adding probabilities, the cumulative probability of the final value of u must be equal to one. This is equivalent to the statement that we are certain that u must assume some one of its permissible values.

2. Continuous Random Variables

If a random variable is continuous, it can assume any value in an interval with a specified probability. We regard the probability distribution as a continuous function of the random variable; for u

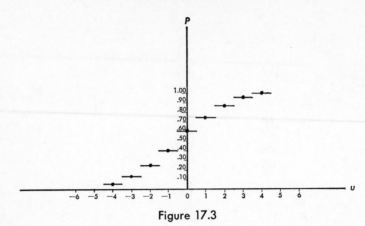

Figure 17.3

continuous, we write $p(u)$ as the function that expresses the probability distribution and call it the probability density function. The continuous formulation clearly brings out the relation between the density function and the cumulative probability function.

Assume that a random variable u can vary continuously from $u = a$ to $u = b$. The function $p(u)$ is such that

$$\int_a^b p(u)\ du = 1$$

That is, the sum of the probabilities is equal to unity. The cumulative probability is given by

$$\int_a^{u_0} p(u)\ du$$

This is the probability that u will be smaller than or equal to the value u_0, which is less than or equal to b. The *probability density function* is the first derivative of the cumulative probability function. If we let $P(u)$ represent the cumulative probability function, then

$$p(u) = \frac{dP(u)}{du}$$

A typical probability density function and its corresponding cumulative probability function are shown in Figures 17.4 and 17.5, respectively.

Consider the continuous random variable u that can assume all values between one and ten with equal probability (hence, its graph is rectangular). The probability density function is

$$p(u) = \tfrac{1}{9} \qquad 1 \le u \le 10$$

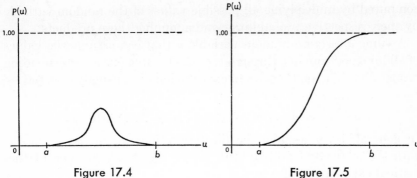

Figure 17.4   Figure 17.5

The reason why the probability equals $\frac{1}{9}$ can easily be seen if we compute the cumulative function over the entire range of u (see Chapter 13):

$$\int_1^{10} p(u)\ du = \int_1^{10} \tfrac{1}{9}\ du$$
$$= \tfrac{1}{9}(10) - \tfrac{1}{9}(1) = \tfrac{9}{9} = 1$$

What is the probability that u will be smaller than or equal to six? We have

$$\int_1^6 \tfrac{1}{9}\ du = \tfrac{1}{9}(6) - \tfrac{1}{9}(1) = \tfrac{5}{9}$$

The probability that u will be between two and four is given by

$$\int_2^4 \tfrac{1}{9}\ du = \tfrac{1}{9}(4) - \tfrac{1}{9}(2) = \tfrac{2}{9}$$

E. MOMENTS OF THE PROBABILITY DISTRIBUTION

A probability distribution contains certain properties, which describe that distribution. By looking at Figure 17.5, for example, we can see there is some value of u that is more probable than any other, there is a given degree of dispersion, a given degree of flatness or peakedness, etc. There are a number of very useful ways to describe the characteristics of a probability distribution. One very common measure is called the *mathematical expectation*, or simply the expectation. This is the arithmetic mean of the probability distribution or, more briefly, the mean value of the random variable. The mathematical expectation describes the general location of the graph of the distribution. It is a measure of the central tendency of the probability distribution. The mathematical expectation is computed by multiplying all possible values of the random variable by their respective probabilities and summing these products.

Assume a discrete random variable u that can assume the values of all integers from one through ten. Each value has a corresponding probability. The mathematical expectation of u, usually denoted by Eu or μ, is computed as follows:

$$\mu = Eu = 1 \cdot p_1 + 2 \cdot p_2 + 3 \cdot p_3 + \ldots + 10 \cdot p_{10}$$

In general, let u assume the discrete values $u_1, u_2, u_3, \ldots, u_n$ with the associated probabilities $p_1, p_2, p_3, \ldots, p_n$. The mathematical expectation of u is

$$\mu = Eu = \sum_{i=1}^{n} u_i p_i$$

Suppose the permissible values of u and their probabilities are those given in the following table.

u_i	p_i
0	$\frac{2}{20}$
1	$\frac{3}{20}$
2	$\frac{4}{20}$
3	$\frac{5}{20}$
4	$\frac{3}{20}$
5	$\frac{2}{20}$
6	$\frac{1}{20}$
	$\frac{20}{20} = 1$

Using the above formula, we obtain

$$\mu = Eu = 0(\tfrac{2}{20}) + 1(\tfrac{3}{20}) + 2(\tfrac{4}{20}) + 3(\tfrac{5}{20}) + 4(\tfrac{3}{20})$$
$$+ 5(\tfrac{2}{20}) + 6(\tfrac{1}{20}) = \tfrac{54}{20} = 2.7$$

This is the average value of u in the probability sense, or the arithmetic mean of the probability distribution.

If u is continuous, varies between $u = a$ and $u = b$, and has the probability density function $p(u)$, then we merely replace the summation by integration:

$$\mu = Eu = \int_a^b u \, p(u) \, du$$

Let u be continuous between one and ten inclusive with the probability density function $p(u) = \frac{1}{9}$. We have seen in Chapter 13 that the indefinite integral of $\frac{1}{9} u$ is given as $\frac{1}{18} u^2 + k$. This is the reverse of differentiation. Applying the methods of Section B in Chapter 13 we obtain the mathematical expectation of u as

$$\mu = Eu = \int_1^{10} \tfrac{1}{9}u \, du = \tfrac{1}{18}(10)^2 - \tfrac{1}{18}(1)^2 = 5.5$$

There are some simple rules for the calculation of expectations that will prove useful for later applications.

(1) The mathematical expectation of a constant is equal to that constant. Let $u = k$, a known constant. Then

$$Eu = Ek = k$$

(2) The mathematical expectation of a random variable times a constant is equal to the constant times the mathematical expectation.

$$Eku = kEu$$

(3) The mathematical expectation of a sum or a difference of random variables is the sum or difference of the mathematical expectations. Let u and v be random variables.

$$E(u + v) = Eu + Ev$$
$$E(u - v) = Eu - Ev$$

1. Moments About the Mathematical Expectation

Given a random variable u and its probability distribution, let us first define the tth *moment* about the origin of the variable, that is, about zero. We define the tth moment about the origin of u as

$$Eu^t = \sum_{i=1}^{n} u_i^t p_i$$

when the variable is discrete and varies between one and n inclusive. We define the tth moment about the origin as

$$Eu^t = \int_a^b u^t p(u) \, du$$

when the variable is continuous and varies between a and b inclusive.

Suppose we set $t = 0$. The 0th moment about the origin is

$$Eu^0 = E1 = 1$$

since any number to the zero power equals one, and since the expectation of a constant equals that constant. Now suppose we set $t = 1$. The first moment about the origin is

$$Eu^1 = Eu = \mu$$

That is, the first moment about the origin of a random variable is the mathematical expectation of the random variable. Hence, it is seen that "moments" is a general term used to describe the characteristics or properties of a probability distribution. One of these moments, the first moment about the origin, is the mathematical expectation of the random variable. It describes the location of the graph of the distribution on the horizontal axis.

This conclusion is clear enough, and it is all that need be said with reference to moments about the origin. We next consider moments about the mathematical expectation itself. For the theory of statistics, these are extremely useful characteristics of a probability distribution. We have already seen that the mathematical expectation of a random variable u is the first moment about the origin. This can be written

$$Eu = E(u - 0)^1$$

Likewise, for the tth moment about the origin, we can write

$$Eu^t = E(u - 0)^t$$

Now in speaking of moments about the mathematical expectation itself, we can merely replace the zero by the mathematical expectation and write

$$E(u - Eu)^t$$

or, more briefly,

$$E(u - \mu)^t$$

for the tth moment about the mathematical expectation. Going the other way around, since μ is the mathematical expectation of u, if we replace μ by zero, we have the formula for the expectation about the origin.

What about the actual computation of moments about the mathematical expectation? We must add an additional step. First, the mathematical expectation of u is computed. Secondly, this is subtracted from the values of u. The difference thus obtained is raised to the tth power if we wish to know the tth moment. Thirdly, the result in each case (that is, for each difference $u_i - \mu$) is multiplied by the corresponding probability. Finally, the products so obtained are summed. In symbolic notation for a discrete variable u, where u assumes the values $u_1, u_2, \ldots, u_n$ with probabilities $p_1, p_2, \ldots, p_n$:

$$\mu_t = E(u - \mu)^t = \sum_{i=1}^{n} (u_i - \mu)^t p_i$$

The symbol μ_t is used to denote the tth moment about the mathematical expectation (mean value) of the random variable. Application of the formula gives the actual numerical value of the tth moment of u about its mathematical expectation. Now if u is continuous from $u = a$ to $u = b$ with probability density function $p(u)$,

$$\mu_t = E(u - \mu)^t = \int_a^b (u - \mu)^t p(u) \, du$$

is the formula for the tth moment about the mathematical expectation of u.

Having given the general formulation for moments about the mathematical expectation, we might ask ourselves how such moments help to describe a probability distribution. What sort of information do the moments impart? We shall interpret five of them. Of these five, we lay special emphasis on the second moment, because it has widespread applicability in statistical analysis. Next in importance are the third and fourth moments. The 0th and first moments will merely be calculated.

(1) The 0th moment about the mathematical expectation is equal to one:

$$\mu_0 = E(u - \mu)^0 = E1 = 1$$

(2) The first moment about the mathematical expectation is zero:

$$\mu_1 = E(u - \mu) = Eu - E\mu = \mu - \mu = 0$$

(3) The second moment about the mathematical expectation is called the *variance*. It is a measure of the dispersion of the probability distribution about the mean of the distribution. The second moment is denoted by σ^2:

$$\sigma^2 = \mu_2 = E(u - \mu)^2$$

A special symbol is given to the variance because it plays such an important role in statistical theory. The variance shows the manner in which the various values of u are distributed in a probability sense. The smaller is the computed value of the variance, the closer do the values of u cluster about the mean of u. Conversely, the larger is the variance, the more widely do the values of u deviate from the average or mean value.

The square root of the second moment is called the *standard deviation* and is represented by σ:

$$\sigma = \sqrt{E(u - \mu)^2}$$

Naturally, this measures the dispersion of the distribution just as the variance does. It is often a more convenient way to express the deviations of the values of a random variable from their mathematical expectation. Consequently, it enters into many computations in statistical analysis.

The remaining two moments, the third and the fourth, have much less practical significance. They are important for the abstract theory of distributions, but one seldom encounters them in actual statistical experiments. Since these moments do help to describe the general shape of a probability distribution, we shall describe them briefly.

(4) The third moment is a measure of the *skewness* of the distribution:

$$\mu_3 = E(u - \mu)^3$$

It measures the degree to which the probability distribution is symmetrical about the mathematical expectation or the degree to which it trails off on one end. If $\mu_3 = 0$, the distribution is symmetrical (see Figure 17.2 as an example of a symmetrical distribution).

(5) The fourth moment is a measure of the *kurtosis* of the distribution—its degree of flatness or peakedness at the highest point on the curve:

$$\mu_4 = E(u - \mu)^4$$

2. Summary

We have defined the concept of probability and illustrated the methods of calculation. We then showed that the entire array of values of a random variable, together with the probability of each value, comprises the probability distribution of that variable. Furthermore, any given probability distribution has certain characteristics that may be used to describe the general form of the distribution. The two most important of these are (1) the mathematical expectation of the probability distribution or mean value of the random variable; (2) the variance or manner in which the various values of the variable are distributed around the mathematical expectation. Two less important moments that describe the distribution are (3) the skewness or degree of symmetry of the distribution around the mathematical expectation; (4) the kurtosis or degree of flatness or peakedness of the distribution.

It is clear that if we know these four properties of a probability distribution, we already know quite a bit about that distribution. If

we wish to draw a graph of the distribution, such as that drawn in
Figure 17.5 for example, we can tell from the mathematical expectation the general position of the graph on the horizontal axis, because
the expectation is the mean value of the random variable. The variance will tell us whether the remaining values of the variable are
grouped closely around the mean or distributed widely about it. The
skewness shows whether the graph is to be drawn as approximately
symmetrical about the expectation or as trailing off in one direction
or the other. Finally, the kurtosis reveals whether the graph is to
have a pronounced peak or is to be relatively flat.

F. PARTICULAR DISTRIBUTIONS

We shall discuss in this section two types of probability distributions that have special importance for statistical analysis. The first
is a discrete distribution derived by fundamental probability processes: the binomial distribution. The other, the so-called normal or
Gaussian distribution, is a continuous distribution that is a limiting
case of the binomial.

1. The Binomial Distribution

In Section B, we discussed the calculation of the probability of
obtaining x successes (occurrences of an event) in n independent
trials. According to the theory of combinations, this probability
involving the so-called binomial coefficient is

$$P_r(E_x) = C_x^n p^x q^{n-x} = \frac{n!}{x!\,(n-x)!} \cdot p^x \cdot q^{n-x}$$

where p is the probability of a success in any one trial, and $q = 1 - p$ is the probability of a failure. The factor C_x^n is called the
binomial coefficient, because it may be obtained by expanding a
binomial expression raised to the nth power. Like any other probability distribution, a binomial probability distribution can be
constructed if the event in question is regarded as a value of a random variable.

Let us consider the example of die casting. Assume we make five
trials so $n = 5$. The probability of the event happening is $p = \frac{1}{6}$.
That is, the probability of a "one" is $\frac{1}{6}$, the probability of a "two"
is $\frac{1}{6}$, etc., since the die has six sides. The probability of the nonoccurrence of the event is therefore $q = 1 - \frac{1}{6} = \frac{5}{6}$. Let the event in
question be the occurrence of a "four." We construct the entire

probability distribution for the number of "fours" occurring in five trials: the probability of no "fours" in five trials, the probability of one "four" in five trials, and so on. In the calculation of each of these probabilities, the formula for $P_r(E_x)$ is used:

$$P_r(E_0) = C_0^5 \left(\frac{1}{6}\right)^0 \left(\frac{5}{6}\right)^5 = \frac{5!}{0!5!} \, (1) \left(\frac{3,125}{7,776}\right) = .4019$$

$$P_r(E_1) = C_1^5 \left(\frac{1}{6}\right)^1 \left(\frac{5}{6}\right)^4 = \frac{5!}{1!4!} \left(\frac{1}{6}\right)\left(\frac{625}{1,296}\right) = .4019$$

$$P_r(E_2) = C_2^5 \left(\frac{1}{6}\right)^2 \left(\frac{5}{6}\right)^3 = \frac{5!}{2!3!} \left(\frac{1}{36}\right)\left(\frac{125}{216}\right) = .1608$$

$$P_r(E_3) = C_3^5 \left(\frac{1}{6}\right)^3 \left(\frac{5}{6}\right)^2 = \frac{5!}{3!2!} \left(\frac{1}{216}\right)\left(\frac{25}{36}\right) = .0322$$

$$P_r(E_4) = C_4^5 \left(\frac{1}{6}\right)^4 \left(\frac{5}{6}\right)^1 = \frac{5!}{4!1!} \left(\frac{1}{1,296}\right)\left(\frac{5}{6}\right) = .0032$$

$$P_r(E_5) = C_5^5 \left(\frac{1}{6}\right)^5 \left(\frac{5}{6}\right)^0 = \frac{5!}{5!0!} \left(\frac{1}{7,776}\right) (1) = .0001$$

Note that the sum of these probabilities is approximately equal to one (any small difference is due to rounding). We could obtain the cumulative probability distribution by successively adding the probabilities.

There are some interesting and useful properties of the binomial distribution. The mathematical expectation is equal to $n \cdot p$, and the variance is equal to $n \cdot p \cdot q$:

$$\mu = Eu = np$$
$$\sigma^2 = npq$$
$$\sigma = \sqrt{npq}$$

Thus, considering the occurrence of a "four" as a random variable u, we have

$$\mu = (5)(\tfrac{1}{6}) = \tfrac{5}{6}$$
$$\sigma^2 = (5)(\tfrac{1}{6})(\tfrac{5}{6}) = \tfrac{25}{36}$$
$$\sigma = \sqrt{\tfrac{25}{36}}$$

It is a worth-while exercise to obtain these same results by computing the mathematical expectation and the variance by the formulas given in Section E.

2. The Normal Distribution

The binomial distribution is developed from a set of first principles, using the probability theory and some specified experimental conditions. This basic distribution serves as a transition to another well-known and widely used distribution. This is the *normal distribu-*

tion. Although the normal distribution too can be derived from basic probability principles, it is also a limiting form of the binomial that is approached as n becomes very large, both p and q remaining finite. Whereas the binomial is a discrete distribution, the normal is a continuous distribution. One can see from the preceding example of a binomial that the computation of the coefficient C_x^n becomes extremely laborious and time consuming if both x and n are very large. Consequently, it is convenient to have a continuous distribution at hand that closely approximates the binomial when this is the case.

The normal distribution is more than an approximation to the binomial, however. Empirical distributions of phenomena in the natural and social sciences frequently are very close to a normal distribution. This is especially true of the distribution of errors of observation. The normal distribution provides a standard pattern with which other distributions may be compared. In some important phases of statistical analysis, the distribution of the observations is assumed to approximate the normal distribution. If the data in the sample actually depart seriously from this pattern, unsatisfactory and even nonsensical results may be secured. It is obvious, therefore, that this distribution plays an important role in statistical estimation and tests of hypotheses for econometric models.

Since the normal distribution is continuous, it can be expressed by an equation, and the curve corresponding to this equation is smooth. For a random variable u, normally distributed with the mean μ and the standard deviation σ, the equation for the cumulative probability distribution is

$$P(u) = \frac{1}{\sigma\sqrt{2\pi}} \int_{-\infty}^{u} e^{-\frac{1}{2\sigma^2}(u-\mu)2}\, du$$

where π is the conventional value 3.1416 used in mathematics, and e is the exponential base equal to 2.71828. The probability density function, obtained by differentiating the cumulative function with respect to u, is given by

$$p(u) = \frac{1}{\sigma\sqrt{2\pi}} e^{-\frac{1}{2\sigma^2}(u-\mu)2}$$

It is very convenient for applications of the normal distribution to standardize it, by which we mean constructing it so that it has a mean of zero and a standard deviation of one. To do this we define another random variable, say z, in the following way:

$$z = \frac{u - \mu}{\sigma}$$

Then we can write the probability density function more simply as

$$p(z) = \frac{1}{\sqrt{2\pi}} e^{-\frac{z^2}{2}}$$

The mean or mathematical expectation of z is zero and its standard deviation is one, while the mean of u is $n \cdot p$ and its standard deviation is $\sqrt{n \cdot p \cdot q}$. That is,

$$\mu_z = Ez = 0 \qquad\qquad \mu_u = np$$
$$\sigma_z^2 = 1 \qquad\qquad \sigma_u^2 = npq$$

This conclusion is proved in most textbooks on statistics. Note that the mean and standard deviation of u are the same as that found in the binomial distribution.

Figures 17.6 and 17.7 depict the normal cumulative probability function and the normal probability density function, respectively. They are drawn with the variable z on the axis, so that the mean of the distribution is zero. The numerical value of the ordinate of the graph in Figure 17.6 at any one value of z, say z_o, is equal to the numerical value of the area under the curve in Figure 17.7 to the left of z_o (the shaded area in Figure 17.7). It is seen from Figure 17.7 that the normal distribution is symmetrical about its mean and ranges from minus infinity to plus infinity. For $z = -\infty$, $P(z) = 0$ and for $z = +\infty$, $P(z) = 1$. But for all practical purposes the value of $P(z)$ extends from nearly zero to nearly one. Published tables exist that give the area under the probability density curve from zero to any value of z. From these one can find the probability of values within any interval of z, between z_1 and z_2, for example. Such a table is given at the end of the book, and we shall have opportunities later to make practical use of it.

There is another characteristic of the normal distribution that proves very useful in the interpretation of statistical measurement. If u is a random variable, normally distributed with mean μ and standard deviation σ, then:

(1) 68.27 per cent of the values of u deviate less than *one* standard deviation, σ, from the mean μ.

(2) 95.45 per cent of the values of u deviate less than *two* standard deviations, 2σ, from the mean μ.

(3) 99.73 per cent of the values of u deviate less than *three* standard deviations, 3σ, from the mean μ.

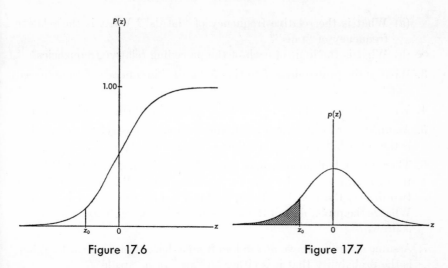

Figure 17.6   Figure 17.7

In terms of the variable z, which has $\mu = 0$ and $\sigma = 1$, this means that 68.27 per cent of the values of z fall within $z = -1$ to $z = +1$; 95.45 per cent fall within $z = -2$ to $z = +2$; 99.73 per cent fall within $z = -3$ to $z = +3$. We shall see that these characteristics of the normal distribution are valuable in judging the reliability of empirical measurements.

PROBLEMS

1. A true die is thrown 45 times with the following outcomes:

1, 6, 3, 2, 4,	4, 4, 2, 1, 3,
6, 6, 4, 5, 2,	5, 3, 5, 1, 2,
3, 1, 3, 1, 4,	6, 4, 5, 1, 2,
1, 6, 5, 2, 3,	1, 2, 3, 4, 5,
	6, 5, 4, 3, 2.

(a) What is the relative frequency of a 4 occurring among all throws? of a 2? of a 5?

(b) What is the limit of each of the preceding relative frequencies?

2. An unbiased coin is tossed 20 times with the following results:

H T T H H
T H H H T
H H T H H
H T T T T

where **H** denotes the occurrence of "heads" and **T** the occurrence of "tails."

(a) What is the relative frequency of "heads"? What is the relative frequency of "tails"?

(b) What is the limit of each of the preceding relative frequencies?

3. What is the probability of getting 5 "heads" in 9 tosses of an unbiased coin?

4. What is the probability of getting 3 "sixes" in 10 throws of a true die?

5. Assume a card is drawn at random from a deck of playing cards. What is the probability that it is either a "king" or a "queen"?

6. There are 10 balls in an urn, of which 4 are white and 6 are red. What is the probability of drawing at random one white ball and one red ball in two draws, the first ball being replaced before the second is drawn? What is the probability if the first ball is *not* replaced before the second is drawn?

7. Assume a card is drawn at random from a deck of playing cards. What is the probability that it is either an "ace" or a "spade"?

8. If $x, y, z, \ldots$ are a series of exclusive events that exhaust all possibilities, it follows that $P_r(x) + P_r(y) + P_r(z) + \ldots = 1$. Explain.

9. Assume a discrete random variable v that can assume the values shown in the table with the associated probabilities.

v_i	p_i
0	$\frac{1}{16}$
1	$\frac{1}{16}$
2	$\frac{2}{16}$
3	$\frac{4}{16}$
4	$\frac{5}{16}$
5	$\frac{2}{16}$
6	$\frac{1}{16}$
	1.00

(a) Construct the histogram for this probability distribution.

(b) Construct the graph of the cumulative probability distribution.

10. Assume a continuous random variable u whose probability density function is given as

$$p(u) = \frac{1}{5u} \qquad u \geq 1$$

(a) Graph the probability density function from $u = 1$ to $u = 10$.

(b) Find $p(3), p(5), p(8), p(10), p(12)$.

(c) Find the cumulative probability function, $P(u)$, from $u = 1$ to $u = u_0$.

(d) Graph the cumulative function from $u = 1$ to $u = 10$, that is, let u_0 vary from 1 to 10.

(e) Find $P(3), P(5), P(8), P(10)$.

11. The following probability distribution of the discrete random variable u is given.

u_i	p_i
0	$\frac{2}{40}$
1	$\frac{3}{40}$
2	$\frac{4}{40}$
3	$\frac{4}{40}$
4	$\frac{6}{40}$
5	$\frac{10}{40}$
6	$\frac{5}{40}$
7	$\frac{3}{40}$
8	$\frac{2}{40}$
9	$\frac{1}{40}$
	1.00

(a) Find the mathematical expectation and variance of the probability distribution.

(b) Graph the distribution and indicate the mathematical expectation of u on the diagram.

12. Construct the probability distribution of the number of "heads" occurring in 5 tosses of an unbiased coin. From the probability distribution find the following:

(a) Mathematical expectation.

(b) Variance.

(c) Skewness.

(d) Kurtosis.

CHAPTER 18

Sample Theory and Statistical Inference

The fundamental theory of probability sets the foundation for the statistical theory of sampling. And the theory of sampling in turn establishes the basis for statistical estimation of econometric models. Having surveyed probability theory, we turn next to sample theory and the general methods of statistical inference. This is the final preparatory step before discussing the actual methods of statistical measurement used in econometrics.

A. INTRODUCTION

We have seen that the central problem of analytical statistics is that of inductive inference. Theoretical propositions are generalizations; they refer to all conceivable observations on the subject matter to which the theory applies. For example, the theoretical economic proposition that unionization in a labor market will, under given conditions, raise wage rates is meant to apply to all instances in which these conditions hold. To test this prediction we cannot, in general, observe all the conceivable instances. It is impractical and often impossible to do so. We can, however, observe a limited number of these instances. The problem is then to infer from the characteristics of a limited number of empirical observations, called a *sample*, the characteristics of all conceivable observations, called the *population*.

1. The Statistical Population

As used in statistics, the term population means the total of all conceivable observations of some specified kind. This abstract concept is sometimes called the universe. The weights of all human beings form a statistical population; the weights of all Americans form another; the weights of all male Americans form a third; the heights of all human beings form a fourth, and so on. Notice that it is the heights and weights, not the individuals themselves, which comprise the observations that go to make up the population. This is made clear by consideration of another population, namely the set of all conceivable measurements of the area of a piece of land. If one were to measure the area with a yardstick time and time again, it is unlikely that any two of the measurements would be exactly equal. The set of measurements (not the land) forms a statistical population. Furthermore, the observations that form the population need not be measurements, as in the preceding examples; they may also be designations of the presence or absence of some specified characteristics. Thus, repeated draws from a deck of playing cards form a population in which the observations may be "clubs" or "not clubs"; again, repeated tosses of a coin comprise a population in which the observation is either "heads" or "tails."

Populations may be *finite* or *infinite*, depending on whether there is a limit to the number of possible observations. In our previous example, the weights of all Americans is a finite population, because there is a definite limit to the number of observable weights. The example of land measurements, on the other hand, is one of an infinite population, since the number of possible different measurements is infinite. To take an example from economics, the set of all conceivable observations on wheat prices in the United States may be regarded as an infinite population.

Sometimes populations are susceptible to only qualitative specification. A population consisting of observations on color of eyes or on sex would be such a population. Each observation can consist only of a color in the first case and a sex specification in the second. When the population consists of a characteristic that is amenable to numerical expression, however, the quantitative values of the measurements are regarded as values of a variable. The variable may be continuous or discrete, and it is very convenient to think of a population in this way.

The term "parameter" is familiar to us from our discussion of mathematical formulation in Part I. It is a term used to indicate the constants in an equation. The purpose of such constants is to designate a certain one of many qualitatively similar equations. A linear equation has the general form

$$y = a + bx$$

where x and y are variables, and a and b are constants. All linear equations are qualitatively similar in that they have this form, but they have different numerical values for a and b. The particular values of the parameters tell us which one linear equation is to be given out of the family of all possible linear equations. Different values for a and b yield different straight lines when graphed, but the graphs of all linear equations show straight lines.

In statistics, the term parameter has a similar interpretation. The parameters of a population are those measures that differentiate a population quantitatively from all other populations of the same form. For instance, the population given by all possible throws of a coin has a parameter: the proportion of heads occurring. This characteristic (a constant) is given for this population but will differ from one population to another. All throws of another coin will have a different proportion of heads—a different parameter. All possible observations on the price of wheat in the United States forms a population; a parameter of this population is the arithmetic mean or average value of wheat prices. The mean price of corn is a parameter of the population consisting of all observations on corn prices. In both of these cases, the average price is a constant characteristic of the population.

2. The Statistical Sample

Ordinarily the data one has to work with consist of a limited number of observations rather than all possible observations. Such a partial collection is called a *sample*. The statistical problem then becomes one of providing information about the unknown population characteristics from knowledge of the characteristics of the sample. When doing this, special importance attaches to *random samples*, so that we make inferences about the population from samples drawn at random from that population. When a given sample is random, it means that if a very large number of samples were selected in the same way from the population, each observation in the population would be included in the same proportion of the samples, and this would also be true of any part of such samples. That is, a random sample is one obtained in such a way that any observation in the population is as likely to be included in the sample as any other observation in the population. We shall treat only random samples, but it should be kept in mind that under some conditions other methods of sampling may be preferable. Such methods may be more effective in yielding information about the population.

Just as a population has certain characteristics that describe it, so a sample has such characteristics called *statistics*. A sample statistic corresponds in meaning to a population parameter. We have seen that the proportion of heads occurring is a parameter of the population formed by all possible tosses of a coin. The sample will consist of a limited number of random tosses, say 50. The proportion of heads in 50 tosses is a statistic of the sample. Suppose we have observations on the consumption and income of 1,000 American families. Assume we are interested in the ratio of consumption to income, so we record this ratio for each family. Our sample consists of 1,000 observations on the ratio of consumption to income. The arithmetic mean or average value of this ratio for all 1,000 observations is a sample statistic. It corresponds in meaning to the mean ratio in the population that consists of observations on *all* American families: the population parameter.

B. ELEMENTS OF SAMPLING THEORY

In the preceding chapter some of the elementary laws of probability were described. We might now ask how these laws enter into statistical analysis. The answer is that they form the foundations for a theory of random sampling. The population mean, the degree of variation in the observations of the population, the range of observations, the largest value, the smallest value, etc., are parameters of the population. The sample mean, variability, range, etc., are the statistics of the sample. In practical situations, one begins with a known sample and certain known sample statistics. One then has to deal with the problem of making inferences about the unknown population, that is, about its unknown parameters. Sampling theory uses probability theory to establish laws for making these inferences. Thus, in sampling theory one starts from a population having known parameters and treats the problem of calculating probabilities about samples, and their statistics, drawn at random from the known population. Once such theoretical laws are established, the reliability of moving in the opposite direction is greatly enhanced.

The methods of statistical inference involve four elements: (1) the population as it actually is, (2) the relationship between the characteristics of this population and the characteristics of many samples drawn from the population, (3) the relationship between the characteristics of the many samples and the characteristics of one sample, and (4) the one sample that we do observe in practice. Now the problem is to infer from the statistics of one sample, element (4), the characteristics of the true but unknown population, element (1). To do this we use the laws provided by elements (2) and (3). We can never know the population precisely, but the object of the theory of sampling is to provide a steppingstone from the one sample to the population.

1. Relation of Population Parameters to Many Samples

Let us examine the several rules derived by statisticians that relate known parameters to the characteristics of a set of many samples drawn at random from the population. We shall show that experimental sampling yields results which can also be achieved by a purely mathematical approach founded on the theory of probability. The normal distribution plays an important role in this mathematical derivation, but we shall not go through the mathematical steps involved in the derivation itself. The interested reader can find proofs for the conclusions in most textbooks on mathematical statistics.

    a. *Finite Populations.* Suppose we have a known finite population consisting of N observations. The number of samples, each consisting of n observations, it is possible to draw from this population is given by C_n^N. We already know this from the theory of probability. For example, this population might be comprised of ten balls in an urn, $N = 10$, each marked 1, 2, 3, 4, . . . , 10 respectively. The number of samples of four balls, $n = 4$, is

$$C_4^{10} = \frac{10!}{4!6!} = 210$$

where each sample is replaced before the next is drawn.

Now suppose that one were to actually undertake the sampling process. One selects four balls at random from the urn. Consider the observed numbers marked on the balls as values of the random variable x, so x may assume the values 1, 2, 3, . . . , 9 or 10. Suppose the statistic we are interested in is the mean value of x, so we compute the mean of this sample by adding the numbers on the four balls and dividing by four. Let the mean value of x in this first sample be designated by $\bar{x}_1$. In this case, suppose we observe the following four values of $x:$ 2, 6, 1, and 8 (that is, these numbers appear on the four balls drawn). Then

$$\bar{x}_1 = \frac{2 + 6 + 1 + 8}{4} = \frac{17}{4} = 4.25$$

for this sample. For the ith sample consisting of n observations on x, the mean has the general formula

$$\bar{x}_i = \frac{x_1 + x_2 + x_3 + \ldots + x_n}{n} = \frac{\sum_{t=1}^{n} x_t}{n}$$

where x_t is the value of x occurring on the tth observation. In general, the symbol $\bar{x}_i$ designates the mean of the ith sample. But let us proceed step by step. After having computed the mean of the first sample, we replace the four balls, draw a second sample at random, and compute its mean. The mean of the first sample is denoted by $\bar{x}_1$, and the mean of the second sample by $\bar{x}_2$. We would repeat this process until we have chosen 210 samples and computed 210 sample means: $\bar{x}_1, \bar{x}_2, \bar{x}_3, \ldots, \bar{x}_{210}$.

Now a frequency distribution of the 210 means can be computed by noting the relative frequency with which each mean appeared. For example, if the mean 4.25 appeared twelve times, then the relative frequency of this mean is $\frac{12}{210}$. The same would be done for all other means. This is an experimental sampling distribution. But from the known population the theoretical sampling distribution of the means can also be computed by using pure probability theory. This is nothing other than a probability distribution, and it is a prediction of the distribution one would get by drawing a larger and larger number of samples of four observations each in experimental sampling. The probability distribution is determined mathematically without actually performing the sample operation.

Given a theoretical (mathematical) sampling distribution and an experimental one, our next step is to calculate the mean of the distribution of means for both distributions. Let $\bar{x}$ (without a subscript) represent the mean of all means in the experimental sampling distribution. The mean of the theoretical sampling distribution we shall designate by $\mu_{\bar{x}}$. Its value is obtained by the formula for the mathematical expectation given in Chapter 17. It is sometimes written $E\bar{x}$ to designate that it is the mathematical expectation of the sample means. We would find that the values $\bar{x}$ and $\mu_{\bar{x}}$ would be very close to one another. That is, we obtain approximately the same results by the use of probability theory as those obtained by actually carrying out the repeated sampling process.

What does this imply? The important question is the relation between the sampling distribution mean $\mu_{\bar{x}}$ and the true population mean, which we may call μ. In general for a finite population of N

elements or observations, consider all possible samples of n observations each drawn from this population. There are C_n^N such samples. The theoretical sampling distribution of means, $\bar{x}_i$, has the mean $\mu_{\bar{x}}$. The following result has been demonstrated by statisticians:

$$\mu_{\bar{x}} = \mu$$

In other words, the mean of the means of all possible samples of n observations each is equal to the population mean.

This result applies to the mean or mathematical expectation of the sample means. The standard deviation of the sample means is a measure of how the various sample means are distributed around the mean of the sample means. A general rule has likewise been developed for this concept, namely: The standard deviation of means of all possible samples of n observations each is equal to the population standard deviation times the factor

$$\frac{1}{n}\sqrt{\frac{N-n}{N-1}}$$

where N is the total number of observations in the population. We express this symbolically as follows:

$$\sigma_{\bar{x}} = \frac{\sigma}{\sqrt{n}}\sqrt{\frac{N-n}{N-1}}$$

where σ represents the population standard deviation. If N is very large, then $\sqrt{\dfrac{N-n}{N-1}}$ is almost equal to one and so $\sigma_{\bar{x}}$ is nearly equal to $\dfrac{\sigma}{\sqrt{n}}$.

We have carried through the explanation for the mean and the standard deviation of the distribution of *sample means*. A similar type of argument can be made for other statistics besides the sample means. For example, the argument can be applied to the distribution of sample sums (if x_t is the value of the tth observation in a sample, the sample of n observations has the sample sum $\sum\limits_{t=1}^{n} x_t$). The only difference here is that one deals with a sampling distribution of sums rather than means. There are sample statistics that have very complicated theoretical sampling laws, and in such cases one often has to resort to experimental sampling based on published random numbers to discover characteristics of the sampling fluctuations.

Before discussing infinite populations it is worth noting the relation of the distribution of sample means to the normal distribution.

Under a very broad set of conditions the distribution of sample means can be approximated by the normal distribution. Both N and n must be large with N much larger than n. Even in some special cases where N and n are rather small, the normal distribution gives a fairly good approximation to the distribution of sample means.

b. Infinite Populations. Most often the data with which economists work are considered as random samples from a hypothetically infinite population. For instance, a series of automobile prices quoted or recorded on the market may be considered as a random sample of all possible automobile prices. These possible prices form a hypothetically infinite population of prices. Therefore, we shall consider the general theory of sampling from an infinite population. Here also statisticians have shown that by the use of mathematical probability theory, a relationship can be established between the population and samples drawn at random from the population. We shall continue to use the sample mean as our statistic.

Assume a population having a known probability distribution with mean μ and standard deviation σ. The population may represent either a discrete or a continuous random variable. The results of successive observations from an infinite population are independent of one another, since the probability that the random variable x has a particular value on one observation is not affected by its value on any other observation. We state the following general maxim for the mean of sample means: The mean of the distribution of means of an indefinitely large number of samples drawn from an infinite population is equal to the mean of the population. In symbolic notation, we write

$$\mu_{\bar{x}} = \mu$$

or

$$E\bar{x} = \mu$$

which expresses the same result in the notation of the mathematical expectation of the probability distribution of the sample means.

Furthermore, the standard deviation of the distribution of means of indefinitely many samples, consisting of n observations each, from an infinite population is equal to the standard deviation of the population divided by $\sqrt{n}$. Briefly we write

$$\sigma_{\bar{x}} = \frac{\sigma}{\sqrt{n}}$$

As in the case of theoretical sampling from a finite population, so the distribution of means of samples from an infinite population can be approximated by the normal distribution under certain conditions. As a matter of fact, the following general rule can be demonstrated: For samples of large size the distribution of means of samples from an infinite population is approximately normal. Moreover, if n is the number of observations in each sample and n is large, then

$$\mu_{\bar{x}} = \mu \qquad \text{and} \qquad \sigma_{\bar{x}} = \frac{\sigma}{\sqrt{n}}$$

where $\mu_{\bar{x}}$, μ, $\sigma_{\bar{x}}$, and n have the same meanings as in the preceding formulations. The closeness of the approximation to the normal distribution improves as the size of the samples increases; the approximation becomes perfect in the limit as n increases indefinitely. Nevertheless, in some situations the approximation is sufficiently close for practical purposes for values of n as small as ten. If the population is exactly normally distributed with mean μ and standard deviation σ, then the sample means are exactly normally distributed with mean equal to μ and standard deviation equal to $\sigma/\sqrt{n}$.

This outline of sampling theory is designed to provide an insight into the general nature of the relations between a population and many samples drawn from the population. The results of a number of independent samples drawn at random from a known population can be determined from the probability theory. As the size of each sample is allowed to become larger, the variation from sample to sample decreases and the samples possess more nearly the characteristics of the population from which they were taken.

2. Relation of One Sample to Many Samples

With the connection between population parameters and the statistics of a set of many samples given to us, what can we say about the connection between the population parameters and the statistics of one sample? In practice research workers most often observe but one sample; this is practically always so in economics. The usual procedure is to calculate statistics (mean, variance, range, sum, etc.) from the sample frequency distribution, and then try to figure out from the values of these statistics what the values of the population parameters (mean, variance, range, sum, etc.) are likely to be. We have to consider the known sample, the theoretical distribution of the population values that we construct by inference from the sample, and the population as it actually is. Though we never know the true population precisely, the object of the theory of sampling is to make the theoretical distribution a satisfactory description of the population. The distribution of many sample statistics (not actually observed) may be used in interpreting the results of one sample. Since the general statistical procedure of inference from samples has applicability to many fields, we shall illustrate here the general statistical principles for the sample mean. In the following two chapters, we shall examine particular methods that have special importance in economics.

Let us suppose we have a sample that consists of 1,000 observations on some variable x. Our first step is to construct a frequency distribution of the values of x. No one observed value of x may be exactly the same as any other observed value. To simplify construction of the frequency distribution we, therefore, group the observed values into classes and record each value of x at the midpoint of a class interval. Thus, in Table 18–A the classes and the midpoints of x are shown in columns (1) and (2). For example, if a value of x between 4 and 6 is observed, say 4.4, it is recorded at the midpoint of this class interval and treated as if the observed value were 5. We have only one sample, so the letter i is used to designate the ith observation on x in the sample.

Table 18–A

(1)		(2)	(3)	(4)	(5)
Class Limits of x		Midpoint of Class	Frequency of Occurrence		
From	But Less Than	x_i	f_i	$x_i f_i$	$x_i^2 f_i$
0 – 2		1	50	50	50
2 – 4		3	90	270	810
4 – 6		5	150	750	3,750
6 – 8		7	225	1,575	11,025
8 – 10		9	200	1,800	16,200
10 – 12		11	160	1,760	19,360
12 – 14		13	85	1,105	14,365
14 – 16		15	40	600	9,000
Totals			$n = \sum_{i=1}^{8} f_i$ $= 1,000$	$\sum_{i=1}^{8} x_i f_i$ $= 7,910$	$\sum_{i=1}^{8} x_i^2 f_i$ $= 74,560$

The third column shows the frequency with which a value of x occurred that fell inside each class interval. Naturally, the total number of frequencies, n, is equal to the total number of observations. If the relative frequency, f_i/n, is recorded for each class midpoint, we have the relative frequency distribution of the variable x. Columns (4) and (5) will be used to compute the statistics of the sample.

Our next step is to compute the sample statistics. We shall compute the sample mean and variance. Earlier we saw that the mean of ungrouped data is defined as

$$\bar{x} = \frac{1}{n} \sum_{i=1}^{n} x_i$$

where the variable x assumes the values x_1, x_2, x_3, . . . , x_n.

For grouped data like that in Table 18–A, the sample mean has the formula

$$\bar{x} = \frac{1}{n} \sum_{i=1}^{m} x_i f_i$$

where $n = \sum_{i=1}^{m} f_i$ and m is the total number of classes (in our sample $m = 8$). That is, the products of all values of x are multiplied by their respective frequencies and summed; then this sum is divided by the total number of frequencies or observations.

In our example, we have

$$\bar{x} = \frac{1}{1{,}000} (7{,}910) = 7.91$$

from the totals of columns (3) and (4) in the table.

The sample variance is a measure of the distribution of the values of x in the sample around the mean. The greater is the variance the greater is the dispersion of the values of x from the mean; the smaller is the variance the closer are the values of x grouped around the mean. We use the symbol s^2 to denote the sample variance. For ungrouped data, the sample variance is given by

$$s^2 = \frac{\sum_{i=1}^{n} (x_i - \bar{x})^2}{n - 1}$$

We take the difference between the mean value of x and the observed value of x for each observed value of x in the sample. These differences are squared and then summed over all observations. The resulting figure is then divided by the number of observations in the sample minus one $(n - 1)$. The quantity $n - 1$ is called the *degrees of freedom* used to compute the variance.[1] Note the similarity of this formula to that given for the population variance in Chapter 17, where $\bar{x}$ is replaced by the mathematical expectation of x in the population. For *grouped* data the formula becomes

$$s^2 = \frac{\sum_{i=1}^{m} (x_i - \bar{x})^2 f_i}{n - 1} = \frac{\sum_{i=1}^{m} x_i^2 f_i - n\bar{x}^2}{n - 1}$$

In our example with the number of classes $m = 8$, the quantity $\sum_{i=1}^{m} x_i^2 f_i$ is given at the bottom of column (5) in Table 18–A. Substituting this quantity and the sample mean already computed, we have for the sample variance

$$s^2 = \frac{74{,}560 - (1{,}000)(7.91)^2}{1{,}000 - 1} = \frac{11{,}991.9}{999} = 12.00$$

carried out to two decimal places.

Grouping the data has led to some inaccuracy in the computation of the variance. By substituting the midpoint of a class for the observed value of x some error has been committed. The so-called Sheppard's correction is often applied to the result in order to rectify this error. By subtracting from the variance the size of the class interval squared and dividing by twelve, we correct for the error introduced by grouping. In our example the size of the class interval is two; hence, we square this quantity and divide by twelve. Sheppard's correction is

$$\frac{(2)^2}{12} = \frac{4}{12} = .33$$

The computed variance is 12.00 so the corrected variance is

$$s^2 = 12.00 - .33 = 11.67$$

[1] We divide by $n - 1$ rather than by n because some of the information contained in the sample was used to compute the sample mean. The so-called *degrees of freedom* decreases as the amount of information in the sample is used up. A sample of, say, 50 observations contains more information than a sample of 49 observations or less. We use some of the information in the sample to compute the sample mean. This uses up one degree of freedom, so for a sample of 50 observations we have only 49 degrees of freedom left to compute the variance, since to compute the variance we need to know the mean.

The standard deviation is defined as the square root of the variance. Hence, we have

$$s = \sqrt{11.67} = 3.42$$

as our sample standard deviation.

Having computed these sample statistics, let us concentrate attention on the sample mean $\bar{x} = 7.91$. If we were to take another sample from the same population, it is almost certain that the second sample would not have the same mean. This is likewise true of a third, a fourth, and so on. Even if many additional samples were to be drawn, we probably would not obtain exactly the same value for the mean twice. But would these other sample means vary greatly from the one we have observed? Sample theory helps us to decide how all possible means are distributed around the population mean. We can see how our one sample mean fits into this distribution, and we can thereby establish some grounds for an inference about the population mean.

The *standard error of the sample mean* is an estimate of the variability that would occur among the means of many samples if many samples were to be drawn at random from the same population. If we are to estimate the variability that would appear among the means of many samples, we must take into account the magnitude of the standard deviation of our observed sample and the size of the sample. The standard error of the mean is denoted by $s_{\bar{x}}$ and is given by the formula

$$s_{\bar{x}} = \frac{s}{\sqrt{n}}$$

In the case of the sample illustrated in Table 18–A, the standard error of the mean rounded to two decimal places is

$$s_{\bar{x}} = \frac{3.42}{\sqrt{1,000}} = \frac{3.42}{31.61} = .11$$

This is an estimate of the standard error of the mean that would have been secured had we (1) taken a large number of random samples from the population, (2) computed the mean of each sample, (3) arranged these means in a frequency distribution, and (4) calculated the standard deviation of these means. If this distribution of means is approximately normal, we know that about 68.27 per cent of the sample means would lie within plus or minus .11 of the mean of this distribution of sample means; 95.45 per cent would fall within plus or minus .22, and 99.73 per cent would fall within plus or minus .33 of the mean of the sample means.

Let us pause now to see where we have come up to this point. Tracing our steps backwards we have seen that from knowledge of the sample mean and the sample standard deviation of the one observed sample, we can compute the standard error of the sample mean. This quantity tells us the degree to which our sample mean might be expected to differ from the mean value of the distribution of many sample means—without our having actually to draw many samples. The theory of sampling in Section B establishes a relationship between the mean value of many sample means and the population mean. Therefore, we have a link between the mean of one observed sample and the unobserved population mean. The final problem, then, is to consider the conditions under which one can estimate population parameters directly from knowledge of the statistics of one sample.

C. STATISTICAL ESTIMATION

1. Confidence Intervals

We have seen that we cannot make statements about the population parameters with certainty; "errors" of sampling prevent our doing so. On the basis of the sample evidence, what sort of an estimate of a population parameter can one make? One kind is such that for a preassigned "degree of confidence," the statistician can establish a *confidence interval* or *confidence limits* on the basis of the information in the sample. We then say that with a given degree of probability the population parameter will be within these limits. We choose a probability in advance and refer to it as the *confidence coefficient*. Suppose this preassigned coefficient is 95 per cent. We then say that if the statistician were to compute many confidence limits (from many samples) on the 95 per cent probability basis, then in the long run these limits would include the unknown population value in 95 per cent of the cases. In the other 5 per cent of the cases the population value will fall outside the confidence limits. For some samples the population value will lie within the limits and for other samples it will not. But in the long run, the confidence limits will contain the true population value in approximately 95 per cent of the samples.

In Section B, we presented the general rule that the mean of a sample of n observations has itself the mathematical expectation equal to the population mean:

$$\mu_{\bar{x}} = \mu$$

We saw also that the variance of the sample means equals the population variance divided by the number of observations in the sample:

$$\sigma_{\bar{x}}^2 = \frac{\sigma^2}{n}$$

In our discussion of the normal distribution, we saw that we can define the variable

$$z = \frac{x - \mu}{\sigma}$$

which has the mean zero and variance of one if x is normally distributed. If the sample comes from a normal population, moreover, the variable

$$z = \frac{\bar{x} - \mu}{\sigma_{\bar{x}}}$$

is distributed normally with a mean of zero and a variance of one. Even when the population is not normally distributed but the sample is large, z will under certain conditions still be normally distributed. Finally we recall that the standard error of the mean is given by

$$s_{\bar{x}} = \frac{s}{\sqrt{n}}$$

For large samples, the sample standard deviation, s, is a reasonably good estimate of the unknown population standard deviation. Now we can compute $s_{\bar{x}}$ from our known sample, so we substitute $s_{\bar{x}}$ for $\sigma_{\bar{x}}$ in the definition of z:

$$z = \frac{\bar{x} - \mu}{s_{\bar{x}}}$$

where z is approximately normally distributed with mean zero and variance of one. The larger the sample the closer will be the approximation.

Note that in the definition of z, the quantities $\bar{x}$, $s_{\bar{x}}$, and z are either observed or can be computed from the sample data. We can now use this formulation to determine confidence limits for the estimation of the unknown population mean μ. For we can write

$$\mu = \bar{x} - z s_{\bar{x}}$$

We first choose a confidence coefficient; let us suppose it is to be 95 per cent. We see, from Table D on the normal distribution at the end of the book,[2] the probability that z is between -1.96 and 1.96 is $.95$, so we compute the limits

$$\mu = \bar{x} + 1.96s_{\bar{x}} \quad \text{and} \quad \mu = \bar{x} - 1.96s_{\bar{x}}$$

We estimate that the unknown population mean, μ, will lie within these limits. In the long run following such a procedure, we will be correct in 95 cases out of 100. Notice that this statement is equivalent to the statement that in 95.45 per cent of the cases for the normal distribution, the observations will deviate less than two standard deviations from the mean (see the second characteristic in Section F.2 of Chapter 17). That is, for a normally distributed variable with mean zero and standard deviation equal to one, 95.45 per cent of the values of the variable fall within plus or minus 2 (measured from the mean of the distribution, that is, zero).

We have not yet specified the numerical values of the limits. Let us therefore return to our sample of 1,000 observations on the variable x. We have

$$\bar{x} = 7.91 \quad \text{and} \quad s = 3.42$$

The standard error of the mean was computed as

$$s_{\bar{x}} = .11$$

Choosing a value of 95 per cent for the confidence coefficient, we have the limits

$$\bar{x} + 1.96(.11) = 8.13$$
$$\bar{x} - 1.96(.11) = 7.69$$

From our single sample, we estimate that the (unknown) true population mean lies between 7.69 and 8.13. But we are not certain of being correct; our inference is probable. We make this statistical estimate with 95 per cent confidence; we know that if we were to make many such estimates, we would be correct about 95 times out of 100 in the long run.

2. Point Estimation

Sometimes we wish to obtain a single figure for an estimate of the unknown population parameter rather than intervals. A number of

---

[2] The use of Table D is discussed in the next section on tests of hypotheses. Note here that we have chosen a 95 per cent probability level in advance. With the mean of z equal to zero, the table gives the probability of z from zero to any of the values of z shown in the left-hand margin. But we want to know the deviation of z from its mean (zero) in *both* the positive and the negative directions. Hence, we must find the value of $2p$ that equals .95, chosen in advance. When $p = .4750$, then $2p = .9500$, the chosen probability level. Therefore, we read off the value of z corresponding to .4750 as 1.96. Since we are going in both directions from the mean of z (we have multiplied p by 2), we have $+1.96$ and -1.96 as the values of z corresponding to a probability level of .95.

methods have been developed by statisticians. The two most important are the method of maximum likelihood and the method of least squares.

The method of maximum likelihood chooses as the population estimate the value of the random variable that maximizes its probability of being observed. The estimate of the population parameter should be that value of the variable which, if it were correct, would maximize the probability of obtaining the sample actually observed. For every possible value of the population parameter, the probability of the observed sample's occurring in random sampling is calculated. The particular value that maximizes this probability is selected as the estimate of the parameter.

The method of least squares chooses the value that minimizes the sum of the squares of the deviations from the chosen value. This method has been used extensively in econometrics, and we shall have more to say about it in the next chapter. Besides the methods of maximum likelihood and least squares, there are other methods available for point estimation. They are not very often used, however.

D. TESTS OF HYPOTHESES

A hypothesis is a theoretical proposition that is capable of empirical verification or disproof. It is an explanation of some event or events, and it may be a true or a false explanation. The following statements are statistical hypotheses: "The average height of American males between 14 and 40 years of age is greater than the average height of American males 40 years of age or over." "The proportion of white balls in an urn containing 100 balls, each of which is either black or white, is $\frac{2}{3}$." "The price elasticity of demand for food products in the United States is less than unity." "The cause of the decline in national income was an autonomous decline in investment." Notice that these are statements about the statistical population. The problem is one of determining from a sample whether the hypothesis is probably true or probably false.

Often econometric problems are phrased in terms of a hypothesis. Empirical tests of hypotheses are called *tests of significance*. Such a test essentially amounts to this: it is a probability test based on sampling theory designed to determine whether a given sample could reasonably come from a specified population. Suppose we have a given hypothesis about the population and a sample drawn at random from the population. We intend to judge the truth or falsity of the hypothesis on the basis of the evidence in the sample. To do this, we compute the probability that this particular sample would have arisen if the hypothesis were true. A so-called level of significance is specified in advance. This significance level is used to decide whether we will accept the hypothesis as true or reject it as false. Acceptance or rejection turns on the probability of an error we might commit in making the decision. If the probability of making a wrong decision is less than a preassigned value, we go ahead and make the decision.

The significance level is this preassigned value. One significance level that is commonly chosen is 5 per cent; another is 1 per cent. Suppose one were to choose a 5 per cent level of significance. This means we will reject the hypothesis whenever the probability of wrongly rejecting it is less than 5 per cent. In this case, the probability of rejecting it when it is in fact true is less than 5 per cent. If this probability is greater than 5 per cent, the hypothesis is to be accepted as true. If we decide to accept the hypothesis, we will not reject it, because in this case the probability of rejecting it when it is in fact true is greater than 5 per cent. This latter conclusion does not mean that one has proved the hypothesis; it merely means that one has verified it, that is, failed to disprove it.

Two types of error may be made in testing hypotheses. One, called the error of the first kind, occurs if a true hypothesis is rejected. The probability of this error is given by the level of significance chosen. An error of the second kind occurs if a false hypothesis is not rejected. These errors are, in a sense, competing; by reducing the chance of one error we increase the chance of the other. The usual procedure, therefore, is to hold constant the probability of an error of the first kind and minimize the probability of an error of the second kind. This is what we do when we specify the level of significance in advance of the test to be applied.

Let us consider tests of hypotheses regarding the population mean, μ, of a normal population for a large sample. Again we compute the quantity

$$z = \frac{\bar{x} - \mu}{s_{\bar{x}}}$$

We can substitute $s_{\bar{x}}$ for $\sigma_{\bar{x}}$ because in large samples s is a good approximation to σ. Then z is normally distributed with mean zero and variance equal to one.

This being the case, let p represent the probability of z (obtained from the normal probability Table D). The probability q is the probability of obtaining the sample mean $\bar{x}$, or another sample mean with the same or greater deviation from the true mean μ. This probability is

$$q = 1 - 2p$$

Let the hypothesis in question be that $\mu = 8$. We wish to test this hypothesis from knowledge of the sample given in Table 18–A. For that sample we have

$$\bar{x} = 7.91 \qquad \text{and} \qquad s_{\bar{x}} = .11$$

We choose a level of significance of 5 per cent, let us say. On the basis of the sample statistics, shall we accept or reject the hypothesis? We have

$$z = \frac{7.91 - 8}{.11} = \frac{-.09}{.11} = -.82$$

We can ignore the sign of z, since the positive or negative direction of the deviation does not matter. For $z = 0$, then $\mu = \bar{x}$. But in general, there will be some difference. Is it large enough to reject the hypothesis? If the difference is probably due to chance, we will accept the hypothesis; otherwise, we will reject it. For $z = .82$, we have from Table D that $p = .2939$. Therefore, the probability of observing in the sample as large a value of z or a larger value due to chance and not a "real" difference between $\bar{x}$ and μ is

$$q = 1 - 2(.2939) = 1 - .5878 = .4122$$

This probability, about 41 per cent, is greater than the chosen level of significance of 5 per cent. Hence, we will accept the hypothesis that $\mu = 8$ at the 5 per cent level of significance upon the basis of the sample data.

Suppose the hypothesis had been that the population mean equals 7.50. Would we have accepted this hypothesis at the 5 per cent level of significance? Again, from our sample we compute

$$z = \frac{7.91 - 7.50}{.11} = \frac{.41}{.11} = 3.73$$

For $z = 3.73$, $p = .4999$ from Table D. Hence,

$$q = 1 - .9998 = .0002$$

This value, only about two tenths of 1 per cent, is much less than the level of significance, so the hypothesis that $\mu = 7.50$ must be rejected.

The preceding test is valid for large samples. If the sample is small, say less than 30 observations, the test is not applicable. For samples from a normal population, however, the so-called quantity t follows a distribution that closely approximates the normal distribution, where

$$t = \frac{\bar{x} - \mu}{s_{\bar{x}}}$$

Its distribution is called *Student's distribution* or the t distribution. Table C gives the t distribution for various degrees of freedom. The larger the number of degrees of freedom (the larger the sample) the closer does t approximate the normal distribution.

This quantity is especially appropriate for testing hypotheses when the sample size is small. For example, assume the hypothesis that $\mu = 20$ is to be tested. We select the 5 per cent level of significance. Suppose the given sample consists of 16 observations from which the following statistics are computed:

$$\bar{x} = 24$$
$$s = 9.20$$
$$s_{\bar{x}} = \frac{9.20}{\sqrt{16}} = 2.30$$

We next compute t:

$$t = \frac{\bar{x} - \mu}{s_{\bar{x}}} = \frac{24 - 20}{2.30} = \frac{4}{2.30} = 1.74$$

This is our empirical value of t. For $n - 1 = 15$ degrees of freedom, we see from Table C that

$$t = 2.131$$

at the 5 per cent level of significance. Our empirical t computed from the sample is less than this. Hence, the probability of t exceeding 1.74 is greater than 5 per cent, and the hypothesis that the true or population mean of 20 is verified. The difference between the sample mean and the hypothetical population mean is not so great that it cannot be explained by random errors of sampling. Had our empirical t been greater than 2.131, we should have had to reject the hypothesis; the difference between the hypothetical mean and the observed mean would have been too great to be accounted for by random errors of sampling alone.

E. THE RELATIONSHIP OF ESTIMATION TO TEST OF HYPOTHESES

The reader may have realized by now that there is an intimate connection between statistical estimation and testing hypotheses. The error of rejecting a true hypothesis really amounts to the error of excluding the correct value of a population parameter from the confidence interval. Likewise, including a wrong value in a confidence interval is tantamount to an error of the second kind in testing hypotheses (acceptance of a false hypothesis). Indeed, testing the hypothesis that some parameter has a specified value is ordinarily equivalent to computing the confidence interval for that parameter. If the hypothetical value of the parameter is enclosed by the confidence interval, the hypothesis is verified and accepted; if not, it is rejected. The primary reason for treating the two subjects separately is that sometimes hypotheses refer to more than population parameters. When this is the case, the two methods are not equivalent.

PROBLEMS

1. Let the variable x represent the height of Americans over twenty years of age. The following sample of measurements on x is given in feet.

x	x	x	x	x
5.5	5.1	5.8	6.0	7.0
5.8	5.7	5.2	5.6	6.1
6.0	5.3	5.4	5.4	5.6
5.3	5.0	6.5	6.1	5.8
6.1	6.2	5.3	5.9	5.2
5.7	5.5	5.9	5.9	5.7
5.0	6.5	4.5	5.6	4.1
4.8	4.9	5.8	6.4	6.3
5.9	5.3	5.1	5.0	5.9
4.5	5.6	4.2	5.2	5.7

(a) Compute the sample mean for the ungrouped data.
(b) Compute the sample standard deviation.
(c) Assuming the population is normally distributed and using Table D at the end of the book, establish the 95 per cent confidence limits for the population mean.
(d) How do you interpret the limits found in part (c)?

2. Using the sample given in Problem 1, test the hypothesis that the average height of Americans is 6.0 feet. Test the hypothesis that the average height is 5.50 feet. Choose the 5 per cent level of significance.

3. Let the variable x represent scores on an aptitude test. The following sample of test scores is given.

x	x	x	x	x
33	84	41	68	48
45	91	56	66	72
52	88	77	36	79
76	13	28	82	39
64	27	83	75	58
72	87	61	65	75

Group the data in class intervals of

0 − 9.99 with a midpoint of 5, 10 − 19.99 with a
midpoint of 15, . . . , 90 − 99.99 with a midpoint of 95.

(a) Compute the sample mean for the grouped data.

(b) Compute the sample standard deviation.

(c) Assuming the population is normally distributed and using Table D, establish the 95 per cent confidence limits for the population mean.

4. Using the sample given in Problem 3, test the hypothesis that the average test score is 85. Test the hypothesis that the average test score is 65. Choose the 5 per cent level of significance.

5. Explain briefly the connection between tests of hypotheses and statistical estimation by confidence limits.

CHAPTER 19

Simple Regression and
Correlation

The general methods of statistical inference outlined in Chapter 18 apply to data taken from any field of empirical research. The principles of statistical estimation and tests of hypotheses are used in physics, chemistry, psychology, economics, and other fields of empirical research. There is a particular kind of point estimation, however, that has proved to be very appropriate in economics: the method of least squares. The method of *least squares* chooses as an estimate of the unknown population value that sample value such that the sum of the squares of the deviations of the sample observations from that sample value is a minimum. Let $\hat{X}$ represent the true or population value to be estimated from the sample of observations $x_1, x_2, x_3, \ldots, x_n$. We will use the sample value $\hat{x}$ as an estimate of $\hat{X}$. To find $\hat{x}$ from the sample data, we construct the sum of the squared deviations of the sample observations from $\hat{x}$:

$$D = (x_1 - \hat{x})^2 + (x_2 - \hat{x})^2 + (x_3 - \hat{x})^2 + \ldots + (x_n - \hat{x})^2$$

In this expression the x_1, x_2, $\ldots$, x_n are all known quantities; the expression is minimized with respect to $\hat{x}$ and the resulting equation is solved for the value of $\hat{x}$. $\hat{x}$ is then used as an estimate of $\hat{X}$.

In economics, the data in the sample ordinarily consist of pairs, triplets, etc., of measurements—not observations on a single variable only. For example, the sample may be comprised of observations on the consumption and the income of a number of American families. Or it may be comprised of observations on the interest rate and net investment. Sometimes more than two variables are involved, as when the sample consists of observations on the quantity of beef purchased by consumers and its price and the prices of other meats. It is the relationship among these variables in which the economist is interested, and the method of least squares does, under certain conditions, yield an estimate of the relationship among variables. When applied to a relationship among variables rather than to a single variable, the method of least squares is called *regression analysis*.

A. SIMPLE LINEAR REGRESSION

Simple regression refers to a relationship between two variables. When more than two variables are involved, the regression analysis is called multiple regression. In this chapter, we treat only simple regression. Assume there is a random variable y that is related to another variable x by the linear equation

$$y = a + bx$$

This is the relationship that is presumed to hold in an infinite population. Now our sample will consist of pairs of observations. Let us suppose that we have ten pairs of observations: $x_1, x_2, x_3, \ldots, x_{10}$ and also $y_1, y_2, y_3, \ldots, y_{10}$. The ten observations (the total of ten pairs) make up the sample in which we associate y_1 with x_1, y_2 with x_2, and so on. Assume the observed values of y and the corresponding observed values of x are those shown in Table 19–A.

Table 19–A

Observation	y	x	Observation	y	x
1	5	10	6	−15	−10
2	−4	−4	7	−8	−12
3	−6	4	8	10	13
4	−2	1	9	−1	5
5	5	16	10	−10	−6

If we plot each pair of values (x, y) as a point, we obtain the so-called *scatter diagram* depicted in Figure 19.1. We see that the scatter of points has a form roughly similar to a straight line with a positive slope, and we can fit a straight line to the scatter diagram. One way to do this is to draw in a line by a freehand method that visually appears to best fit the scatter. There are more systematic ways of doing so, however. We need not at the moment concern ourselves with these; in any event, let us suppose that the line drawn in Figure 19.2 is the one chosen to be fitted to the scatter of points given by the sample. The equation of this line is

$$\hat{y} = -3.81 + .71x$$

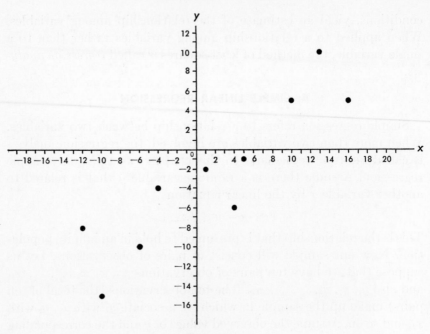

Figure 19.1

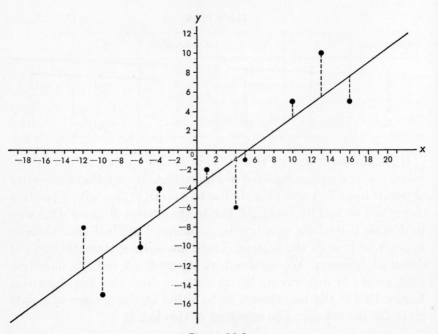

Figure 19.2

We use $\hat{y}$ instead of y in this equation to indicate the predicted value of the "explained" variable—not its actual or observed value. For a known value of x, we can predict a value of y from the equation; for each given x, $\hat{y}$ lies on the line. But we see that the equation does not predict the values of the "explained" variable with perfect accuracy. The sizes of the errors committed in the prediction are shown by the broken lines in Figure 19.2. These are the deviations of the observed values of y from the predicted values for each observed value of x, that is, $y - \hat{y}$. The magnitudes of the errors are shown in Table 19–B.

Table 19–B

For $x =$	From the equation, $\hat{y} = -3.81 + .71x =$	From the sample observations, $y =$	Errors in the prediction: $y - \hat{y} =$
10	3.29	5	1.71
−4	−6.65	−4	2.65
4	−.97	−6	−5.03
1	−3.10	−2	1.10
16	7.55	5	−2.55
−10	−10.91	−15	−4.09
−12	−12.33	−8	4.33
13	5.42	10	4.58
5	−.26	−1	−.74
−6	−8.07	−10	−1.93

We have not said anything about how the equation for this line was determined. It is the primary purpose of regression analysis to predict the value of y from knowledge of a given value of x. However, under suitable conditions it will also yield the best estimates of the constant a and the so-called regression coefficient b (the unknown parameters of the population equation). Let us rephrase our problem as follows: Theoretically we state that a definite positive relationship holds between the variable y and another variable x. This is a statement about the population obtained from theoretical considerations. We furthermore assume that the relationship is linear, so the population equation can be written

$$y = a + bx$$

where a and b are the *unknown* population parameters that we wish to estimate. We observe a sample of n observations: x_1 associated with y_1, x_2 associated with y_2, . . . , x_n associated with y_n. Let $\hat{a}$

denote the empirical (sample) value of the constant y intercept and $\hat{b}$ the empirical value of the constant coefficient. We will use the equation

$$\hat{y} = \hat{a} + \hat{b}x$$

to estimate the population equation. That is, we use $\hat{a}$ as an estimate of a and $\hat{b}$ as an estimate of b. Now we know that this equation will not fit exactly our sample data; certain errors or deviations will appear. We can represent these by a variable, u, which assumes the values $u_1, u_2, u_3, \ldots, u_n$. We then rewrite the empirical or sample equation as

$$y = \hat{a} + \hat{b}x + u$$

with the condition that the mean value of u is zero, and where

$$y_1 - \hat{y}_1 = u_1 = y_1 - \hat{a} - \hat{b}x_1$$
$$y_2 - \hat{y}_2 = u_2 = y_2 - \hat{a} - \hat{b}x_2$$
$$\vdots \qquad \vdots \qquad \vdots$$
$$y_n - \hat{y}_n = u_n = y_n - \hat{a} - \hat{b}x_n$$

That is, u is a measure of the deviations of the predicted values $\hat{y}$ from the observed values y in the sample. The values of u correspond to the values $y - \hat{y}$ in the last column of Table 19–B.

Now we must make some assumptions about the errors u in order to estimate a and b from $\hat{a}$ and $\hat{b}$. We may use the method of least squares if we assume that the errors $u_1, u_2, u_3, \ldots, u_n$ are random and independently distributed. That is, the distribution of any one random error is independent of the distribution of all others; the probability of u_1 occurring is independent of the probabilities of u_2, $u_3, \ldots, u_n$. We need not assume that their distribution is normal. The Markoff theorem assures us that $\hat{a}$ and $\hat{b}$ are the best unbiased linear estimates of the parameters a and b. Best means that the estimates have the smallest variance among all linear unbiased estimates. For example, "best" in this connection means that the variance of the u's is a minimum.

Note that the equation itself need not be linear; the theorem still holds if we substitute x^2, x^3, $\log x$, $\sin x$, etc., for x. The constants must enter the equation linearly—they cannot be, for example, $\log a$ or $(1 - b)^2$.

If we are to use $\hat{a}$ and $\hat{b}$ to estimate the population parameters, we must next compute them by the method of least squares. The regression of y on x is nothing more than the values of y estimated by least squares from the equation

$$\hat{y} = \hat{a} + \hat{b}x$$

To find the values of $\hat{a}$ and $\hat{b}$, we solve the following pair of normal equations:

(1) $$\Sigma y = \hat{a}n + \hat{b}\Sigma x$$
(2) $$\Sigma xy = \hat{a}\Sigma x + \hat{b}\Sigma x^2$$

It can be shown that the simultaneous solution of these normal equations yields those values of $\hat{a}$ and $\hat{b}$ that minimize the sum of the squares of the errors u.[1] All the quantities in the normal equations can be computed from the sample data. If the sample is large, the computation is greatly facilitated with the help of modern calculating machines.

To simplify matters, let us solve the equations, and write $\hat{a}$ and $\hat{b}$ in terms of the other quantities (see Chapter 4). Multiply (1) by Σx and (2) by n and subtract (1) from (2) to eliminate $\hat{a}$ and obtain $\hat{b}$; thus

$$\hat{b} = \frac{n \cdot \Sigma xy - \Sigma x \cdot \Sigma y}{n \cdot \Sigma x^2 - (\Sigma x)^2}$$

Substituting this value for $\hat{b}$ in either (1) or (2), yields

$$\hat{a} = \frac{\Sigma x^2 \cdot \Sigma y - \Sigma x \cdot \Sigma xy}{n \cdot \Sigma x^2 - (\Sigma x)^2}$$

To illustrate, let us return to the example of ten observations given in Table 19–A. These are shown again in Table 19–C, where we have $n = 10$. The quantities other than n used to compute $\hat{a}$ and $\hat{b}$ are shown at the bottom of each column. For the present, we can ignore the last column. We substitute the computed values from the table into the formulas for $\hat{a}$ and $\hat{b}$, and obtain

[1]   Let $D = u_1{}^2 + u_2{}^2 + \cdots + u_n{}^2$
$$= (y_1 - \hat{a} - \hat{b}x_1)^2 + (y_2 - \hat{a} - \hat{b}x_2)^2 + \cdots + (y_n - \hat{a} - \hat{b}x_n)^2$$
This quantity D is to be minimized with respect to $\hat{a}$ and $\hat{b}$. We have the necessary conditions:

(1) $\dfrac{\partial D}{\partial \hat{a}} = 0$ (2) $\dfrac{\partial D}{\partial \hat{b}} = 0$

(1) $\dfrac{\partial D}{\partial \hat{a}} = -2(y_1 - \hat{a} - \hat{b}x_1) - 2(y_2 - \hat{a} - \hat{b}x_2) - \cdots - 2(y_n - \hat{a} - \hat{b}x_n) = 0$

(2) $\dfrac{\partial D}{\partial \hat{b}} = -2x_1(y_1 - \hat{a} - \hat{b}x_1) - 2x_2(y_2 - \hat{a} - \hat{b}x_2) - \cdots - 2x_n(y_n - \hat{a} - \hat{b}x_n) = 0$

Dividing both sides of each equation by 2 and combining like terms gives—

(1) $-\sum_{i=1}^{n} y_i + \hat{a}n + \hat{b}\sum_{i=1}^{n} x_i = 0$

(2) $-\sum_{i=1}^{n} x_i y_i + \hat{a}\sum_{i=1}^{n} x_i + \hat{b}\sum_{i=1}^{n} x_i{}^2 = 0$

These are the normal equations given above. Their solution gives $\hat{a}$ and $\hat{b}$, which minimize D.

$$\hat{a} = \frac{(863)(-26) - (17)(551)}{(10)(863) - (17)^2} = \frac{-31,805}{8,341} = -3.8131$$

$$\hat{b} = \frac{(10)(551) - (17)(-26)}{(10)(863) - (17)^2} = \frac{5,952}{8,341} = .7136$$

Table 19–C

y	x	x^2	xy	y^2
5	10	100	50	25
−4	−4	16	16	16
−6	4	16	−24	36
−2	1	1	−2	4
5	16	256	80	25
−15	−10	100	150	225
−8	−12	144	96	64
10	13	169	130	100
−1	5	25	−5	1
−10	−6	36	60	100
$\Sigma y = -26$	$\Sigma x = 17$	$\Sigma x^2 = 863$	$\Sigma xy = 551$	$\Sigma y^2 = 596$

Hence, our sample data yields the equation

$$\hat{y} = -3.81 + .71x$$

where the computed constants are rounded to two decimal places. Under the stated assumptions this equation provides the estimated values of y, that is, $\hat{y}$, if x is given. Recall it is this equation that was used to fit a straight line to the sample data expressed geometrically as a scatter of points. Hence, the problem of computing the regression of y on x is equivalent to the geometric problem of obtaining the best fit to a scatter of points by means of least square techniques. The size of the errors committed in fitting the line and predicting y from it are equivalent to the values of u (shown in Table 19–B).

Since the residuals $y - \hat{y}$ are expressed as a variable u, we can write the regression equation as

$$y = -3.81 + .71x + u$$

This form of the regression equation emphasizes the fact that we are attempting also to estimate the population parameters a and b. Note that the random errors u are assumed to exist in y but not in x. The sample values $\hat{a} = -3.81$ and $\hat{b} = .71$ are estimates of the population parameters a and b if either of the following conditions are satisfied:

(1) The errors u_1, u_2, . . . , u_{10} are errors of observation. The reason why the regression equation does not predict y exactly in

every instance is because of deficiencies in the sample data. The collection of the sample by interview or questionnaire, and the recording of the sample have led to inaccuracies due to clerical mistakes, incomplete investigation, or other causes.

(2) The errors are errors of omission. That is, they result from certain variables other than x that exert an influence on y but have not been included in the regression equation. Variations in y may be caused partly by variations in x but partly by variations in z, p, q, etc. The omission of these variables will lead to imperfect predictions of y from knowledge of x. These two sources of error have been discussed more completely in Chapter 16.

1. Adequacy of the Estimates

How shall we determine whether the estimates of a and b yielded by the sample are "good" estimates? Stated another way: how shall the general principles of statistical estimation be applied to regression analysis? The values of $\hat{a}$ and $\hat{b}$ are in the nature of averages or means. It is quite possible that no one value of y exactly equals the estimated $\hat{y}$ (no one point in the scatter diagram lies exactly on the line), but the values of $\hat{y}$ may be close to y. Since errors are to be expected in all such estimates, it is necessary to measure the amount of error and infer from this the degree of confidence that we will attribute to the estimates.

We shall first compute the *standard error of the regression coefficient, $\hat{b}$*. This quantity is similar in meaning to the standard error of the mean described in Chapter 18, where we were using the sample mean to estimate the population mean. We designate the standard error of the regression coefficient by $s_{\hat{b}}$. Its square is given by the formula

$$s_{\hat{b}}^2 = \frac{n\Sigma y^2 - (\Sigma y)^2 - \left\{\dfrac{(n\Sigma xy - \Sigma x\Sigma y)^2}{n\Sigma x^2 - (\Sigma x)^2}\right\}}{(n-2)\left\{n\Sigma x^2 - (\Sigma x)^2\right\}}$$

Note the similarity of the quantities in the braces { } to those already used to compute $\hat{a}$ and $\hat{b}$. To find $s_{\hat{b}}$, we merely take the square root of this quantity, thus

$$s_{\hat{b}} = \sqrt{s_{\hat{b}}^2}$$

We have assumed that the errors u are random and independent. We now introduce an additional assumption, namely that they are normally distributed. If the distribution of errors is normal, the quantity

$$t = \frac{\hat{b} - b}{s_{\hat{b}}}$$

follows the t distribution (see Chapter 18, Section D) with $n - 2$ degrees of freedom. The number of degrees of freedom is two less than the number of observations because two constants ($\hat{a}$ and $\hat{b}$) have already been determined from the sample data.[2] We can see that t is a measure of the difference between the empirical coefficient and the hypothetical population coefficient, taking account of sampling variability. It is useful for establishing confidence limits and tests of significance.

The usual procedure is to execute a *test of significance*, that is, to test the statistical significance of the empirical coefficient $\hat{b}$. If there is no linear relationship between x and y in the population, then $b = 0$. The hypothesis to be tested is that $b = 0$, and a level of significance is chosen. If we reject this hypothesis, we say the empirical coefficient $\hat{b}$ is statistically significant—it is significantly different from zero. If we accept this hypothesis, then $\hat{b}$ is not significant and there is probably no linear relation between x and y in the population.

Returning to our example, we first compute $s_{\hat{b}}$ from the sample data in Table 19–C.

$$s_{\hat{b}}^2 = \frac{(10)(596) - (-26)^2 - \left\{\dfrac{[(10)(551) - (17)(-26)]^2}{(10)(863) - (17)^2}\right\}}{(8)\left\{(10)(863) - (17)^2\right\}}$$

$$= \frac{5,960 - 676 - \left\{\dfrac{[5,952]^2}{8,341}\right\}}{8\left\{8,341\right\}} = \frac{5,284 - 4,247}{66,728}$$

$$= \frac{1,037}{66,728} = .0155$$

$$s_{\hat{b}} = \sqrt{.0155} = .1245$$

[2] In regression analysis, the number of observations minus the number of constants, computed from the sample and used to fix the points from which the deviations are measured, constitute the degrees of freedom. Obviously, if we had n observations and n constants, there would be no "errors" (for each constant would fix a point equal to the observed point) and sampling errors would have no role to play. Loosely, the fewer are the number of constants, the greater is the freedom left for additional inferences.

Next we set $b = 0$ in the formula for t and obtain

$$t = \frac{\hat{b} - b}{s_{\hat{b}}} = \frac{.7136 - 0}{.1245} = 5.73$$

Given this empirical or sample value of t, our final step is to choose a level of significance at which we shall test the hypothesis that $b = 0$. Suppose we choose the 5 per cent significance level. Table C tells us that at the 5 per cent level of significance for $(10 - 2) = 8$ degrees of freedom, we may expect a positive or negative value of t that may be as large as 2.306 if the hypothesis is true. That is, if the population coefficient is in fact zero, we may expect a difference between zero and the empirical $\hat{b}$, which is the result of chance or sampling errors. But this difference cannot be so great as to lead to a value of t that exceeds 2.306 (positive or negative). Now our empirical t is much greater than 2.306; hence, we will reject the hypotheses that $b = 0$ (that there is no linear relation between x and y in the population). We say that our regression coefficient is significant at the 5 per cent level of significance. Had our empirical t been less than 2.306, we would say that our regression coefficient is not significant. The difference between it and zero in that case would be small enough to be accounted for by chance alone.

At the end of Chapter 18, we saw that testing the hypothesis that some parameter has a specified value (say the empirical value $\hat{b}$) is equivalent to computing the confidence interval for the parameter. If the hypothetical value of the parameter is enclosed by the confidence interval, the hypothesis is accepted; if not, it is rejected.

Thus in our significance test, we used the 5 per cent level of significance. This really amounts to the error of excluding the correct value of the population parameter from the confidence interval. Hence, the probability of including the correct value of the parameter in the confidence interval is .95. To say $\hat{b}$ is significant at the 5 per cent level of significance, is to say that the probability is .95 that the confidence limits will enclose the true population parameter.

Confidence limits can be established for a confidence coefficient of 95 per cent by substituting the value of t given in Table C for our empirical t:

$$t = \frac{.7136 - b}{.1245} = \pm 2.306$$

As we have seen, this is the value of t at the 5 per cent level of significance for 8 degrees of freedom. Solving this equation for b, we get

$$.7136 - b = + 2.306 \,(.1245) = + .2871$$
$$b = .7136 - .2871 = .4265$$

and

$$.7136 - b = -2.306 \,(.1245) = - .2871$$
$$b = .7136 + .2871 = 1.0007$$

The limits that enclose the true population coefficient at the 95 per cent probability level are .4265 and 1.0007. If many samples were drawn at random from the population and the limits computed for each sample, these limits would enclose the true population parameter in about 95 cases out of 100. In the remaining 5 per cent of the cases, it would fall outside the limits.

Incidentally, we can see from the foregoing discussion that the t test can be used to test the hypothesis that b is equal to some stated value. This is similar to testing the significance of an estimated coefficient $\hat{b}$. The only difference is that in the significance test we are testing the hypothesis that $b = 0$, whereas in this case we are testing whether b equals any number we may choose in advance. Suppose the hypothesis is that $b = 3$. We substitute this hypothetical value for b in the formula for t:

$$t = \frac{.7136 - 3.000}{.1245} = -18.3646$$

For 8 degrees of freedom at the 5 per cent level of significance, the maximum (positive or negative) t that could arise by chance is 2.306. But our empirical t is much greater. Hence, the probability that the difference between $\hat{b}$ and the hypothetical b could have arisen purely by chance is less than 5 per cent if the hypothesis were true. We, therefore, reject the hypothesis that $b = 3$.

In summary, the primary purpose of simple regression analysis is prediction of the values of a dependent variable y from knowledge of given values of an independent variable x. A linear functional relation between y and x is determined from the sample by computing the constants of the sample equation, $\hat{a}$ and $\hat{b}$. Furthermore, $\hat{a}$ and $\hat{b}$ are the best unbiased linear estimates of the hypothetical population parameters a and b, if $\hat{a}$ and $\hat{b}$ are computed by least squares and if the residuals u are random and mutually independent. Assuming u is normally distributed, the significance of the regression coefficient $\hat{b}$ can be determined by use of the t test. If $\hat{b}$ is found to be significant at, say, the 5 per cent level of significance, then we can say that the 95 per cent confidence limits will enclose the true or population coefficient b.

B. SIMPLE CORRELATION

A measure of the degree to which two variables are related is given by the sample correlation coefficient, usually designated by r. If two variables x and y are assumed to have a linear relationship, the value of r measures the extent to which sample observations on x are co-related with sample observations on y. It is a pure number, so that the units in which x and y are quoted do not affect its value. The number r may vary from -1 to $+1$. If r is positive, then y increases when x increases and y decreases when x decreases. If r is negative, then y increases when x decreases and y decreases when x increases. If r is zero, then we say that there is neither a positive nor a negative relationship between x and y.

Suppose r turns out to be equal to $+1$. In this case, there is perfect positive correlation between x and y in the sample. Diagrammatically, all of the observed sample points (x, y) lie on a straight line running from lower left to upper right (see Figure 19.3a). If r turns out to be -1, there is perfect negative correlation between x and y.

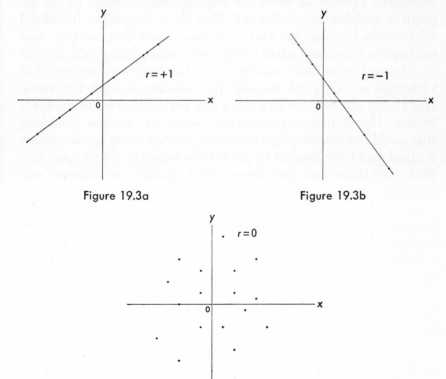

Figure 19.3a   Figure 19.3b

Figure 19.3c

All the sample points lie exactly on a line running from upper left to lower right (see Figure 19.3b). When r is found to be zero, there is no distinguishable line formed by the sample scatter diagram. An example of zero correlation is depicted in Figure 19.3c.

In practice, we almost never observe either perfect correlation or zero correlation. Usually r is some (positive or negative) number between zero and one. But the closer that number is to one, the greater is the degree of correlation—the closer will the scatter of points approach a straight line. Naturally, the more the scatter of points diverge from a straight line, the closer r is to zero.[3] In Figure 19.2, for example, we can see that r will be positive but less than one, because there are deviations of the observations from the fitted line with a positive slope.

The concepts of correlation and regression give different types of information, but there is a connection between them. First, how do they differ?

(1) Regression analysis selects one of the variables as the independent variable or predictor and the other variable as the dependent variable or predictand. That is, it imputes a functional relationship between the two variables. Correlation analysis does not imply a functional relationship—only some relationship. It seeks to discover if a mutual variation exists, but it does not suggest that variations in, say, y are "caused" by variations in x, or vice versa. Knowledge of the value of r alone will not enable one to predict y from x. Correlations are sometimes observed between quantities that could not conceivably be causally related (such as soil erosion in Alaska and the amount of alcohol consumed in South America). Such correlations are sometimes called spurious or nonsense correlations.

(2) A given correlation coefficient is consistent with an infinite number of straight lines. Obviously, if we were to shift every point in Figure 19.3a upward or downward by an equal amount, the correlation coefficient would still be equal to $+1$. The regression equation would have a different y intercept, however. Likewise, if we rotate all the points around one given point in Figure 19.3b so that they fall exactly on a different straight line (with a different slope), the regression coefficient $\hat{b}$ would change (and perhaps $\hat{a}$) but the

---

[3] If all the points lie on a straight line with zero slope, the correlation coefficient will be zero also. For variations in one variable are not associated with variations in the other. Changes in x, for example, are not corelated with changes in y.

correlation coefficient would still equal one. In other words, the correlation coefficient measures the degree to which the points scatter around a fitted straight line, but it does not give the equation for the fitted line.

There is, nevertheless, a connection between the correlation coefficient and the regression coefficient. We know that if r is positive, then a fitted line must have a positive slope. But $\hat{b}$ is the slope of a fitted line, so it must be positive. Conversely, if r is negative, then $\hat{b}$ must be negative. Finally, it follows that if r is zero, then $\hat{b}$ must be zero.

1. Computation of the Correlation Coefficient

To grasp the importance of the correlation coefficient, we shall first consider its statistical meaning. It is the ratio of the standard deviation of the predicted values of the dependent variable to the standard deviation of the observed values of the dependent variable. Let s_y represent the standard deviation of the actual values of y in the sample. Let $s_{\hat{y}}$ designate the standard deviation of the predicted values of y. Hence,

$$r = \frac{s_{\hat{y}}}{s_y}$$

This then is a measure of the closeness of the relationship between the two variables y and $\hat{y}$. It compares the total variation in y with the variation in y that is associated with variations in x.

The formula for the practical computation of the numerical value of the simple correlation coefficient is given as

$$r = \frac{\Sigma(x - \bar{x})(y - \bar{y})}{\sqrt{\Sigma(x - \bar{x})^2 \Sigma(y - \bar{y})^2}}$$

where $\bar{x}$ and $\bar{y}$ are the sample means of x and y. Remembering the definition of the mean as

$$\bar{x} = \frac{\Sigma x}{n} \qquad \text{and} \qquad \bar{y} = \frac{\Sigma y}{n}$$

this expression may be simplified to

$$r = \frac{\Sigma xy - n\bar{x}\bar{y}}{\sqrt{(\Sigma x^2 - n\bar{x}^2)(\Sigma y^2 - n\bar{y}^2)}}$$

Let us compute the correlation coefficient for our sample of ten observations given in Table 19–C. We note that

$$\bar{x} = \frac{17}{10} = 1.7 \qquad \text{and} \qquad \bar{y} = \frac{-26}{10} = -2.6$$

So we have

$$r = \frac{551 - (10)(1.7)(-2.6)}{\sqrt{[863 - (10)(1.7)^2] \cdot [596 - (10)(-2.6)^2]}}$$

$$= \frac{595.20}{\sqrt{(834.1)(528.4)}} = \frac{595.20}{663.88} = .897$$

This value is positive, indicating that x and y are positively related. But does it yield any other information? The following important rule can be demonstrated: The square of the correlation coefficient, r^2, tells the percentage of the variance of the dependent variable that can be explained by the independent variable. Given a linear regression of y on x, r^2 tells the proportion of the variation in y that is accounted for by variations in x. This quantity is called the *coefficient of determination*.

If r equals $+1$ or -1, then $r^2 = 1$, and all the variation in y can be explained by the variation in x. This implies that the errors u in the regression equation are all equal to zero; there are no unexplained deviations. At the other extreme if r equals zero, then r^2 must equal zero, and none of the variation in y can be explained by the variation in x. All of the variation in y is due to the "unexplained" component u. We say there is no linear relation between x and y (though there may be a nonlinear one). In our example, we found $r = .897$; therefore $r^2 = .805$. We may conclude that about 80 per cent of the variation in y, in the sample, can be explained by the linear regression of y on x:

$$\hat{y} = -3.81 + .71x$$

The remaining 20 per cent of the total variation in y is unaccounted for: the errors in the prediction of y amount to 20 per cent.

2. Tests of Significance

Just as for other sample statistics, it is possible to test the statistical significance of r. Assuming a joint normal distribution of x and y, we compute

$$t = \frac{r\sqrt{n-2}}{\sqrt{1-r^2}}$$

which follows the t distribution with $n - 2$ degrees of freedom. Assume the hypothesis to be tested is that the population correlation coefficient R is equal to zero. If we reject this hypothesis, we say that r is significant. Choosing the 5 per cent level of significance, we compute the empirical t:

$$t = \frac{.897\sqrt{8}}{\sqrt{1-.805}} = \frac{.897(2.828)}{\sqrt{.195}} = \frac{2.537}{.442} = 5.74$$

Since Table C shows t may be as large as 2.306 for 8 degrees of freedom at the 5 per cent level of significance, we reject the hypothesis that the population correlation coefficient R is zero. We say r is significant at the 5 per cent level of significance. Two properties of this test may be noted. (1) The larger is r, the more likely is it to be significant for a given sample size. (2) The empirical t is approximately equal to the empirical t obtained when testing the significance of $\hat{b}$. As a matter of fact, they are only approximately equal because of rounding to two decimal places. It can easily be shown that, except for differences due to rounding, they have identical values. This should not be surprising, since we have already seen that the hypothesis that $b = 0$ implies the hypothesis that $R = 0$.

C. CURVILINEAR REGRESSION

Generally, theoretical considerations will enable one to judge whether a relationship between two variables should be positive or negative. For instance in economics, we expect a positive relation between total consumption and income. We expect a negative relation between the quantity demanded of a commodity and its price. Even if this is known from theoretical considerations, however, the theory does not permit one to tell if the relation is linear or not except in some special instances. The usual procedure is to take an over-all look at the sample data by constructing a scatter diagram. The general form of the scatter may suggest that a linear equation gives a close approximation to the observed points. But sometimes a nonlinear curve is suggested. Simple linear regression is easily extended to the case of nonlinear equations.

Suppose it is decided that the regression equation should be a parabola of the form

$$\hat{y} = \hat{a} + \hat{b}x + \hat{c}x^2$$

For a least-squares estimate, the normal equations are formed from the condition that the sum of the squares of $y - \hat{y}$ be a minimum. Since there are three constants to be determined, we have three normal equations:

$$\Sigma y = \hat{a}n + \hat{b}\Sigma x + \hat{c}\Sigma x^2$$
$$\Sigma xy = \hat{a}\Sigma x + \hat{b}\Sigma x^2 + \hat{c}\Sigma x^3$$
$$\Sigma x^2 y = \hat{a}\Sigma x^2 + \hat{b}\Sigma x^3 + \hat{c}\Sigma x^4$$

These equations are solved (by the methods of Chapter 4) to obtain the values of $\hat{a}$, $\hat{b}$, and $\hat{c}$.

Similarly, our equation might be a cubic of the form

$$\hat{y} = \hat{a} + \hat{b}x + \hat{c}x^2 + \hat{d}x^3$$

or even a polynomial of higher degree. In the case of a cubic regression equation, four normal equations would result from the minimization of errors. The methods used for the solution of the normal equations will become clear after reading Chapter 20 on multiple regression.

There are other types of nonlinear equations. Assume we wish to compute the constants of the equation

$$\hat{y} = \hat{a}x^b$$

by least squares. In this case, we wish to find the value of a power of x that is unknown. By taking logarithms to the base e of both sides of the equation, we obtain

$$\log_e \hat{y} = \log_e \hat{a} + \hat{b} \log_e x$$

Set $\log_e \hat{y} = \hat{z}$, $\log_e x = w$, and $\log_e \hat{a} = \hat{A}$ (a constant). Then we can rewrite the equation as

$$\hat{z} = \hat{A} + \hat{b}w$$

This is a linear equation, and a simple regression of z on w can be computed by the methods of Section A. The practical procedure is to to find $\log_e y$ and $\log_e x$ from published logarithmic tables for each observed value of y and x in the sample. Record these quantities as z and w, and then proceed as we did with x and y in Section A. The regression of z on w will yield least-squares values for $\hat{A}$ and $\hat{b}$. Now since $\hat{A} = \log_e \hat{a}$, then $\hat{a} = e^{\hat{A}}$, so $\hat{a}$ is known. Hence, we reconvert the regression equation into its original form:

$$\hat{y} = \hat{a}x^b$$

where $\hat{a}$ and $\hat{b}$ are now known.

Likewise, the exponential

$$\hat{y} = \hat{a}e^{bx}$$

can be converted into a linear equation. Again we take the logarithms of both sides of the equation and write

$$\log_e \hat{y} = \log_e \hat{a} + \hat{b}x$$

Set $\log_e \hat{y} = \hat{z}$ and $\log_e \hat{a} = A$, so we have the linear equation

$$\hat{z} = \hat{A} + \hat{b}x$$

where A and $\hat{b}$ can be computed by least squares from measurements on (z_1, x_1), (z_2, x_2), etc. When $\hat{A}$ and $\hat{b}$ are found, we find $\hat{a}$ from the relation

$$\hat{a} = e^{\hat{A}}$$

We then insert the known values of the constants into the original equation, getting

$$\hat{y} = \hat{a}e^{\hat{b}x}$$

Essentially, what is required is the conversion of curvilinear regression into linear regression by the definition of new variables. From the original variables of the nonlinear equation, new variables are defined that result in a linear equation. After the linear equation is computed, these definitions permit a reconversion into the original form. In nonlinear regression, the regression coefficients are least-squares estimates; like linear regression, under specified conditions they are estimates of the population parameters. Tests of significance, tests of hypotheses and confidence limits can be established in a manner like that described for linear regression.

Correlation has the same meaning as in the case of linear functions. When a curvilinear function is used to describe the relationship between two variables, the *index of correlation* is computed. It is obtained by relating the variance explained to the total variance, as before when linear regressions were used. Since the curve does not have the same slope at each point and since the slope can change signs at various points, no plus or minus sign can be attached to the index of correlation. It is always expressed as a positive number. But since it is a pure number like the coefficient of correlation, it can vary from zero to one. Except for the absence of sign, the index of correlation is interpreted like the coefficient of correlation, and it is used in statistical analysis in much the same way.

D. ECONOMIC APPLICATIONS

1. Estimation of Demand Parameters

Much econometric research has been devoted to fitting empirical demand and supply curves to sample data. The equilibrium price of a good and the quantity traded on the market are determined by the intersection of the demand and supply curves for the good. The equilibrium price and quantity are the observable price and quantity. At any one interval of time we can observe only the points on the demand and supply curves at which the intersection occurs.

Suppose we wish to estimate the demand curve for a commodity Q, and we have good reason to believe that the demand curve does not shift during the period being studied: its parameters do not change. Assume we also have good reason to believe that the supply curve for Q does shift. There are many agricultural commodities, for example, that are characterized by this situation. Then the supply curve shifting over the stable demand curve should result in a series of points, all of which lie on the demand curve. Theoretically, we can describe this by a diagram like that in Figure 19.4, where q represents the quantity of Q exchanged per unit of time and p denotes the price of Q. DD is the demand curve and S_1S_1, S_2S_2, S_3S_3 and S_4S_4 designate the supply curve in different positions as it shifts. The observable (equilibrium) prices and quantities are given by the intersection points (p_1, q_1), (p_2, q_2), etc.

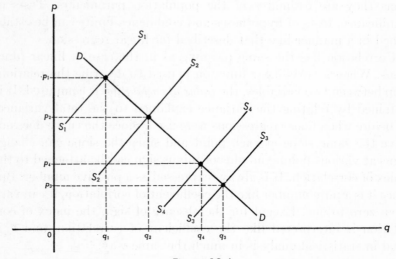

Figure 19.4

Now our data might consist of a time series, that is, a series giving equilibrium prices and quantities for many points in time. Suppose the price data chosen are annual average prices of Q, and the quantities are the total quantities of Q purchased per year. The sample, we assume, consists of 16 observations covering the period 1940 to 1955 inclusive. The observations are shown in columns (1) and (2) of Table 19–D. From this sample, we wish to estimate the parameters of the true (population) demand equation

$$q = f(p) \qquad \frac{dq}{dp} \leq 0$$

where q denotes the quantity of Q demanded per year and p designates the annual average price of Q.

Table 19–D

Year	(1) q Thousand of Units	(2) p Dollars per Unit	(3) p^2	(4) qp	(5) q^2
1940	10	8.00	64.00	80.00	100
1941	28	4.50	20.25	126.00	784
1942	34	3.80	14.44	129.20	1,156
1943	32	7.10	50.41	227.20	1,024
1944	18	6.00	36.00	108.00	324
1945	60	4.00	16.00	240.00	3,600
1946	60	2.00	4.00	120.00	3,600
1947	78	1.00	1.00	78.00	6,084
1948	87	2.30	5.29	200.10	7,569
1949	66	3.00	9.00	198.00	4,356
1950	48	7.00	49.00	336.00	2,304
1951	41	6.40	40.96	262.40	1,681
1952	44	2.50	6.25	110.00	1,936
1953	25	7.40	54.76	185.00	625
1954	53	6.80	46.24	360.40	2,809
1955	65	6.10	37.21	396.50	4,225
	$\Sigma q = 749$	$\Sigma p = 77.90$	$\Sigma p^2 = 454.81$	$\Sigma qp = 3,156.80$	$\Sigma q^2 = 42,177$

$$n = 16 \quad \bar{q} = \frac{\Sigma q}{n} = 46.81 \quad \bar{p} = \frac{\Sigma p}{n} = 4.87$$

The first step in the estimation procedure is to construct a scatter diagram from the sample observations. This is depicted in Figure 19.5. Imagine for the moment that the line is not shown in the diagram; we will discuss it later. We notice that the points do not lie exactly on a line, but the general form of the scatter suggests that a straight line will give the best fit to the distribution of the points. Hence, we assume the population demand equation is given as

$$q = a + bp$$

where a and b are the unknown population parameters. We shall estimate a and b by least squares from the regression equation

$$q = \hat{a} + \hat{b}p + u$$

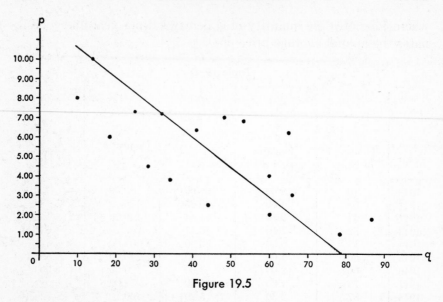

Figure 19.5

where the errors or deviations u are assumed to be random and independently distributed. We compute the regression of q on p. Columns (1) through (4) of Table 19–D provide the necessary data. Using the methods of Section A, we have

$$\hat{a} = \frac{(454.81)(749) - (77.90)(3,156.80)}{(16)(454.81) - (77.90)^2} = 78.39$$

$$\hat{b} = \frac{(16)(3,156.80) - (77.90)(749)}{(16)(454.81) - (77.90)^2} = -6.49$$

Our estimate of the true demand equation for the commodity Q is

$$q = 78.39 - 6.49p$$

The straight line corresponding to this equation is shown in Figure 19.5.

To test the significance of this regression coefficient, we compute

$$s_{\hat{b}} = \sqrt{\frac{(16)(42,177) - (749)^2 - \left\{ \dfrac{[(16)(3,156.80) - (77.90)(749)]^2}{(16)(454.81) - (77.90)^2} \right\}}{(16 - 2)\{(16)(454.81) - (77.90)^2\}}}$$

$$= \sqrt{\frac{113,788.8799}{16,919.70}} = \sqrt{6.7252} = 2.5933$$

From the formula given for t in Section A, we have

$$t = \frac{-6.49 - 0}{2.5933} = -2.5026$$

Recalling that there are 14 degrees of freedom, Table C tells us that we may expect a (positive or negative) value of t as large as 2.145 at the 5 per cent level of significance if the population coefficient b is in fact zero. Since our empirical t is larger than 2.145, we conclude that $\hat{b}$ is significant at the 5 per cent level of significance.

Note that for the one per cent level of significance, Table C gives the value of t as 2.977, so we know our regression coefficient is *not* significant at the one per cent level of significance. There is more than one chance in 100 that the difference $\hat{b} - b$, if b is in fact zero, could have arisen by chance.

We may also wish to know what proportion of the variation in q can be explained by the variation in p. For this purpose, we compute the coefficient of determination:

$$r^2 = \left[\frac{\Sigma qp - n\bar{q}\bar{p}}{\sqrt{(\Sigma p^2 - n\bar{p}^2)(\Sigma q^2 - n\bar{q}^2)}} \right]^2$$

$$= \frac{[\Sigma qp - n\bar{q}\bar{p}]^2}{(\Sigma p^2 - n\bar{p}^2)(\Sigma q^2 - n\bar{q}^2)}$$

$$= \frac{[3156.80 - (16)(4.87)(46.81)]^2}{[454.81 - (16)(4.87)^2][42{,}177 - (16)(46.81)^2]}$$

$$= .4489$$

Changes in the price of the commodity Q explain about 45 per cent of the changes in the quantity of Q exchanged on the market. The remainder of the variation in q is due to "errors." We have seen that these errors are assumed to result from errors of observation or errors of omission (such as income changes, changes in other prices, and changes in tastes).

Once the demand equation has been estimated, one can compute its characteristics. The price elasticity of demand for the commodity Q at the mean price and the mean quantity traded is

$$\frac{dq}{dp} \cdot \frac{\bar{p}}{\bar{q}} = (-6.49)\left(\frac{4.87}{46.81}\right) = -.68$$

We see that the demand for the commodity Q is relatively inelastic.

2. The Consumption Function: Lagged Regression

We have already seen that economic theory may postulate a *lagged* functional relationship between two economic variables. Study of institutions may lead one to expect that there are certain rigidities that cause changes in the dependent variable to lag in time behind changes in the independent variable. To take an example from income theory, it may be postulated that consumption in the current period depends upon income in the preceding period. That is, when income in the current period rises, consumption in the next period will rise. This can be expressed in functional notation as

$$c_t = f(y_{t-1}) \qquad \frac{dc_t}{dy_{t-1}} > 0$$

where c denotes total national consumption and y national income. The subscript t refers to time period t.

The period might be chosen as one month, so the sample data consist of observations on monthly consumption and monthly income expressed in appropriate units. For illustrative purposes assume the sample is that shown in Table 19–E (in practice it would normally consist of more observations). The left side shows the data for each month. But since the population functional relationship is assumed to be lagged, we must shift the series on income back one month. If we were to plot c_t against y_{t-1}, we would see that a linear relation is suggested, so we specify that the population equation is of the form

$$c_t = a + by_{t-1}$$

We can estimate the population parameters a and b by least squares under the usual assumptions from a regression of c_t on y_{t-1}:

$$c_t = \hat{a} + \hat{b}y_{t-1} + u$$

We proceed exactly as we did in Section A, where c_t replaces y and y_{t-1} replaces x.

Table 19–E

Month t	Consumption in t: c_t	Income in t: y_t	Month t	c_t	y_{t-1}
Jan.	70	120	Jan.	70	110
Feb.	85	160	Feb.	85	120
Mar.	93	180	Mar.	93	160
Apr.	110	135	Apr.	110	180
May	98	140	May	98	135

No additional difficulties are created for regression analysis by introducing lags in the theoretical equations. Tests of significance, tests of hypotheses, confidence limits, and correlation coefficients can be established in the usual manner. The computation of the regression constants, the correlation coefficient and the test of significance for the sample shown in Table 19–E is left to the reader as an exercise.

3. Liquidity Preference: Curvilinear Regression

The liquidity preference theory of the interest rate states that for a given level of income the demand for money to hold as cash balances is a decreasing function of the rate of interest. Symbolically

$$m = l(i) \qquad \frac{dm}{di} < 0$$

may denote the quantity of money demanded, m, as a decreasing function, l, of the rate of interest, i.

Assume the sample data are those given in columns (1) and (2) of Table 19–F, where m designates the stock of money and i is defined

Table 19–F

Year	(1) m	(2) i	(3) z	(4) $u = m - \hat{m}$
1	130	.07	14.29	17.25
2	125	.05	20.00	6.14
3	115	.03	33.33	−18.12
4	170	.02	50.00	19.04
5	185	.01	100.00	−19.46
6	145	.03	33.33	11.88
7	130	.02	50.00	−20.96
8	110	.05	20.00	−8.86
9	135	.06	16.67	19.70
10	105	.07	14.29	−7.75
11	120	.06	16.67	4.70
12	133	.04	25.00	8.79
13	100	.06	16.67	−15.30
14	110	.04	25.00	−14.21
15	140	.02	50.00	−10.96
16	230	.01	100.00	25.54

as the annual average rate of interest. The scatter diagram is shown in Figure 19.6 (according to economic convention the dependent variable m is measured on the horizontal axis). Theoretical considerations may indicate that the demand is stable, and changes in the quantity demanded are due to changes in the money supply. Note that the scatter does not assume the form of a straight line. Some familiarity with equations and their graphs indicates that an equation of the form

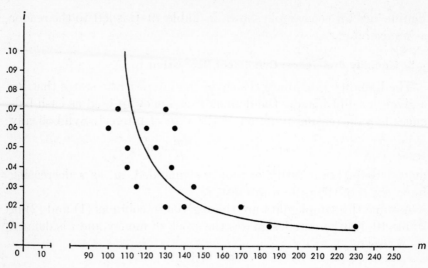

Figure 19.6

$$m = a + \frac{b}{i}$$

gives a rather close approximation to the scatter diagram. For the purposes of regression analysis, we can define a variable $z = 1/i$ and compute the regression of m on z from the equation

$$m = \hat{a} + \hat{b}z + u$$

This is a linear equation in which $\hat{a}$ and $\hat{b}$ enter linearly, so $\hat{a}$ and $\hat{b}$ will yield unbiased least-squares estimates of a and b. The values of z for given values of i are shown in column (3) of Table 19–F. For the least-squares computation of $\hat{a}$ and $\hat{b}$, we have the following quantities:

$$n = 16 \qquad\qquad \Sigma z^2 = 33,013.85$$
$$\Sigma z = 585.25 \qquad\qquad \Sigma zm = 92,216.80$$
$$\Sigma m = 2,183 \qquad\qquad \Sigma m^2 = 314,839$$

Substituting in the formulas for $\hat{a}$ and $\hat{b}$, we obtain

$$\hat{a} = \frac{(33,013.85)(2,183) - (585.25)(92,216.80)}{(16)(33,013.85) - (585.25)^2} = 97.46$$

$$\hat{b} = \frac{(16)(92,216.80) - (585.25)(2,183)}{(16)(33,013.85) - (585.25)^2} = 1.07$$

Reconverting the regression equation into the nonlinear form:

$$\hat{m} = 97.46 + 1.07z = 97.46 + \frac{1.07}{i}$$

This is our estimate of the "true" liquidity preference function. It is a worthwhile exercise to find the values of $\hat{m}$ for given values of i and to fit the resulting curve to the scatter diagram. The errors committed in the prediction of m from $\hat{m}$ are shown in column (4) of Table 19-F.

These examples serve to illustrate how the method of least squares can be used to estimate the parameters of structural equations that comprise econometric models. When only two variables are assumed to be related in the population, simple regression can under suitable conditions yield the desired estimates. Which of the two variables is to be designated as the independent variable and which as the dependent variable cannot be decided on the basis of statistics. This decision requires knowledge of economic theory. A variety of applications are possible. If the independent variable is chosen as time, then one attempts to estimate trends or cycles like those discussed in Chapter 3. Even if a trend is nonlinear, it may be possible to approximate a segment of the trend curve by a simple linear regression. The results achieved by regression analysis depend partly upon the ingenuity with which these statistical procedures are applied.

PROBLEMS

1. The following sample of observations on the price and quantity exchanges of a commodity X is given.

Price of X	Quantity of X
10	110
8	98
20	75
16	100
24	80
30	58
36	54
40	40
35	55
25	60
28	55
30	65
35	80
40	30
45	40
40	40

(a) Construct a scatter diagram from the observations and establish the form of the population demand equation for X.

(b) Estimate the parameters of the demand equation by least squares.

(c) Compute the coefficient of determination. How do you interpret it?

(d) Is the regression coefficient statistically significant at the 5 per cent level of significance? How do you interpret this?

(e) Compute the price elasticity of the demand for X at the mean values of price and quantity traded.

2. The following sample of observations on the price and quantity exchanged of a commodity Y is given.

Price of Y	Quantity of Y
15	44
20	60
25	4
20	110
40	45
35	85
60	52
50	50
45	45
60	140
70	100
40	125
80	90

(a) Construct a scatter diagram from the observations and establish the form of the population supply equation for Y.

(b) Estimate the parameters of the supply equation by least squares.

(c) Test the statistical significance of the regression coefficient at the 1 per cent level of significance and at the 5 per cent level of significance.

3. The following observations on the total money supply for the economy as a whole and the general price level are given.

Year	Money Supply	General Price Level
1920	200	100
1921	212	104
1922	220	104
1923	228	110
1924	240	107
1925	245	125
1926	260	120
1927	270	132
1928	280	125

Compute the correlation coefficient. Is it significant at the 5 per cent level of significance? How do you interpret this?

4. The total net investment function for the economy as a whole is assumed to be of the form

$$I = ai^b$$

where I denotes net investment, i denotes the interest rate and a and b are the unknown parameters of the investment function. The following sample is given.

I (Billion Dollars)	i (Per Cent)
9.0	2
5.5	3
8.5	2
4.0	4
3.5	5
2.5	6
3.0	4
1.5	6
1.2	8
1.8	7
1.5	9

(a) Construct a scatter diagram.

(b) Estimate the parameters of the investment function by least squares.

(c) Test the statistical significance of the regression coefficient at the 1 per cent level of significance and at the 5 per cent level of significance.

(d) Establish the confidence limits of the regression coefficient for a 95 per cent confidence coefficient.

5. Assume the following observations on Gross National Product are given.

Year	GNP	Year	GNP	Year	GNP
1937	115	1944	127	1951	130
1938	108	1945	120	1952	140
1939	90	1946	125	1953	133
1940	112	1947	122	1954	143
1941	125	1948	120	1955	155
1942	130	1949	128	1956	145
1943	132	1950	138	1957	140

(a) Plot GNP over time.

(b) With 1936 as the origin ($t = 0$ in 1936), estimate the trend equation for GNP by least squares.

(c) What percentage of the total variation in GNP is explained by the trend?

6. Assume it is given from theoretical considerations that the total amount of inventories of a commodity X held in stock is an increasing linear function of the rate of change of the price of X. In symbolic notation

$$y_t = a + b(p_t - p_{t-1})$$

where y_t denotes inventories in month t and p_t is the price in month t. The following sample of observations is given.

Month t	y_t	p_t	Month t	y_t	p_t	Month t	y_t	p_t
0	15	10	5	40	5	10	60	19
1	20	9	6	50	7	11	55	21
2	15	6	7	45	9	12	40	21
3	25	4	8	55	13	13	35	20
4	30	4	9	50	16	14	25	19

(a) Estimate the parameters of the inventory function by least squares.

(b) What percentage of the total variation in inventories is explained by the price spread?

(c) Test the significance of the regression coefficient at the 5 per cent level of significance.

(d) Find the confidence limits of the regression coefficient for a confidence coefficient of 95 per cent.

CHAPTER 20

Multiple Regression and Correlation

In Part I, the mathematical formulation of economic theory was discussed in some detail. We saw that one variable may be expressed as a function of two or more other variables. For instance, the quantity demanded of a commodity may be expressed as a function of the price of the commodity, consumer income, other prices, etc. The methods of simple regression apply only to explicit functions of one variable—to cases in which the dependent variable is related to one independent variable only. When we relate the quantity demanded to the price of the commodity only in our empirical calculations, we thereby assume that the sum of influences exerted by other variables is relatively small and approximately random in its effect upon the quantity demanded. We then summarize the sum of these influences in a random variable or "error" (which we have been designating by u). But suppose that this is not the case; suppose there is a systematic relation found between the quantity demanded and the residuals u. Then we may seek additional systematic variables that ought to be explicitly included in the regression equation. This is what multiple regression analysis accomplishes. Instead of relating a dependent variable y to another variable x, we relate y to x and z— perhaps to x, z, and w or more variables.

The method of multiple regression is an extension of simple regression to the case of two or more explanatory variables or predictors. One attempts to predict the value of an "explained" variable y from known values of two or more explanatory variables, say x and z, rather than from knowledge of the value of x alone. Suppose one formulates the population equation as

$$y = a + bx + cz$$

where a, b, and c are the population parameters. Then from the multiple regression

$$\hat{y} = \hat{a} + \hat{b}x + \hat{c}z$$

one obtains least-squares estimates of y. As in the case of simple regression, the computed values of the constants $\hat{a}$, $\hat{b}$, and $\hat{c}$ give the best unbiased linear estimates of y. These computed values are also the best unbiased linear estimates of the population parameters a, b, and c if y only is a random variable (subject to errors) but not x and z, or if the errors in the regression equation are due to errors of omission.

A. MULTIPLE LINEAR REGRESSION: FUNCTIONS OF TWO VARIABLES

Let us assume it is decided that the population equation relates y to x and z. Furthermore, we assume the true or population function is linear, so we write

$$y = a + bx + cz$$

where a, b, and c are again the unknown population parameters. We are given a sample of n observations, each of which consists of a value of y, a value of x, and a value of z: (y_1, x_1, z_1), (y_2, x_2, z_2), . . . , (y_n, x_n, z_n). We set up the same multiple regression equation

$$y = \hat{a} + \hat{b}x + \hat{c}z + u$$

where $u = y - \hat{y}$ is assumed to be random with zero mean. The method of least squares is employed; we minimize the sum of squares of the errors u. Just as for simple regression, the minimization operation yields normal equations that may be solved for the values of the sample constants.

Since we are dealing with a linear function of two variables (x and z), there are three constants and consequently three normal equations:

$$\Sigma y = \hat{a}n + \hat{b}\Sigma x + \hat{c}\Sigma z$$
$$\Sigma xy = \hat{a}\Sigma x + \hat{b}\Sigma x^2 + \hat{c}\Sigma xz$$
$$\Sigma zy = \hat{a}\Sigma z + \hat{b}\Sigma xz + \hat{c}\Sigma z^2$$

The normal equations are obtained from the condition that the sum of squares of the errors be a minimum, following the procedure shown in footnote 1, Chapter 19. All quantities in these three equations except $\hat{a}$, $\hat{b}$, and $\hat{c}$ can be computed from the sample data.[1]

---

[1] Note the similarity of these normal equations to those given for a parabola in Section C of Chapter 19. In particular, if x^2 in the equation for the parabola is set equal to a new variable z, the normal equations are identical.

Once the sums and products have been computed, the three equations can be solved for the values of $\hat{a}$, $\hat{b}$, and $\hat{c}$.

To be more concrete, let us consider a specific example. From theoretical considerations, suppose it is decided that the population function relates a dependent variable y to two independent variables x and z. It is further decided that the population equation is linear. The sample data, we suppose, are given in columns (1), (2), and (3) of Table 20–A. Columns (4) through (8) are computed for the pur-

Table 20–A

(1)	(2)	(3)	(4)	(5)	(6)	(7)	(8)
y	x	z	xy	zy	xz	x^2	z^2
4	2	5	8	20	10	4	25
9	1	2	9	18	2	1	4
12	5	1	60	12	5	25	1
16	8	1	128	16	8	64	1
10	14	3	140	30	42	196	9
5	7	4	35	20	28	49	16
18	16	2	288	36	32	256	4
14	20	2	280	28	40	400	4
12	12	3	144	36	36	144	9
10	19	4	190	40	76	361	16
Σy $= 110$	Σx $= 104$	$\Sigma z = 27$	Σxy $= 1{,}282$	Σzy $= 256$	Σxz $= 279$	Σx^2 $= 1{,}500$	$\Sigma z^2 = 89$
$\bar{y} = \dfrac{110}{10}$ $= 11.0$	$\bar{x} = \dfrac{104}{10}$ $= 10.4$	$\bar{z} = \dfrac{27}{10}$ $= 2.7$					

pose of solving the normal equations. We form the regression equation

$$y = \hat{a} + \hat{b}x + \hat{c}z + u$$

Minimization of the sum of squares of u gives the following normal equations:

$$110 = 10\hat{a} + 104\hat{b} + 27\hat{c}$$
$$1{,}282 = 104\hat{a} + 1{,}500\hat{b} + 279\hat{c}$$
$$256 = 27\hat{a} + 279\hat{b} + 89\hat{c}$$

Solving these equations by the methods of Chapter 4, we obtain

$$\hat{a} = 14.466$$
$$\hat{b} = .319$$
$$\hat{c} = -2.511$$

Our multiple regression equation is, therefore,

$$\hat{y} = 14.466 + .319x - 2.511z$$

where

$$y - \hat{y} = u$$

1. Geometric Interpretation

In Section D of Chapter 2, it was shown that to every equation there corresponds a geometric counterpart, and that an equation in three variables corresponds to a three-dimensional surface. The purpose of the regression of y on x and z was to compute the values of the constants in the linear equation. Once these values are determined, a plane in three-dimensional space is also determined. If y, x, and z are measured on three mutually perpendicular axes, a graph of the plane can be constructed. For a given value of x and a given value of z, a value of y is determined from the regression equation. These three values locate a point in the three-dimensional space. For all possible pairs of values for x and z, all possible values of y are determined—and these form a plane in the space.

The geometric interpretation of the least squares estimates of the constants is the same as that for simple regression. In problems of simple regression, each observation fixes a point in two-dimensional space, and the total of all observations forms a scatter diagram. The regression equation is such that the curve corresponding to it minimizes the sum of the squared values of the deviations of the points from the curve. Likewise, when the sample consists of observations on three variables, each observation fixes a point in three-dimensional space and the set of all observations forms a scatter diagram in this space. The multiple regression equation is such that the sum of the squared deviations of the observed points from the plane is a minimum.

When the multiple regression involves functions of more than two variables (see Section D of this chapter), one cannot present a diagram of the geometric interpretation. One can, however, conceive of (rather than visualize) a space consisting of four or more dimensions. Then each observation of the value of n variables may be regarded as a point in n-dimensional space. The conceptual geometric interpretation of equations involving more than three variables was discussed in Chapter 2 and need not be repeated in detail here.

2. Significance Tests

The t test can be used to test the statistical significance of the multiple regression coefficients $\hat{b}$ and $\hat{c}$. It can also be used to test the hypothesis that the coefficients are equal to some values specified beforehand. The general principles are basically the same as those applicable to problems of simple regression. The computation of the standard errors of the regression coefficients is, however, much more complicated. A sufficient discussion is beyond the scope of this book and will not be given here.[2]

B. MULTIPLE CORRELATION

We have already seen that the *simple correlation coefficient* measures the degree of variation in the dependent or explained variable, which is associated with variation in the independent or explanatory variable, relative to the total variation in the dependent variable. The *multiple correlation coefficient*, often denoted by R, is defined in a similar way. It measures the degree of variation in the explained variable that is associated with two or more explanatory variables, relative to the total variation in the explained variable. The only conceptual difference is that the "explained" part of the variation in the explained variable is now attributed to two or more other variables rather than to one other variable.

More specifically, the value of the multiple coefficient of determination, R^2, measures the percentage of the variance in the explained variable that is accounted for by the variance of all explanatory variables in the regression equation taken in combination. That is, if the regression equation relates a variable y to two explanatory variables, x and z, then R^2 measures the percentage of the total variance in y that is explained by both x and z. The quantity $1 - R^2$ measures the percentage of the total variance of y that cannot be explained by x and z.

We can compute the multiple correlation coefficient from the following formula:

$$R = \sqrt{\frac{\Sigma(\hat{y} - \bar{\hat{y}})^2}{\Sigma(y - \bar{y})^2}}$$

where $\hat{y}$ is a predicted value of the explained variable obtained from the regression equation and $\bar{\hat{y}}$ is the mean of all these predicted

[2] The interested student may consult G. Tintner, *Econometrics* (New York: John Wiley & Sons, Inc., 1952), pp. 83–92

values in the sample. Likewise, y denotes an observed value of the explained variable and $\bar{y}$ is the mean of all those observed values in the sample. The value of R (like the index of correlation in simple nonlinear regression) is nonnegative and varies between zero and one.

For the sample data given in Table 20–A, we shall compute the quantities in the formula; they are shown in Table 20-B. The mul-

Table 20–B

y	$\bar{y}$	$(y - \bar{y})^2$	$\hat{y} = 14.466 \\ + .319x - 2.511z$	$\bar{\hat{y}}$	$(\hat{y} - \bar{\hat{y}})^2$	
4	11	$(-7)^2 = 49$	2.55	11	$(-8.45)^2 =$	71.40
9	11	$(-2)^2 = 4$	9.76	11	$(-1.24)^2 =$	1.54
12	11	$(1)^2 = 1$	13.55	11	$(2.55)^2 =$	6.50
16	11	$(5)^2 = 25$	14.51	11	$(3.51)^2 =$	12.32
10	11	$(-1)^2 = 1$	11.40	11	$(.40)^2 =$	.16
5	11	$(-6)^2 = 36$	6.65	11	$(-4.35)^2 =$	18.92
18	11	$(7)^2 = 49$	14.55	11	$(3.55)^2 =$	12.60
14	11	$(3)^2 = 9$	15.82	11	$(4.82)^2 =$	23.23
12	11	$(1)^2 = 1$	10.76	11	$(-.24)^2 =$	.06
10	11	$(-1)^2 = 1$	10.48	11	$(-.52)^2 =$	.27
		$\Sigma(y - \bar{y})^2 = 176$			$\Sigma(\hat{y} - \bar{\hat{y}})^2 = 147.00$	

tiple correlation coefficient is

$$R = \sqrt{\frac{147.00}{176.00}} = \sqrt{.8352} = .914$$

Since $R^2 = .8352$, we say that approximately 84 per cent of the variation in y can be explained by variations in both x and z. The remaining 16 per cent of the variation in y is not explained by the multiple regression equation.

C. ECONOMIC APPLICATIONS

1. The Demand Function

Our illustrative demand function for simple linear regression related the quantity demanded of a commodity to the price of that commodity only. If the population demand function is linear and the parameters of this demand equation are indeed approximately constant, the simple linear regression will give a good fit to the true demand curve.

Suppose, however, that we find the fit unsatisfactory; the errors are too large and the regression equation is not significant. Perhaps the reason may be found in the fact that consumer income changed significantly during the period covered by the sample. We may then wish to introduce income explicitly in the demand equation. Hence, assuming it is linear, our hypothetical population demand equation would be written as

$$q = a + bp + cy$$

where q represents the quantity of the commodity demanded per unit of time, p its price, and y the level of consumer income per unit of time (all expressed in appropriate units).

The sample consists of triplets of measurements; each observation in the sample includes a measurement of the quantity demand, the price, and income. For n sample observations, we have (q_1, p_1, y_1), (q_2, p_2, y_2), . . . , (q_n, p_n, y_n). We construct the regression equation

$$q = \hat{a} + \hat{b}p + \hat{c}y + u$$

where u is assumed to be random. Now, subject to the assumptions stated in Chapter 19 and Section A of this chapter, we wish to estimate the population parameters a, b, and c from the regression constants $\hat{a}$, $\hat{b}$, and $\hat{c}$. For convenience, let us suppose that the sample data yield the following sums and products:

$$
\begin{array}{ll}
n = 10 & \Sigma p^2 = 120 \\
\Sigma q = 550 & \Sigma py = 1{,}300 \\
\Sigma p = 30 & \Sigma qy = 33{,}800 \\
\Sigma y = 500 & \Sigma y^2 = 31{,}800 \\
\Sigma qp = 1{,}300 &
\end{array}
$$

Applying the principle of least squares, we obtain three normal equations. Substituting the computed sums and products into the normal equations, with the appropriate changes in notation used to designate the variables, we have

$$550 = 10\hat{a} + 30\hat{b} + 500\hat{c}$$
$$1{,}300 = 30\hat{a} + 120\hat{b} + 1{,}300\hat{c}$$
$$33{,}800 = 500\hat{a} + 1{,}300\hat{b} + 31{,}800\hat{c}$$

Solving these equations, we find

$$
\begin{array}{rl}
\hat{a} = & 39.207 \\
\hat{b} = & -6.829 \\
\hat{c} = & .726
\end{array}
$$

Our regression demand equation is

$$q = 39.207 - 6.829p + .726y + u$$

Note that the negative coefficient of p indicates a negative relationship between the quantity demanded and price (as economic theory leads us to expect). The positive coefficient of y indicates a positive relationship of the quantity demanded to income. As income increases, the quantity demanded increases. In the language of economic theory, this is a superior good.

Given the values of the coefficients, the net effect of a change in price and a change in income may be a positive or a negative change in the quantity demanded, depending upon the directions and amounts of the changes in price and income. Furthermore, we can compute from the sample data the multiple coefficient of determination, R^2. This statistic tells us the per cent of the variation in quantity traded that can be explained by variations in *both* price and income.

If the multiple regression equation is found to be statistically significant, we can with confidence make further statements about the properties of the demand for this commodity. We may, for example, wish to know the price elasticity of demand for the commodity. The formula for the price elasticity of demand is

$$e_p = \frac{\partial q}{\partial p} \cdot \frac{p}{q}$$

For our regression equation, we see

$$\frac{\partial q}{\partial p} = -6.829$$

We must next choose the point at which we shall measure the elasticity. A common practice is to choose the mean values of price and quantity. From our sample data:

$$\bar{p} = \frac{\Sigma p}{n} = \frac{30}{10} = 3 \qquad \bar{q} = \frac{\Sigma q}{n} = \frac{550}{10} = 55$$

The price elasticity of demand at the mean values of price and quantity is

$$e_p = (-6.829)\left(\frac{3}{55}\right) = -\frac{20.487}{55.000} = -.37$$

Since this is less than one in absolute value (greater than minus one), we say the demand for this commodity is relatively inelastic with respect to price for a given (constant) level of income. This statement about elasticity is, however, a statement about the population inferred from the sample data, and we have seen that such statements cannot be made with certainty. Since our estimate of the demand parameters is only probable, our statement about the price elasticity of demand is likewise probable. The probability of the correctness of our elasticity statement is no greater than the probability of the correctness of our estimates of the demand parameters.

Similarly, we may wish to compute the income elasticity of demand from the regression equation. At the mean values of quantity traded and income, we find

$$e_y = \frac{\partial q}{\partial y} \cdot \frac{\bar{y}}{\bar{q}} = (.726)\left(\frac{50}{55}\right) = .66$$

For a given percentage change in income, the quantity demanded will change by a percentage that is approximately .66 as large as the percentage change in income, assuming the price is constant. Naturally, this statement, like the price elasticity statement, is made with a specified degree of probability of being correct.

2. The Consumption Function

When discussing national income theory, it is often stated that aggregate consumption is a function of income. But again this theoretical proposition may not be entirely supported by empirical investigation—a simple regression of consumption on income may not adequately explain variations in consumption. We may then seek to find the other systematic variables that determine aggregate consumption. Let us suppose that consumption is to be related to the income of households lagged one period and the current liquid asset position of households. If this relationship is assumed to be linear in both explanatory variables, we write

$$C_t = a + bY_{t-1} + cA_t$$

for the population consumption function, where C_t denotes total national consumption in period t, Y_{t-1} denotes national income in period $t - 1$, and A_t denotes total national liquid assets of households. Each observation in the sample will consist of a measurement on each of these three variables; the constants of the multiple regression equation

$$C_t = \hat{a} + \hat{b}Y_{t-1} + \hat{c}A_t + u$$

can be computed from the sample data by the methods of Section A. The sample constants are estimates of the population parameters under the usual assumptions with respect to the errors u, and significance tests can be executed to judge the statistical reliability of the estimates.

The reader can no doubt think of several other applications of multiple regression analysis to economic problems. Production functions are typically expressed in terms of output as a function of two or more factor inputs. Liquidity preference can be written as a function of the interest rate and income. Regional labor mobility may be expressed as a function of regional income differentials and variables that describe the expected relative industrial growth of regions. Investment decisions can be expressed as dependent upon the current interest rate and the asset position of firms, and so on. In all such theoretical formulations, multiple regression analysis is useful as a technique for estimating population parameters and conducting tests of hypotheses.

D. FUNCTIONS OF MORE THAN TWO VARIABLES AND NONLINEAR MULTIPLE REGRESSION

Sometimes one finds it necessary to relate a dependent variable y to three (or more) variables x, z, and w. The linear population equation is then written

$$y = a + bx + cz + dw$$

where a, b, c, and d are the unknown population parameters. The sample multiple regression equation is written

$$y = \hat{a} + \hat{b}x + \hat{c}z + \hat{d}w + u$$

and the constants are computed by minimizing the sum of the squares of u. Just as in the case of functions of two variables, this minimization operation yields the normal equations that are solved for the least-squares values of the constants. For the above function of three variables, the normal equations are

$$\Sigma y = \hat{a}n + \hat{b}\Sigma x + \hat{c}\Sigma z + \hat{d}\Sigma w$$
$$\Sigma xy = \hat{a}\Sigma x + \hat{b}\Sigma x^2 + \hat{c}\Sigma xz + \hat{d}\Sigma xw$$
$$\Sigma zy = \hat{a}\Sigma z + \hat{b}\Sigma zx + \hat{c}\Sigma z^2 + \hat{d}\Sigma zw$$
$$\Sigma wy = \hat{a}\Sigma w + \hat{b}\Sigma wx + \hat{c}\Sigma wz + \hat{d}\Sigma w^2$$

Again, all quantities in the equations except $\hat{a}$, $\hat{b}$, $\hat{c}$, and $\hat{d}$ can be computed from the sample data, so the four equations can be solved for the values of the four unknowns. Standard errors of the regression coefficients can be computed and tests of significance conducted. The multiple correlation coefficient is computed in the same way as that shown for the case of functions of two variables.

In general for a function of k variables, the same principles apply. Let the general multiple regression equation be written as

$$y = \hat{a} + \hat{b}_1 x_1 + \hat{b}_2 x_2 + \cdots + \hat{b}_k x_k + u$$

where the subscripts on the right side of the equation designate
different explanatory variables and their corresponding coefficients.
Minimization of the sum of squares of u yields the normal equations:

$$\Sigma y = \hat{a}n + \hat{b}_1\Sigma x_1 + \hat{b}_2\Sigma x_2 + \cdots + \hat{b}_k\Sigma x_k$$
$$\Sigma x_1 y = \hat{a}\Sigma x_1 + \hat{b}_1\Sigma x_1{}^2 + \hat{b}_2\Sigma x_1 x_2 + \cdots + \hat{b}_k\Sigma x_1 x_k$$
$$\vdots \qquad \vdots \qquad \vdots \qquad \vdots \qquad \vdots$$
$$\Sigma x_k y = \hat{a}\Sigma x_k + \hat{b}_1\Sigma x_k x_1 + \hat{b}_2\Sigma x_k x_2 + \cdots + \hat{b}_k\Sigma x_k{}^2$$

There are $k + 1$ unknowns $(\hat{a}, \hat{b}_1, \hat{b}_2, \ldots, \hat{b}_k)$ and $k + 1$ normal
equations that can be solved for the values of the unknowns. It is
seen, therefore, that multiple linear regression is essentially an
extension of the case of simple linear regression.

Likewise, curvilinear multiple regression consists of an extension
of the methods of simple curvilinear regression to cases involving
two or more explanatory variables. Suppose theoretical considerations together with a preliminary examination of the data suggest
the sample regression equation is to be of the form

$$\hat{y} = \hat{a}x^{\hat{b}}z^{\hat{c}}$$

where again $\hat{a}$, $\hat{b}$, and $\hat{c}$ are the sample constants. For the least
squares computation of the constants, we can take the natural
logarithms of both sides of this equation; thus

$$\log_e \hat{y} = \log_e \hat{a} + \hat{b} \log_e x + \hat{c} \log_e z$$

We define the following new variables and the constant $\hat{A}$:

$$\hat{Y} = \log_e \hat{y}$$
$$\hat{A} = \log_e \hat{a}$$
$$X = \log_e x$$
$$Z = \log_e z$$

Then we can rewrite the regression equation as

$$\hat{Y} = \hat{A} + \hat{b}X + \hat{c}Z$$

which is linear in all the variables, so we have reduced the problem
to one of multiple linear regression. For each sample observation on
y, x, and z, the values of Y, X, and Z are found from published tables
of logarithms. These values of Y, X, and Z are those that are to be
used to compute $\hat{A}$, $\hat{b}$, and $\hat{c}$ by means of least squares in the same
manner as that followed in Section A. Once these constants are
computed from the normal equations, $\hat{a}$ can be found from the
definition

$$\hat{A} = \log_e \hat{a} \qquad \text{or} \qquad \hat{a} = e^{\hat{A}}$$

since the least squares value of $\hat{A}$ is known. The three constants can then be substituted into the original form of the regression equation.

Similar transformations can be made for other types of nonlinear equations. The procedural rules outlined for simple curvilinear regression are simply extended to include additional explanatory variables.

E. MULTICOLLINEARITY

Simple and multiple regression and correlation methods are used (1) to find which variables are significantly related one to another and (2) to find what type of relation (linear, quadratic, logarithmic, etc.) exists among the variables. Between two defined variables a linear relationship may emerge, but sometimes a nonlinear relationship yields a closer prediction of the dependent or explained variable and a more reliable estimate of the population parameters. The same is true in problems involving three or more variables. The methods of regression and correlation analysis aid the economist in deciding which variables are significantly related and what type of relation exists among them, that is, which type of relation gives the best "fit" (if any fit at all is significant).

In multiple regression problems, very often one wishes to know the separate influences that each of two or more explanatory variables exerts upon the explained variable. For example, if the regression equation is given by

$$\hat{y} = \hat{a} + \hat{b}x + \hat{c}z$$

then once the constants are computed, one can predict the direction and amount of change in y in response to given changes in both x and z combined. Any change in y is the result of changes in both explanatory variables. But what effect will a change in x have upon y if z does not change? And what is the relation between y and z when x is held constant? To answer these questions the methods of partial regression and correlation have been developed. The so-called partial regression coefficient of y on x measures the relationship between these two variables when z is conceptually held constant, and the partial regression coefficient of y on z measures the relationship between these two when x is held constant. It can be shown that the partial regression coefficient is the corresponding coefficient in the multiple regression equation; $\hat{b}$ can be referred to as the partial regression coefficient of y on x and $\hat{c}$ as the partial coefficient of y on

z. Similarly, partial correlation coefficients can be computed in order to determine the correlation between the dependent variable and each one of the several independent variables, while eliminating any (linear) tendency of the remaining independent variables to obscure the correlation. The coefficient of partial correlation is a measure of the extent to which that part of the variation in the dependent variable that is not explained by the other independent variables can be explained by the independent variable in question.

In multiple regression problems there is a particularly bothersome problem that may arise, especially in economics. It is very often the case with economic data that a relationship exists among the explanatory variables themselves. For the above linear multiple regression equation, it may be found that a correlation exists between x and z. When such a linear relation exists among two or more of the explanatory variables, it is not possible to measure their separate influences upon the explained variable. Though the regression equation remains valid for prediction of y from both x and z together, the effect of a change in x (or z) upon y when z (or x) is conceptually held constant cannot be determined. One can see intuitively why this is so. If perfect positive correlation exists between any two explanatory variables in a regression equation, then either of these two correlated variables could be used in place of the other. Since they always change in the same direction, there is no reason to use both of them in the regression equation. It is true that we almost never find perfect correlation between two or more explanatory variables, but we often find a high degree of correlation. In such an event, it may not be possible to find the values of the individual regression coefficients with sufficient accuracy.

Such a linear relation among two or more explanatory variables has been called *multicollinearity* by R. Frisch. When collinearity exists, the standard errors of the estimated population parameters are very large. Hence, the applicability of the probable-error method is called into question. Frisch has developed a visual or geometric technique (called bunch maps) for judging whether multicollinearity exists in a regression equation. This test has the weakness that it depends heavily upon the personal judgment of the statistician in interpreting the results. Another method has been developed by G. Tintner that is not graphical but is appropriate only if there are errors of observation and their relative magnitudes are known. Hence, the test must be considered as a rough approximation to a measure of collinearity. Other tests have been worked out also, but even the very sophisticated ones have not completely solved the problem. Multicollinearity is an inherent characteristic of much economic data about which little can be done at the present time with the given tools of statistical analysis. One can only try to select meaningful explanatory variables that show little correlation among themselves if we wish to know their separate effects upon the variable to be predicted. But this is not always possible. In any event, one must be cautious in the interpretation of the results of multiple regression analysis if these results are not to be misleading.

F. CONCLUSION

By applying the methods of multiple regression and correlation, we are enabled to quantify and measure the relationships among economic variables. The regression equations may be static or dynamic in nature; they may involve difference equations or differential equations, or be in any form appropriate to the model. The choice of explanatory variables is dictated by theoretical considerations—they are initially determined when the model is first constructed. The type of relationship that is to be used depends at least partly upon the sample data. Even when the relationship is obviously not strictly linear, in many cases, however, a linear equation gives a sufficiently close approximation to the "true" relationship among the variables.

If we regard the errors in regression equations as errors of omission, we may improve a simple regression by the inclusion of additional explanatory variables. How many additional variables will be included depends upon the degree of improvement in the prediction of the explained variable that results. An equation using x and z to predict y may be better than one using x alone, but an equation using x, z, and w may show no significant improvement over the one using x and z. To determine whether an improvement occurs from the addition of z as a second explanatory variable, one must test whether the variance in y associated with the addition of the regression on z is greater or less than that associated with the residual (unexplained variance in y). If it is greater than the residual, the addition of z in the regression equation enhances our ability to predict y.

One might be tempted to infer that all we need for perfect prediction of y is enough explanatory variables; at some point the unexplained residual would be zero. It may be possible to do this. However, it would require such a sacrifice of degrees of freedom that the resulting regression equation would be meaningless for significance tests and other statistical analyses. In any practical situation, there will always be some residual variance of y—some unexplained portion of its total variation. If the many (perhaps systematic) factors that cause these errors are individually small and independent of each other, their sum will behave as if it were random. We may then conclude that all of the important systematic determinants of the explained variable have been included in the regression equation. Though, in dealing with social phenomena, we cannot account for all determining variables separately, we can very often specify the quantitatively important ones. If the sum of the remaining variables behaves approximately as if it is random in its effect on the variable to be explained and if it is normally distributed, we may employ the usual probability theory and analytical statistics to make estimates of the population parameters and to conduct tests of hypotheses.

PROBLEMS

1. The quantity supplied of a commodity X is assumed to be a linear function of the price of X and the wage rate of labor used in the production of X. The population supply equation is given as

$$x = a + bp_x + cw$$

where x denotes the quantity exchanged on the market, p_x denotes the price of X, w denotes the wage rate, and a, b, and c are the unknown supply parameters. The sample data are given in the following table.

x	p_x	w
20	10	12
35	15	10
30	21	9
47	26	8
60	40	5
68	37	7
76	42	4
90	33	5
100	30	7
105	38	5
130	60	3
140	65	4
125	50	3
120	35	1
135	42	2

(a) Estimate the supply parameters by least squares.

(b) Compute the price elasticity of supply at the mean price and mean quantity traded.

2. The production function of a firm is given as $x = al^b k^c$ where x denotes the quantity produced of the commodity X, l and k denote the quantities of the factors of production L and K, respectively, and a, b, and c are the unknown parameters of the production function. The sample data are given in the following table.

x	l	k	x	l	k
100	1.0	2.0	165	2.5	2.8
120	1.3	2.2	190	3.0	3.0
140	1.8	2.3	200	3.0	3.3
150	2.0	2.5	220	4.0	3.4

(a) Estimate by least squares the parameters of the production function.

(b) Find the marginal productivity functions of the two factors L and K.

3. The savings function for the economy as a whole is given as

$$s_t = a + by_{t-1} + ci_t$$

where s_t denotes aggregate saving in year t, y_{t-1} denotes national income in year $t - 1$ and i_t denotes the average interest rate in year t. The symbols a, b, and c denote the unknown population parameters. The sample data is given in the following table.

Year	s	y	i
1948	20	100	.02
1949	25	110	.02
1950	25	130	.03
1951	30	140	.02
1952	33	160	.03
1953	38	170	.04
1954	35	170	.03
1955	45	200	.04
1956	43	240	.04
1957	50	250	.05
1958	55	260	.05

(a) Estimate by least squares the parameters of the savings function

(b) What percentage of the total variation in saving is explained by both income and the interest rate?

(c) Compute the marginal propensity to save out of income.

CHAPTER 21

Problems of Economic Time Series

The sample data from which economists make inferences about theoretical models are of two kinds: (1) cross-section data and (2) time series data. Cross-section data consist of observations on the values of economic variables at a given point in time—or, more practically, during a given interval of time. Each observation on a defined variable x may be the observed value of x in a specified geographic locality or in a given institution, such as a household. The total number of observations in the sample would then be the total of such observed values of x for all localities or all institutions included in the sample. For example, x might represent the amount of cotton produced in a given year. An observation on x might be the amount of cotton produced in a given state during that year; the total sample of 50 observations might consist of the amounts of cotton produced for all 50 states in the United States during that year. Or the sample data on the ratio of consumption to income may be comprised of many observations on this ratio, one observation for each household included in the sample during a given year. The economic variable in question may be wage rates, and wage rates in various cities or various countries during a specified month could make up the cross-section sample. Thus, the primary reference of cross-section data is spatial; the factor that separates different observations is a difference in spatial locality at a given time.

Time series data, on the other hand, consist of observations on a variable at different points in time—or during different intervals of time. Each successive observation is separated from the others by its occurrence at a different time rather than its occurrence in a different place. A sample comprised of the total output of steel per month in the United States from 1940 to 1955 is a time series. So is the set of observations on national income per year in the United States for each year from 1910 to 1950. The sample data contained in Table 19–D on page 319 includes two time series: one on price and the other on the quantity of the commodity purchased by consumers. Any economic variable (such as employment, savings, production, and cost) whose values are ordered with respect to time is called an economic time series.

Both cross-sectional and time series data are used in regression analysis. The problem of multicollinearity may be inherent in either type of data used in multiple regression. There is another problem, however, that attaches to the use of time series data: the phenomenon of mutual dependence among successive observations on a variable. Given a series of observations on some variable x (x_1, x_2, x_3, . . . , x_n) that occur in successive time intervals, we may find that the several observations are not independent of each other. As a matter of fact, most economic time series are characterized by mutual dependence, and this fact should not be surprising. Consider, for example, a price series. If successive observations from, say, one year to the next were indeed independent of one another, we would be living in a kind of chaotic economy. In such a world, prices would be determined like random throws of a die or like numbers chosen at random from an urn. Knowledge of the price in one time period would in no way permit us to predict price in the next period, for in the succeeding time period any price would be as likely as any other.

This mutual dependence of successive observations raises a thorny problem for statistical analysis; it may seriously affect the interpretation of the least squares estimates of the population parameters. The Markoff Theorem assures us that the method of least squares gives the best unbiased linear estimate of the dependent or explained variable under conditions that do not require a normal distribution or even independence of the errors. Least squares also gives valid estimates of the population parameters without the assumption that the distribution of the errors is normal, if only the errors are independently distributed.[1] Furthermore, if we assume both a normal distribution and mutual independence of the errors, statistics can be computed to establish confidence limits for the estimates of the parameters, to conduct significance tests, and to test hypotheses.

In other words, in order that such statistical procedures be valid the value of one deviation or error in prediction should in no way

[1] It has been shown that even the assumption of independence may be dropped under certain conditions. See A. C. Aitken, "On Least Squares and Linear Combinations of Observations," *Proceedings of the Royal Society of Edinburgh*, Vol. 55 (1934–1935), pp. 42 ff.

determine or influence the magnitude of any other error. The probabilities of obtaining a given size of error must not change as a result of the size of any other error. In a regression equation of the form $y = \hat{a} + \hat{b}x + u$, the functional analysis assumes the variable y is a random variable (because u is a random variable) but not x. That is, y has a systematic component (determined by x) and a random component (determined by u). The validity of traditional statistical tests is dependent upon the randomness of u—more specifically that successive values of u be independent of one another, and normally distributed. If such is not the case, the sample cannot be treated as the result of random sampling, and many of the usual statistical analyses are not applicable.

Now there is reason to believe that small deviations from normality will not seriously affect the results of significance tests, confidence limits, etc. But if the successive errors are not independent—if they are correlated—then the consequences are more serious. The number of degrees of freedom is greatly reduced, because the number of degrees of freedom is related to the number of independent observations.

A. AUTOCORRELATION

Economic data ordered in a time sequence can seldom be regarded as random samples. An observation on price, production, inventory stocks, savings, and other economic variables in a given year is usually correlated with (not independent of) the value of that same variable in a previous year. The term *autocorrelation* is used to describe the lag correlation of a particular time series with itself, lagged by a number of time units. A variable x observed in a time series is autocorrelated if the value of x in period t, x_t, is correlated with the value of x in period $t - 1$, x_{t-1}. The variable x is said to be autocorrelated also if x_t is correlated with x_{t-2} or x_{t-3}, etc. Sometimes the term "serial correlation" is used to describe this same concept, but some writers distinguish serial correlation from autocorrelation. When this distinction is made, serial correlation is used to describe the lag correlation between two different time series rather than the lag correlation of the series with itself.

One can readily see how autocorrelation would enter into economic time series. Most series exhibit a secular trend or long-run movement over time (discussed in Section H, Chapter 3). This fact alone will introduce autocorrelation into the series; the values of the trend appear in ordered sequence and each value is, in a sense, determined by the value that precedes it. The so-called business cycle produces the same effect. Cyclical fluctuations impose a regularity among successive observations of the variable over time. A regular seasonal pattern in monthly data obviously imposes the same sort of autocorrelation.

The problem of statistical estimation is complicated by the presence of autocorrelation. It often detracts from the desirable characteristics that good estimates of the population parameters should possess. The loss is not considerable if the autocorrelation is not too strong. Tests of significance, however, may be seriously influenced by existing autocorrelation.

1. A Test for Autocorrelation

Several statistical tests have been developed to detect mutual dependence of successive observations in a time series. A relatively powerful one devised by B. I. Hart is the ratio of the mean square successive difference to the variance, sometimes called the *mean-square-successive-difference* method. For a time series of n observations on a variable x $(x_1, x_2, \ldots, x_n)$, the statistic k is defined as

$$k = \frac{m^2}{s^2}$$

where the denominator is the variance of x:

$$s^2 = \frac{\sum_{i=1}^{n} (x_i - \bar{x})^2}{n}$$

and the numerator is the mean square successive difference:

$$m^2 = \frac{\sum_{i=1}^{n-1} (x_{i+1} - x_i)^2}{n - 1}$$

The quantity k is closely related to the variance of the first difference of the series (to be discussed in Section B). If the successive differences are small (so that k is small), there is some pattern such as a trend or a cycle in the series, and *positive autocorrelation* exists. If these differences are very large (so k is large), *negative autocorrelation* is present. Thus very small and very large values of k indicate autocorrelation. Very large values of k, however, could arise only from a somewhat artificial set of observations such as alternating very large and very small values of the observed variable and so have little practical applicability.

The test is designed primarily as a test of randomness in a given series. We proceed in the following way: we test the hypothesis that the series is a random series. All observations are assumed to be normally distributed and mutually independent. Therefore, our hypothesis states that there is no autocorrelation among the successive observations, and we test the significance of this hypothesis. A table of significance levels and corresponding permissible values of k is available.[2]

We compute the empirical value of k from the sample. In general, the empirical k will differ from the permissible value shown in the table. If the (positive or negative) deviation is small enough so that the empirical k does not lie outside the upper or lower boundaries permitted, we say that the difference is not significant at the given level of significance. If this is the case, then it is very likely that the series behaves like a true random series. If, on the other hand, the empirical k does lie outside the permissible values, we say the value of k is significant at the given level of significance, and the series does not behave like a random series. It is very likely in this latter case that autocorrelation exists in the sample data. Although very large and very small values of the empirical k are significant and suggest autocorrelation, in practical situations in economics one is more likely to find significant values of k that are small rather than large (relative to the permissible values given in the table).

Let us consider a specific illustration. Suppose the sample consists of 48 observations on a variable x, and we wish to discover whether a significant degree of autocorrelation is present. We compute the sample variance s^2 and the mean square successive difference m^2. Assume they turn out to be

$$s^2 = 6.0504 \qquad \text{and} \qquad m^2 = 1.1213$$

We compute

$$k = \frac{m^2}{s^2} = \frac{1.1213}{6.0504} = .1853$$

According to the table of significance, for 48 observations and a 5 per cent level of significance, we have a permissible k of 1.57. At the 1 per cent level of significance, this permissible ratio is 1.38. Since our empirical k is much smaller than either of these, we say it is signifi-

[2] B. I. Hart, "Significance Levels for the Ratio of the Mean Square Successive Difference to the Variance," *Annals of Mathematical Statistics*, Vol. 13 (1942), pp. 445 ff.

cant at the one per cent level of significance. It is very unlikely that the observed time series is a random series.

An extremely useful application of this test is to be found in problems of regression analysis. We may wish to test for randomness in the errors or residuals in a regression equation, for the standard errors of the regression coefficients are to be used to conduct tests of significance only if the residuals are random and independent. If it turns out that the errors are not random, some other form of regression must be sought. As an example, we may use the data presented in Tables 20–A and 20–B, assuming the observations are time series. The regression equation obtained from these data was

$$y = 14.466 + .319x - 2.511z + u$$

and we wish to test for autocorrelation in u. The computed values of u are shown in Table 21–A. From these computations, we find

$$m^2 = \frac{89.25}{9} = 9.917$$

$$s^2 = \frac{28.96}{10} = 2.896$$

Hence,

$$k = \frac{9.917}{2.896} = 3.424$$

Table 21–A

i	$u_i = y_i - \hat{y}_i$	$(u_{i+1} - u_i)^2$	$(u_i - \bar{u})^2$
1	1.45	$(-2.21)^2 = 4.88$	$(1.453)^2 = 2.11$
2	−.76	$(-.79)^2 = .62$	$(-.757)^2 = .57$
3	−1.55	$(3.04)^2 = 9.24$	$(-1.547)^2 = 2.39$
4	1.49	$(2.89)^2 = 8.35$	$(1.493)^2 = 2.23$
5	−1.40	$(-.25)^2 = .06$	$(-1.397)^2 = 1.95$
6	−1.65	$(5.10)^2 = 26.01$	$(-1.647)^2 = 2.71$
7	3.45	$(5.27)^2 = 27.77$	$(3.453)^2 = 11.92$
8	−1.82	$(3.06)^2 = 9.36$	$(-1.817)^2 = 3.30$
9	1.24	$(-1.72)^2 = 2.96$	$(1.243)^2 = 1.55$
10	−.48		$(-.477)^2 = .23$

$\bar{u} = \dfrac{-.03}{10} = -.003$ | $\displaystyle\sum_{i=1}^{9}(u_{i+1} - \mu_i)^2 = 89.25$ | $\displaystyle\sum_{i=1}^{10}(u_i - \bar{u})^2 = 28.96$

We find in B. I. Hart's tables for the 5 per cent level of significance and for $n = 10$ a lower permissible ratio of 1.18. At the 1 per cent level of significance, we find .84 as the lower permissible ratio. The upper permissible ratios are 3.26 at the 5 per cent level of significance and 3.61 at the 1 per cent level. Our empirical k is about 3.42. Hence, we may conclude that our empirical k is not significant, that is, it is not significantly different from the permissible values, and so it is unlikely that significant autocorrelation exists in the series of residuals u. The test is efficient in indicating the absence of autocorrelation where in fact none exists, but we must keep in mind that it may sometimes not indicate autocorrelation when in fact some does exist.

The problem of autocorrelation is one of the most important in time series analysis. Though progress has been made, the results of research in this area are not yet entirely satisfactory. The mathematical problems involved are often quite difficult. Moreover, the most reliable methods designed to cope with autocorrelation are applicable only to large samples, but most economic time series are rather short. At the present time, we lack adequate small sample tests. Furthermore, the results of some tests are strongly influenced by a trend in the series. If the data show a strong trend, the applicability of these tests is thrown into doubt.

B. TRANSFORMATION OF OBSERVATIONS

If a given time series is characterized by autocorrelation, can it be removed? Several methods have been suggested in the literature on this problem, but often their validity in practical situations is doubtful. We shall discuss some of the simpler and more practical techniques.

1. Elimination of Linear Trend

To remove autocorrelation, the economist may attempt to transform his observations in such a way that they become mutually independent. One way of doing this is to eliminate the trend from the original data and work with deviations from the trend. We have seen that the presence of a trend introduces a dependence between successive observations. It is the intent of trend elimination to reduce and possibly to eliminate the source of this mutual dependence. If it is successful, customary statistical methods can then be employed.

Suppose our problem involves a multiple linear regression of y on x and z:

$$y = \hat{a} + \hat{b}x + \hat{c}z + u$$

Assume that each of the three explanatory variables has a linear secular trend. By the method of least squares, we can compute the three individual time trends. For the variable x, we have

$$x_t = \hat{d} + \hat{e}t \qquad (t = 1, 2, 3, \ldots, n)$$

as the trend equation, where the subscript t on x denotes the value of x in period t and the variable t denotes time. The same can be done for the variables y and z. Given the computed trend equations and the known values of t, each value of t included in the sample can be substituted into the trend equations to obtain the trend values of y, x, and z. Then the deviations of the observed values of y, x, and z from their trends can be obtained by subtracting the fitted trend values from the observed values. These deviations are represented by y', x', and z'. We have the new regression equation

$$y' = \hat{a} + \hat{b}x' + \hat{c}z' + v$$

where v is assumed to be a random variable. Each value of y', x', and z' will be more or less independent of the original series if the orginal series consisted of a linear trend plus a random component.

There is, however, a simpler way to achieve this same result. It can be proved that the multiple regression of one variable on two or more others, all of which are deviations from linear trends, is tantamount to introducing time explicitly into the regression equation. Hence, if we write the multiple regression equation as

$$y = \hat{a} + \hat{b}x + \hat{c}z + \hat{d}t + v$$

where t denotes time with a defined origin and measured in appropriate units and v is assumed random, this formulation is equivalent to the above regression equation in terms of the deviations y', x', and z'. One can then test for autocorrelation in the residuals v in the manner outlined in Section A.

The original regression equation need not be linear in the variables y, x, and z. If the equation is, for example, logarithmic, the logarithms of y, x, and z can be computed and new variables defined in terms of the logarithms—as was shown in Section D, Chapter 20. The resulting regression equation is then linear in the logs of y, x, and z, but the trend component is linear in t. The regression equation has the form

$$\log_e y = \hat{a} + \hat{b} \log_e x + \hat{c} \log_e z + \hat{d}t + v$$

Indeed, it is not difficult to extend these procedures of trend elimination to nonlinear trends represented by, say, (orthogonal) polynomials. One should keep in mind, however, that the method of trend elimination may not always be successful. A regular pattern may remain in the residuals so that autocorrelation persists. Tests for the randomness of v will aid in determining this.

2. Finite Differences

Another method available for the transformation of observations so that they become mutually independent is the method of finite differences. We have seen (Section I, Chapter 3) that the first difference of a series is the rate of change in that series. For a variable x, we denote an observation on x in time t as x_t. Then the first difference of x is $x_t - x_{t-1}$. Note the use of first differences in the formula for the mean square successive difference in Section A. The second difference is the rate of change of the series of first differences; the third difference is the rate of change of the series of second differences; and so on. By taking some finite differences of the series, it may be possible to reduce or eliminate the autocorrelation in the series.

A general description of the principles involved runs as follows. Let the variable on which a time series is available be denoted by x, and let an observed value of this variable in period t be represented by x_t $(t = 1, 2, 3, \ldots , n)$. We assume each observed value x_t consists of two additive components: a systematic component s_t and a random component u_t. Thus, we write

$$x_t = s_t + u_t \qquad (t = 1, 2, 3, \ldots , n)$$

Some additional assumptions are made about u_t: it is not autocorrelated, it has zero mean and constant variance; it must be assumed to be normally distributed for some statistical tests. Now if the systematic (autocorrelated) part s_t may be expressed as a "smooth" mathematical function of time, we can approximate it (at least segments of it) by a polynomial. As can be seen from our discussion of calculus in Part II, it is a characteristic of a polynomial of degree k that its kth derivative is a constant. Furthermore, its $(k + 1)$th, $(k + 2)$th, . . . derivatives are all zero. Since the derivative is a limiting case of a finite difference, we can say the kth finite difference is a constant and the $(k + 1)$, $(k + 2)$, . . . finite differences are zero. Therefore, by finding the appropriate finite difference of x one can eliminate (or at least greatly reduce) the systematic part of x_t.

This leaves only the random component u_t, and autocorrelation has been removed from the series.

That successful application of this technique is widespread, is somewhat doubtful. There exist certain conditions under which it definitely is not. In the final analysis, one must admit that the problem of autocorrelation remains one of the primary difficulties in dealing with economic time series. One may hope that continued research in this area eventually will produce more effective methods for coping with the problem.

PART V

Econometric Models Reconsidered

CHAPTER 22

Some Aspects of Model Construction

The basic properties of econometric models were discussed in Part III, but we are now in a position to introduce some additional refinements. Both static and dynamic models were treated in Chapters 14 and 15 under the assumption of perfect certainty. Since econometric models are designed, however, with an eye to statistical measurement and tests of hypotheses, account must be taken of errors. This in turn involves the concepts of probability and the random variable. Knowledge of the principles of the probability theory and statistical inference enables us to treat econometric models under conditions of uncertainty. One type of useful application of these principles immediately comes to mind—the formulation of individual decision processes. Let us, therefore, turn once more to the theory of the single firm. This time, however, we shall assume that the entrepreneur is not certain about the values of economic variables that enter into his decisions with respect to production, sales, etc.

A. MODELS OF THE SINGLE FIRM

In Section A of Chapter 15, a static model of the firm under the assumption of perfect knowledge was presented. At that point, we also considered a dynamic model under certainty. In planning multidate production and sales, the entrepreneur was assumed to have not only perfect knowledge of the present market price and present costs of production, but also perfect knowledge of the values of these variables in future time periods. Let us first discuss the simpler case of a static-uncertainty model, so we do not have to cope with the problem of planning over time.

1. Single-Date Uncertainty

Assume that the market for a commodity X is purely competitive. The total profit of a single firm was defined in Chapter 14 as

$$(1) \qquad P(x) = R(x) - C(x)$$

where R denotes total revenue as a function of the output x, and C signifies the total cost of production of x. Maximum profit is determined from the condition

$$(2) \qquad \frac{dP}{dx} = \frac{dR}{dx} - \frac{dC}{dx} = 0$$

That is, x must be set at that level for which marginal revenue equals marginal cost of production. Under pure competition

$$R(x) = px$$

where p is the given price of the commodity X, so profit is a maximum when

$$(3) \qquad p = \frac{dC}{dx}$$

From knowledge of the market price and the cost-of-production function, equation (3) can be solved for $\hat{x}$, the value of x that maximizes P.

But what if the market price, p, is not known with certainty? The fact that entrepreneurs do make decisions even though they are uncertain about the values of relevant variables calls for some changes in the model. This uncertain world can be viewed as one in which the values of the relevant variables occur with definite probabilities. After long investigations of games of chance, probability theorists found that if a gambler knows the probabilities of alternative events, he is advised to choose a decision that will maximize the "expected return" from the game. This is the mathematical expectation of total net returns. Now let the profit that the firm seeks to maximize be the expected profit. Since the uncertainty of profit at alternative outputs springs from the uncertainty of total revenue—which in turn is due to the uncertainty of price—multiply the probability of the occurrence of each possible price by the profit that a given decision (with respect to x) will yield at that price. The sum of all these products is the mathematical expectation of profit. It is thus the average of profits, weighted by their respective probabilities.

Note that this concept is not the same as the "profit one expects." The use of expected profit assumes that the entrepreneur is economically "rational" in a world characterized by uncertainty. This rationality takes the form of viewing the world in terms of probabilities. Hence, it assumes also that the entrepreneur knows the probabilities involved; though the prices are not known, their probabilities are. It is, of course, possible that the entrepreneur may not even know the probabilities unless the price occurrences are something like a game of chance. Moreover, even if the probabilities are known, it may be asked whether, for example, large profits and large losses of equal probability are to be assigned the same weights in formulating the expression that the firm is assumed to maximize. For our purposes, it is not necessary to delve into these problems. We shall assume a probability distribution exists and is known. Our acceptance of the rule of maximizing expected profit follows; it is justified by the fact that many practical people (engineers, actuaries, etc.) do apply this rule in their respective fields. Then it must be granted that this decision principle, if applied again and again an indefinitely large number of times, will in the long run make the firm's actual profit larger (or not smaller) than any other decision principle. This conclusion follows from the definition of probabilities as, roughly, a limit of relative frequencies as the number of trials increases indefinitely.

For purposes of comparison, consider the following model of an individual firm in a competitive market under conditions of certainty:

$$P(x) = R(x) - C(x) = px - wx^2$$

where the symbols P, R, C, x, and p have the same meaning as in the previous example. The symbol w denotes the wage rate, assumed to be the only relevant factor price entering total cost. For maximum P, we have

$$\frac{dP}{dx} = p - 2wx = 0$$

$$\hat{x} = \frac{p}{2w}$$

Suppose that it is known that $p = 10$ and $w = 1$. Then $\hat{x} = 5$.

Suppose, on the other hand, that p and w are not known, but the values of the pairs (p, w) will occur with known probabilities. Let the pairs shown in Table 22–A be the only possible pairs. They occur with the probabilities shown in the table.

Now the firm is assumed to maximize *expected* profit, EP, where

$$EP = x \cdot Ep - x^2 \cdot Ew$$

Table 22–A

Values	Probability
$p = \;\;8, w = 5$	.1
$p = 10, w = 1$	.2
$p = 12, w = 1$	.3
$p = 14, w = 2$	.2
$p = 16, w = 3$	.2
	1.0

and where Ep and Ew denote the expected price and the expected wage rate respectively. The rule for the maximization of expected profit is

$$\frac{dEP}{dx} = Ep - 2x \cdot Ew = 0$$

$$\hat{x} = \frac{Ep}{2Ew}$$

More specifically, we have from Table 22–A and the definition of mathematical expectation:

$$EP = (.1)(8x - 5x^2) + (.2)(10x - 1x^2) + (.3)(12x - 1x^2)$$
$$+ (.2)(14x - 2x^2) + (.2)(16x - 3x^2) = 12.4x - 2x^2$$

Consequently,

$$\frac{dEP}{dx} = \frac{d(12.4x)}{dx} - \frac{d(2x^2)}{dx} = 12.4 - 4x = 0$$

$$\hat{x} = \frac{12.4}{4.0} = 3.1$$

Note that the output decision differs from that which results under conditions of certainty. Note also that $\hat{x}$ is not equal to the average of outputs that are best under each of the five pairs (p, w). It is rather the output that yields the best expected profit, not the expected best output.

This simplified model illustrates the way in which probability theory can be used in economics to cope with the problem of uncertainty. Since economists are primarily interested in aggregate market behavior, there remains the problem of aggregation over all firms to obtain the market supply function for the commodity. Such a supply function will differ from that under assumed certainty, in that the total market supply is a function of an expected price (for a given expected wage rate) rather than the actual price.

2. Multidate Uncertainty

Let us now turn to a more interesting application of probability theory: the case of multidate planning by the firm. In Section A, Chapter 15, a multiperiod planning model for an individual firm was constructed under the assumption that all future and present values of the variables were known by the entrepreneur. The definition of profit included prices, sales, and production in more than one period. Profit was maximized with respect to sales and production—hence, with respect to inventories also. We concluded that such a model can be considered only as a provisional one. Account must be taken of the fact that the future is uncertain. Consequently, in his ignorance the entrepreneur can make only conditional decisions, depending on the values of the variables that can occur in future periods.

Let us reconstruct the two-period model of Chapter 15 with an allowance for uncertainty about the future. The following symbols are defined:

p_t = price at the end of period t

x_t = production during period t

s_t = sales at the end of period t

y_t = inventories in stock at the end of period t

wx_t^2 = total cost of production of the amount x in period t, where w denotes the *known* (constant) wage rate

ky_t = total cost of storing the amount y for the period t, where k is a *known* constant (known cost per unit stored)

Let the two periods be designated by 1 and 2. The firm is to make its decision at the beginning of period 1. p_1 and p_2, prices at the *end* of periods 1 and 2 respectively, are assumed unknown and in general different. What *is* known about the prices is their joint probability distribution, like the distribution of the pairs (p, w) in the previous model.

Just like equation (3) in Section A.2 of Chapter 15, when y_2 is set equal to zero, total profit is written

(3) $\quad P = s_1 p_1 + s_2 p_2 - w x_1^2 - w x_2^2 - k y_1$

Since by definition $y_1 = x_1 - s_1$ and $s_2 = x_1 + x_2 - s_1$, total profit can be rewritten like equation (4) in Chapter 15:

(4) $\quad P = p_1 s_1 + p_2(x_1 + x_2 - s_1) - w x_1^2 - w x_2^2 - k(x_1 - s_1)$

Separating the terms in the variables x_1, x_2, and s_1, we have

(5) $\quad P = [s_1(p_1 - p_2 + k) + x_1(p_2 - k) - w x_1^2] + [x_2 p_2 - w x_2^2]$

Since p_1 and p_2 are assumed random variables, so is P. But the mathematical expectation of P is not itself a random variable. This follows from the fact that the mathematical expectations of prices are not random variables but constants. The expression for expected profit is given as

(6) $\quad EP = [s_1(Ep_1 - Ep_2 + k) + x_1(Ep_2 - k) - wx_1^2] + [x_2Ep_2 - wx_2^2]$

Now s_1, x_1, and x_2 have to be chosen so as to make EP a maximum. But s_1 and x_1 must be chosen with both p_1 and p_2 unknown, while x_2 is chosen when p_1 is already known. Therefore, EP is maximized not with respect to x_2, a number, but rather with respect to a function that prescribes for each p_1 a value of x_2. This is a so-called decision function or "rule"; call it g_2. For more than two periods the sequence $x_1, g_2, g_3, \ldots$ is called a *strategy*.

Let us now proceed to maximize EP. In this case, we can regard EP as the sum of two components: EP_1 and EP_2. Thus

(7) $\qquad EP_1 = s_1(Ep_1 - Ep_2 + k) + x_1(Ep_2 - k) - wx_1^2$
(8) $\qquad EP_2 = x_2Ep_2 - wx_2^2$

We can maximize each component separately. The procedure follows that outlined in Chapter 15:

Case 1: If $Ep_1 > Ep_2 - k$
then set $s_1 = x_1$
and $y_1 = 0$
The equation (7) becomes
(7′) $\qquad\qquad EP_1 = x_1Ep_1 - wx_1^2$

Case 2: If $Ep_1 < Ep_2 - k$
then set $s_1 = 0$ and store all production
and $y_1 = x_1$
The equation (7) becomes
(7″) $\qquad\qquad EP_1 = x_1(Ep_2 - k) - wx_1^2$

Case 3: If $Ep_1 = Ep_2 - k$
then the firm is indifferent, and the rule for either Case 1 or Case 2 may be followed.

Maximizing both (7′) and (7″) with respect to x_1, we obtain

$$\hat{x}_1 = \frac{Ep_1}{2w} \qquad \text{if } Ep_1 \geq Ep_2 - k$$

$$\hat{x}_1 = \frac{Ep_2 - k}{2w} \qquad \text{if } Ep_1 \leq Ep_2 - k$$

That is, the marginal cost of production must equal either Ep_1 or $Ep_2 - k$, whichever is larger. The common sense of this is clear. If the expected price in period 2 minus the storage cost per unit exceeds the expected price in period 1, it is more advantageous to produce for storage rather than for sale in period 1. If the reverse condition holds, it is more advantageous to produce for sale in period 1.

But now what about the decision for output in period 2, $\hat{x}_2$, that maximizes EP_2? The prices p_1 and p_2 are mutually dependent. In general, if two random variables x and y are mutually dependent, the conditional probability of x is the probability of x, given that y has occurred. The output x_2 is to be chosen with p_1 already known, so EP_2 is the conditional expected profit in the second period. It is denoted by the following expression:

$$(9) \qquad EP_2\bigg|_{p_1} = x_2 Ep_2\bigg|_{p_1} - wx_2^2$$

where the "slant" is read "given the value of." Maximization of EP_2 with respect to x_2 gives

$$(10) \qquad \hat{x}_2 = \frac{Ep_2\big|_{p_1}}{2w}$$

The marginal cost of production in the second period must equal the conditional expectation of the price in the second period, given the price in the first period. Remember that the firm makes this plan with respect to period 2 at the beginning of period 1. Therefore, this decision about $\hat{x}_2$ is a function. The function prescribes the best output in the second period for each possible value of p_1. The plan at the beginning of the first period is of the form: if p_1 should turn out to be equal to a, then produce $\hat{x}_2 = b$ in period 2; if p_1 should be equal to c, produce $\hat{x}_2 = d$ in period 2; and so on. This is what is meant when we say uncertainty leads to conditional decision functions or rules that plan behavior for future periods in such a way as to maximize expected profit.

This type of analysis can be extended to planning that involves more than two time periods. For n periods, we would obtain a whole sequence of functions: $x_1, g_2, g_3, \ldots, g_n$. Each g denotes a function relating output and storage decisions to possible values of the relevant random variables. The entire set of such functions is called a strategy.

More specifically, if price is assumed to be the uncertain variable, each decision must be made with a whole sequence of unknown future prices. Granted that the price at the end of period t, p_t, obeys some joint probability distribution with all previous and future prices, the conditional distribution of p_t, given p_{t-1}, p_{t-2}, p_{t-3}, $\ldots$

can be determined. The sequence of future prices can be estimated on the basis of previous prices. If the relationship between the price in period t and all past prices is linear, then the expected price in period t assumes the form

$$Ep_t\Big|_{p_{t-1},\ p_{t-2},\ \ldots} = a + b_1 p_{t-1} + b_2 p_{t-2} + \ldots$$

The expected price in period t can in this case be estimated by a least-squares linear regression on past prices. Other methods of forecasting are possible; they depend largely upon the ingenuity of the research worker. The formulation presented here indicates the kinds of problems faced in multidate uncertainty models and the general procedure used to contend with the difficulties inherent in multidate planning.

B. MODELS OF MARKET BEHAVIOR

1. The Use of Expectations

Economists as social scientists are primarily interested in predicting market behavior. It follows from the preceding discussion that behavioral equations describing total market behavior may involve future values of an economic variable. Consider the case of a market supply function for some commodity. If the decisions of firms with respect to sales in any period are dependent upon expected future prices, then the aggregate supply of all firms together will also be dependent upon expected future prices. The construction of a market supply function as one structural equation in a complete model implies the summation of individual supplies as functions of expected prices. There are numerous mathematical and statistical problems inherent in such aggregation procedures. Nevertheless, it is not uncommon for economists to disregard these problems and to deal directly with the market relationships; it is often unnecessary to be concerned with the aggregation technique, and we shall ignore it here.

Let us consider a relatively simple structural equation involving expectations. Suppose we are studying the total supply of some agricultural commodity in the United States. Farmers plant the crop in advance of harvest. We assume the yield per acre is given (constant) and the number of acres actually harvested at the end of the year is a constant proportion of the number of acres planted in this crop. Thus, decisions with respect to final output at the end of the year are made at the beginning of the year. Farmers base their planting decisions on the price that will prevail at the time of harvest and sale, but this price is unknown at the time of planting. Hence, we may write the market supply function for the commodity X as

$$x_t = f(Ep_{t+1})$$

where x_t refers to the actual output at the end of period t, and Ep_{t+1} is the price expected to prevail at the beginning of period $t + 1$. Since there is only some indefinitely small interval between the end of t and the beginning of $t + 1$ (one day, one hour, one minute, or whatever small unit one wishes to choose), the two variables x_t and p_{t+1} (not expected p_{t+1}) may be regarded as occurring simultaneously for all practical purposes. But the decisions about x_t are made at the beginning of period t; likewise, the expectation of p_{t+1}, that is, Ep_{t+1}, is formed at this same time, which follows from the fact that p_{t+1} is unknown at the time of planting.

We cannot directly observe the expected price, but we can estimate it if we assume the p_{t+1} obeys some joint probability distribution with all previous and future prices. Then the conditional distribution of p_{t+1}, given p_t, p_{t-1}, p_{t-2}, . . . can be determined (more generally, information on variables other than past prices could be used). This being the case, a multiple regression of p_{t+1} on p_t, p_{t-1}, . . . can be used to estimate the expectation of p_{t+1}. That is to say, we assume that farmers use their knowledge of past prices to predict the future prices. If this regression is linear, we have the so-called distributed lag:

$$Ep_{t+1}\bigg|_{p_t,\ p_{t-1},\ \cdots} = a + b_0 p_t + b_1 p_{t-1} + b_2 p_{t-2} + \cdots,$$

where a, b_0, b_1, etc., are constants. The weights attached to each past price in forming the expected price (b_0, b_1, b_2, . . .) may possibly, but not necessarily, form a decreasing sequence as we go back in time. If they do, this is equivalent to the statement that more recent prices are of greater importance than more distant past prices in the formation of the expected price.

Though one cannot observe the expected price, the past prices are observable. Assuming that the quantity supplied is a linear function of the expected price, the empirical estimation of the parameters of the supply function is derived by least-squares from the multiple regression

$$x_t = f(Ep_{t+1}) = c + d_0 p_t + d_1 p_{t-1} + d_2 p_{t-2} + \cdots$$

Sample data exist for all of the independent variables, and the reliability of the estimates can be tested by the usual statistical methods discussed in Part IV. Though the problem reduces to a typical kind of multiple regression analysis, what has been accomplished by the substitution of past prices for an expected price is the substitution of observable variables for an unobservable variable.

2. The Definition of Real Variables

We have discussed the construction of an econometric model, its structural equations and the variables that enter into these structural equations. If uncertainty is assumed to exist, the expected value of a variable (and possibly other characteristics of its distribution, such as its variance) may replace the value of the variable itself. There remains one important aspect of the systematic variables that we have not discussed. When economists state an economic relationship, it is usually the real value of the variable to which they refer. For example, the consumption function states that real consumption is an increasing function of real income. When reference is made to net investment, this concept is defined as the net addition to the stock of real capital goods.

This much is clear. How then can a problem arise? When we write the consumption function as

$$C = a + bY$$

where C denotes real consumption and Y real income, and where a and b represent positive constants, we know exactly what we mean. But since econometric models are designed with a view to empirical measurement, we must ask how we are to obtain the sample data on real consumption and income. We know that consumption refers to the total of all goods and services consumed by households. These will include such items as pairs of shoes, quarts of milk, tons of coal, amperes of electricity, numbers of books, hours of medical consultation, etc. These must be added, but they are expressed in different units. One must find some unit of measurement to express the sum. Similarly, for investment goods, such diverse items as blast furnaces, industrial plants, wrenches, and steam power, must be summed.

Money provides a standard of value. All goods and services have a price, so that we can add their values and obtain a sum in terms of units that are common to all. Therefore, when we refer to total consumption, for example, we mean real consumption, but we measure this real consumption in money values. This is not enough, however. For the money value of consumption is $P \cdot C$, where P signifies the general price level; likewise $P \cdot Y$ is money income. It is clear then that a change in $P \cdot C$ can occur as a result of a change in P alone, or a change in C alone, or a change in both. The same is true of changes in money income. Consider the time series sample data shown in Table 22–B. The changes in money income and consump-

Table 22–B

Year	National Money Income	Money Value of National Consumption
	$P \cdot Y$	$P \cdot C$
1950	$1 \cdot 10 = 10$	$1 \cdot 5 \ = \ 5$
1951	$2 \cdot 10 = 20$	$2 \cdot 5 \ = 10$
1952	$1 \cdot 20 = 20$	$1 \cdot 10 = 10$
1953	$2 \cdot 20 = 40$	$2 \cdot 10 = 20$

tion from 1950 to 1951 are due entirely to price changes. If we were to accept uncritically the money figures, we would conclude that a change in the variables of our model has occurred, whereas actually neither variable has changed. Comparison of 1952 with 1950 shows the same increases in money income and consumption, but these changes are due to changes in the real variables themselves. The over-all 1950–1953 change results from changes in prices and the real variables.

Granted that the real variables must be expressed in money units for aggregation purposes, how shall we eliminate the effects of price changes on these monetary expressions? The answer is that we deflate the money values: we divide the money values by an index of price. Before this procedure can be described, it will be necessary to briefly describe the meaning of an index.

a. *Index Construction.* An *index* is a set of numbers designed to measure the value of some variable over time. A base period (year or month, depending on the problem) is chosen, and changes in the index are measured relative to the base period. Take two variables x and y and assume the two observable time series show the values of x and y. We choose one year as the base year; let us designate the observed magnitudes in that year as x_0 and y_0. We wish to construct an index of x. For a year different than the base year, call it year 1, we compute

$$I_1 = \frac{x_1 \cdot y_0}{x_0 \cdot y_0}$$

For year 2, we compute

$$I_2 = \frac{x_2 \cdot y_0}{x_0 \cdot y_0}$$

We do this for each year included in the time series, so in general for year t ($t = 0, 1, 2, 3, \ldots, n$)

$$I_t = \frac{x_t \cdot y_0}{x_0 \cdot y_0}$$

The actual procedure can be clarified by consideration of a specific example. Suppose we have a commodity X whose quantity is designated by x and whose price is designated by p. For each year t, the values of x and p are shown in Table 22–C. The price index is

Table 22–C

t	p_t	x_t	Index of Price			
0	$p_0 = 9$	$x_0 = 60$	$\dfrac{p_0 \cdot x_0}{p_0 \cdot x_0} =$	$\dfrac{(9)(60)}{(9)(60)} =$	$\dfrac{540}{540} =$	$1.00 = I_0$
1	$p_1 = 10$	$x_1 = 70$	$\dfrac{p_1 \cdot x_0}{p_0 \cdot x_0} =$	$\dfrac{(10)(60)}{(9)(60)} =$	$\dfrac{600}{540} =$	$1.11 = I_1$
2	$p_2 = 15$	$x_2 = 80$	$\dfrac{p_2 \cdot x_0}{p_0 \cdot x_0} =$	$\dfrac{(15)(60)}{(9)(60)} =$	$\dfrac{900}{540} =$	$1.67 = I_2$
3	$p_3 = 12$	$x_3 = 90$	$\dfrac{p_3 \cdot x_0}{p_0 \cdot x_0} =$	$\dfrac{(12)(60)}{(9)(60)} =$	$\dfrac{720}{540} =$	$1.33 = I_3$
4	$p_4 = 5$	$x_4 = 87$	$\dfrac{p_4 \cdot x_0}{p_0 \cdot x_0} =$	$\dfrac{(5)(60)}{(9)(60)} =$	$\dfrac{300}{540} =$	$.56 = I_4$

shown in the last column for year zero chosen as the base year. Note that the index is a pure number. The index is not expressed in either the price or quantity units. It shows the movements of price relative to the base year, which by definition is always equal to unity. Many times in practice the index is multiplied by 100, in which case the base year is always equal to 100.

There is no reason why an economic index must be limited to prices. In this illustration, we could have just as well allowed x to vary in the numerator. Our resulting index would then have been an index of the quantity of X traded on the market. Similarly, there exist production indexes, cost indexes, income indexes, etc.

The index in Table 22–C was constructed for one commodity X. Suppose, however, that we wish to construct an index of consumer prices, which we may regard as a rough measure of the "cost of living." Then we must take account of all consumer goods and services by summing the products in the numerator and denominator over all these goods and services. Assume there are k goods and services in the economy. The value of the "cost of living" index in period t is

$$I_t = \frac{\sum_{1}^{k} p_t \cdot x_0}{\sum_{1}^{k} p_0 \cdot x_0}$$

The only adjustment required is that the numerator and denominator now consist of a sum of k products (each price times each quantity) rather than one product. This process is carried out for each year t: $t = 0, 1, 2, 3, \ldots, n$. The resulting set of numbers is the general consumer price index.

The index we have been describing here is called Laspeyre's Index. Other indexes are available. Two of these are Paasche's Index (denoted by P below) and Fisher's Index (denoted by F below):

$$P_t = \frac{\sum_{1}^{k} p_t \cdot x_t}{\sum_{1}^{k} p_0 \cdot x_t}$$

$$F_t = \sqrt{I_t \cdot P_t}$$

Note that the Paasche price index differs from the Laspeyre price index in that it allows x to vary with the period t. Under some restrictive assumptions it can be shown that the Laspeyre index gives the upper limit and the Paasche index the lower limit of "true" changes in the cost of living. Fisher's so-called ideal index gives an approximation to "true" changes in the cost of living under some very restrictive assumptions.

b. *Deflation.* Price indexes, production indexes, etc., are published regularly by government and business agencies. It is not very often that an economist finds it necessary to construct his own. Regardless of the source, we must now ask how such indexes are to be used to convert the sample data from money values to real values expressed in money. Returning to the consumption-income relationship, we find real income by deflating money income by an index of the cost of living. Since we shall use a price index as an estimate of the cost-of-living index, money income and the money value of consumption will be deflated by the price index. Suppose the time series on money income and money consumption are the hypothetical figures given in columns (2) and (3) of Table 22–D. The index of the "general price

Table 22–D

(1) Year	(2) National Money Income (Billions of Dollars)	(3) National Money Consumption (Billions of Dollars)	(4) Price Level Index (1950 = 1.00)	(5) Real Income (Billions of Dollars)	(6) Real Consumption (Billions of Dollars)
	$P \cdot Y$	$P \cdot C$	P	Y	C
1950	200	150	1.00	200.00	150.00
1951	210	155	1.30	161.54	119.23
1952	230	160	1.10	209.09	145.45
1953	215	150	1.50	143.33	100.00
1954	250	170	.90	277.78	188.89

level" is shown in column (4). The resulting measures of real income and real consumption are those shown in columns (5) and (6). It is these last two columns of data that one would use for computation purposes. More specifically, in the case of a least-squares estimate of the population parameters, it is the data in columns (5) and (6) from which the regression

$$C = a + bY + u$$

would be computed.

Another view of the role played by deflation is obtained from consideration of the demand function for a single commodity. We express the demand for commodity X as

$$x = a + bp + cy$$

where x represents the quantity of X demanded, p its price, and y consumers' real income. The symbols a, b, and c represent constants. We must, however, take a closer look at what we mean by the price of the commodity X. From economic theory, we know it is the price of X relative to other commodity prices that influences the quantity of X demanded. Therefore, by p we mean the relative price of X. Operationally, we obtain a measure of the relative price of X by deflating its absolute price by an index of other prices. The multiple regression of quantity demanded on the relative price of X and real consumers' income is

$$x = \hat{a} + \hat{b}\frac{P_x}{P} + \hat{c}\frac{Y}{P} + u$$

where P_x is the quoted absolute price of X, Y is money income, and P is an index of the general price level. The variable $\frac{P_x}{P}$—the price of X deflated by an index of all prices—is an approximation to the relative price of X. We say it is an approximation, because the absolute price of X enters into the computation of the general price level. To be strictly correct, P should designate an index of all prices but the price of X. The error from inclusion of the price of X in the computation of P, however, is normally very slight, so the quoted price of X can be deflated by the index of the general price level without seriously affecting the empirical results.

For deflation purposes, it is sometimes more desirable to use an index of prices other than all prices. In the demand or supply function for an agricultural commodity, for example, it may be preferable to deflate the price in question by an index of the prices of agricultural commodities only. If one other commodity is a very strong substitute for the commodity in question, and all other commodities besides this one are weak substitutes, it would be desirable to deflate the price of the commodity in question by the price of this one strong substitute only. No general rule can be given as to the choice of an appropriate index for deflation purposes. The best index for one problem may not be the best index for another. In the last analysis, the choice of an appropriate index is determined by the economist's judgment and his knowledge of the institutions involved.

C. SUMMARY

Let us now summarize the ways in which these aspects of model construction alter the general description given in Part III. We may outline the steps usually followed prior to the computation of the statistical estimates.

(1) Choice of the appropriate economic variables: In the case of uncertainty, this may involve the use of expected values, variances, etc., of probability distributions of the random variables. In other cases, certainty on the part of the decision makers may be assumed, and the value of the variable itself is appropriate. Whether the value

of a variable be assumed known or unknown, that variable may be defined as a real variable or as the money value of a real variable. If it is defined as a real variable and is assumed unknown, then its expected value is likewise the expectation of a real variable.

(2) Formulation of the structural equations: This was discussed at length in Part III and is not altered by the aspects of model construction covered in this chapter.

(3) Collection of the sample data: Two additional considerations are introduced. First, if a variable in the model is defined as a real variable, an operational procedure is necessary to obtain data on the values of the real variable. This operational procedure is the deflation of the sample observations on the money value of the variable in question by an appropriate price index. Deflation of a price series is also necessary if the price variable in the model is defined as a relative price (which is practically always the case in studies of particular markets). Second, if the expectation of a future value of a variable (real or money) is used in the construction of the theoretical model, sample observations on some estimates of the expectations are required. Such estimates may involve a regression on past actual values of the variable—or some other forecasting technique.

When these three steps have been completed, the econometrician is prepared to estimate the population parameters of the structural equations. As an illustration, suppose the population supply equation to be estimated statistically is

$$x_t = a + bEp_{t+1}$$

where x_t is the quantity supplied of the commodity X in year t, and Ep_{t+1} is the expected relative price of X at the beginning of year $t + 1$. The letters a and b denote positive constants. Assume a time series on x_t is already at hand. A time series on Ep_{t+1} is needed for least-squares estimates of the parameters of the supply equation. It may be decided by the economist that EP_{t+1} is to be estimated from the equation

$$Ep_{t+1}\Big|_{p_t,\ p_{t-1},\ p_{t-2}} = c + d_0p_t + d_1p_{t-1} + d_2p_{t-2}$$

where c, d_0, d_1, and d_2 are constants. Substitution into the supply equation yields

$$x_t = (a + bc) + (bd_0)p_t + (bd_1)p_{t-1} + (bd_2)p_{t-2}$$
$$= e + k_0p_t + k_1p_{t-1} + k_2p_{t-2}$$

where e, k_0, k_1, and k_2 are constants different in general from a, b, c, and d. This final equation can be estimated by least squares. But since each price is a relative price, the sample data for the multiple regression must include three price series, each of which is deflated by the appropriate price index. After each of the past prices has been deflated, the lag multiple regression of x_t on p_t, p_{t-1}, and p_{t-2} can be used under the usual assumptions to yield least-squares estimates of the parameters e, k_0, k_1, and k_2. It is also possible under certain conditions to solve back to obtain the values of the original parameters a and b.

PROBLEMS

1. Assume the market supply function for a commodity X is given as

$$x_t = f(Ep_{t+1}) = -10 + 2Ep_{t+1}$$

where x_t denotes the quantity supplied in period t and Ep_{t+1} is the expected price in period $t + 1$. Assume also that the price in any period obeys a joint probability distribution with all past and future prices and that the regression of the expected price on past prices is given as

$$Ep_{t+1}\Big|_{pt,\ p_{t-1}} = 5 + .5p_t + .1p_{t-1}$$

The actual prices from period zero through period five are given as

$$p_0 = 10 \qquad p_2 = 30 \qquad p_4 = 18 \qquad p_6 = 40$$
$$p_1 = 20 \qquad p_3 = 12 \qquad p_5 = 10$$

Find the values of x_t from period one through period six and plot the time path of x_t.

2. Given the following prices and quantities traded of the commodity X, construct (a) a Laspeyre price index and (b) a Paasche price index with $t = 0$ as the base year.

t	Price of X	Quantity of X
0	10	100
1	12	110
2	20	105
3	28	110
4	24	114
5	20	120
6	16	124
7	10	112
8	15	90

3. Time series on the money values of aggregate United States consumption and national income are given in the following table.

Year	Consumption	Income
1948	65	70
1949	88	80
1950	90	100
1951	107	100
1952	110	118
1953	120	120
1954	122	120
1955	125	140
1956	150	160
1957	190	200
1958	164	190

The index of the general price level is given as

Year	General Price Index
1948	1.00
1949	1.05
1950	1.05
1951	1.10
1952	1.15
1953	1.20
1954	1.30
1955	1.25
1956	1.30
1957	1.40
1958	1.30

(a) Plot the scatter diagram relating the money value of consumption to the money value of income.

(b) Estimate the parameters of the consumption function, relating the money value of consumption to the money value of income. Compute the marginal propensity to consume.

(c) Deflate the money values of consumption and income and plot the scatter diagram relating real consumption to real income.

(d) Estimate the parameters of the consumption function relating real consumption to real income. Compute the marginal propensity to consume and compare it with the marginal propensity to consume computed in part (b).

(e) Test the statistical significance of the regression coefficient in (d).

4. A sample consists of time series on the quantity exchanged of a commodity X, the price of X, and an index of the prices of all commodities.

Year	Quantity of X	Price of X	Index of General Price Level
1945	84	10	1.00
1946	75	30	1.10
1947	82	20	1.10
1948	70	25	1.05
1949	70	30	1.15
1950	62	40	1.20
1951	60	35	1.15
1952	56	50	1.25
1953	40	60	1.30
1954	30	65	1.40
1955	36	70	1.50
1956	40	65	1.40

(a) Estimate the parameters of the demand function for X, relating the quantity demanded to the relative price of X.

(b) Test the significance of the regression coefficient.

CHAPTER 23

Identification

An econometric model has three aspects: its economic content, its mathematical structure, and its statistical properties. The logical consistency and completeness of the model are determined by its mathematics. The statistical aspects are concerned with the estimation of the model's parameters. How successful this estimation will be depends upon the empirical data and the form of the model. If the model is not in proper statistical form, it may turn out that the parameters cannot be uniquely estimated, even though adequate data are available. In the language of econometrics, the model may not be identified.

A. THE PROBLEM OF IDENTIFICATION

Consider a simple static econometric model of the market for a single commodity X:

(1) $$x_d = a_0 + b_0 p + u$$
(2) $$x_s = a_1 + b_1 p + v$$
(3) $$x_d = x_s$$

In this model, x_d and x_s are the quantities of X demanded and supplied respectively, p is the price of the commodity, u and v are (different) random variables, and a_0, a_1, b_0, and b_1 are the population parameters. If the constants are known, the three structural equations can be solved for the equilibrium price and quantity exchanged (subject to the random errors u and v). The actual price and the actual quantity exchanged are the result of the interaction of the demand and supply functions.

For given values of the parameters a unique pair (p, x) is determined, and this can be represented geometrically as the intersection of the demand curve and the supply curve. Suppose the sample data consist of two time series, showing the equilibrium price and quantity exchanged during each period of time. Now a question arises.

How do we know which equation, if either, is approximated by the observed data? The time series can be plotted as a scatter diagram, but how can we be sure that the points lie on the demand curve only or on the supply curve only? This is an example of the problem of *identification* that must be faced in the construction of all econometric models. In this case, we must question whether the data identify the demand curve, the supply curve, or some mixture of both.

In some instances, it is relatively easy to determine what the data show. Under the following conditions we can reach the conclusions indicated:

(1) It is known that the demand curve has been unchanged over time, and that the supply curve has shifted substantially. If this is the case, the parameters of the demand equation in the above model are indeed constant, but the parameters of the supply equation have in fact changed. The resulting sample data will show a scatter of points that lie on the demand curve; this situation was depicted in Figure 19.4. More generally, if the demand curve is highly stable relative to the supply curve, then changes in the price and quantity traded are due mostly to supply shifts. The sample scatter diagram will appear like that shown in Figure 23.1. We may then say the demand curve is identified by the data. This situation characterizes the market for many agricultural commodities, where the effects of rainfall, the harvest period, and seasonal patterns of milk production

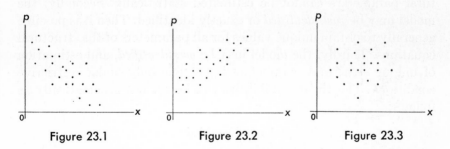

| Figure 23.1 | Figure 23.2 | Figure 23.3 |

cause violent shifts in the supply curve. When there is good evidence that the parameters of the demand curve (consumers' income, other prices, etc.) have changed little or not at all, while the parameters of the supply curve have, then a demand equation like (1) above can be estimated by simple regression analysis. The supply equation like (2) cannot be estimated, however.

(2) It is known that the supply curve has been unchanged while the demand curve has shifted substantially. This is the reverse case. If it is known that the parameters of the supply function (factor prices and technological conditions) have changed little or not at all, but the parameters of the demand function have, the sample data will appear like that shown in Figure 23.2. The points trace out approximately the supply curve, and we say the supply curve is identified. In this situation, simple regression analysis can be used to estimate a supply equation like (2) above, but the demand equation cannot be estimated.

(3) It is known that both the demand curve and the supply curve have shifted substantially. This is perhaps the most common case. The sample data may show a scatter like that depicted in Figure 23.3. Then a simple regression of the quantity traded upon the market price will reveal neither the demand equation nor the supply equation but rather some mixture of both. We say that neither the demand curve nor the supply curve is identified.

B. THE MEANING OF IDENTIFICATION

The foregoing discussion should provide some insight into the importance of identification. Nevertheless, the explanation is by no means complete, for there are three possibilities open. First, the model may be underidentified, in which case the entire set of structural parameters cannot be estimated statistically. Secondly, the model may be *just identified* or exactly identified. Then it is possible generally to obtain unique values for all parameters of the structural equations. Thirdly, the model may be *overidentified*, and estimation of unique structural parameters is possible only under restrictive conditions. The three possibilities can be set out schematically as follows:

(1) Underidentified
(2) Identified
    (a) Just Identified
    (b) Overidentified

If any one equation in the model is underidentified (not identified), the model is said to be underidentified. Thus, the model presented in the previous section is underidentified, regardless of whether the sample outcome is that shown in Figure 23.1, 23.2, or 23.3. Likewise, a model is said to be overidentified if any one equation is over-identified; and a just identified model requires that every one of the equations be just identified.

Underidentification and overidentification are qualitatively different properties of a model. The former is nonstochastic. By this we mean the structural parameters cannot be estimated statistically regardless of the size or accuracy of the sample data. On the other hand, all parameters of overidentified models could be estimated by better sample observations or longer computations. For this reason, in the present chapter we shall stress the difference between under-identified and identified models—whether the identified models are exactly identified or overidentified. In the next chapter just identified and overidentified models will be contrasted from the viewpoint of statistical estimation.

The effects of identification properties upon the model can be interpreted in more than one way. Before entering into a discussion of the effects, however, we shall explain the rules for determining the identification properties of a model—the procedures for finding out into which of the three categories a model falls.

C. RULES FOR IDENTIFICATION

We will treat only models consisting of linear structural equations in which it is assumed that the errors are errors of omission. The random variables in the model summarize the influence of variables that have been omitted from the equations, because they are not known to influence the dependent variable, their separate influences are individually small, no observations on them exist, or for some other similar reason. For illustrative purposes, we shall use a model of the market for a single commodity, but it should be remembered that the principles developed here apply equally to other econometric models.

For the commodity X, we have

(1) $\quad x_d = a_0 + b_0 p + u \quad$ (demand equation)
(2) $\quad x_s = a_1 + b_1 p + v \quad$ (supply equation)
(3) $\quad x_d = x_s$

This is seen to be the same model presented at the beginning of the chapter, and the symbols have the same meanings.

We shall first ask ourselves whether the model is logically complete. That is to say, if the values of the constants a_0, a_1, b_0, and b_1 were known, could the model be solved for the equilibrium values of the endogenous variables (subject to the errors u and v)? We see that there are three variables and three equations in these variables. Hence, the model is a logically complete model.

Having satisfied ourselves that the values of the variables can be determined if the constants are known, we must next ask whether it is possible to statistically estimate the constants or population parameters. This is the problem of identification. Before establishing the conditions that must hold in order for a model to be identified, we must recall some of the definitions given in Chapter 14. We saw there that structural equations are of two kinds: behavioral equations and definitions or statements of equilibrium. Behavioral equations contain systematic and random variables of which the systematic variables are either endogenous or exogenous. *With respect to identification, we shall be interested in behavioral equations containing endogenous variables.* In the above model equations (1) and (2) are of this kind. There are no exogenous variables in the model. Equation (3) is a definition, more specifically a definition of equilibrium.

We now turn to the rules for identification developed by members of the Cowles Commission at the University of Chicago. For a model to be identified, it is necessary that each behavioral equation containing one or more endogenous variables be identified. If *any one* of these equations is not identified, we say the model itself is not identified. The necessary condition for the identification of one such equation is:

The number of variables excluded from this equation (but contained in the model) must be at least one less than the total number of endogenous variables in the entire model.

The necessary and sufficient conditions for identification of one behavioral equation containing endogenous variables is given as follows: Let there be n behavioral equations containing one or more endogenous variables each. Then:

It must be possible to construct at least one nonzero determinant of order $(n - 1)$ from the coefficients of the variables excluded from the equation in question but contained in the other $(n - 1)$ behavioral equations.

The construction of determinants was discussed in Chapter 6. The full meaning and significance of these rules becomes clear from applications to specific models.

1. Model 1

Consider first the model given above. Equations (1) and (2) are behavioral equations containing the endogenous variables x_d, x_s, and p. Hence, both of these equations must be identified if the model is to be identified.

We treat first equation (1). Is the necessary condition satisfied? There are three endogenous variables in the entire model. For (1) to be identified, the number of variables excluded from (1) must be at least two, that is, one less than the total number of endogenous variables. But there is only one variable in the model that is excluded from (1), namely x_s. Therefore, the demand equation is not identified, so the model is not identified. Let us test equation (2) for identification anyway. There must be at least two variables excluded from it but contained in the model. Since there is only one, x_d, the supply equation is not identified either.

2. Model 2

Suppose an econometric model is similar to Model 1, but the demand equation contains an exogenous variable:

$$\text{(1)} \qquad x_d = a_0 + b_0 p + c_0 y + u$$
$$\text{(2)} \qquad x_s = a_1 + b_1 p + v$$
$$\text{(3)} \qquad y = y_0$$
$$\text{(4)} \qquad x_d = x_s$$

The symbol y represents real income; its constant value is y_0 given by equation (3). There are four systematic variables and four structural equations, so the model is complete. Equations (1), (2), and (3) are behavioral equations, but only (1) and (2) contain endogenous variables. We test these two equations for identification by the rule for the necessary condition.

Consider first the demand equation. Since there are three endogenous variables in the model, there must be at least $3 - 1 = 2$ variables (endogenous or exogenous) that appear in the model but not in equation (1). We see that there is only one such variable, x_s. Hence, the demand equation is not identified. Turning to equation (2), there must be $3 - 1 = 2$ variables excluded from (2) but contained in the model. There are indeed two such variables, namely x_d and y (note again that the variables excluded may be endogenous or exogenous). The necessary condition for the identification of the supply equation is met.

For the necessary and sufficient condition, it is required that at least one nonzero second-order determinant can be formed from the coefficients of the two variables excluded from (2). The coefficient of x_d is 1, and the coefficient of y is c_0. We saw in Chapter 6 that the second-order determinant

$$\begin{vmatrix} q & r \\ s & t \end{vmatrix}$$

has the value $qt - sr$. The question is: Can we form such a second-order determinant from 1 and c_0 which is not equal to zero? The only condition under which we can do this is that c_0 not be zero. Therefore if $c_0 \neq 0$, then the necessary and sufficient condition for identification of the supply equation is satisfied. We have seen, however, that the demand equation does not satisfy the necessary condition, so even if $c_0 \neq 0$, the model is still not identified.

3. Model 3

Let us now introduce an exogenous variable into the supply equation. This variable might be the price of some factor input, such as the wage rate for labor used in the production of X. Denote it by w. The new model is

(1) $x_d = a_0 + b_0 p + c_0 y + u$
(2) $x_s = a_1 + b_1 p + c_1 w + v$
(3) $y = y_0$
(4) $w = w_0$
(5) $x_d = x_s$

This model is also logically complete. Furthermore, both the demand and supply equations are identified if certain very likely conditions are met. There are three endogenous variables. There must be excluded from equation (1) at least $3 - 1 = 2$ variables, which appear in the other equations. These two variables are x_s and w. Likewise, there are two variables excluded from equation (2): x_d and y. The necessary condition for identification is satisfied for both behavioral equations that contain endogenous variables.

The necessary and sufficient condition is also satisfied if both $c_0 \neq 0$ and $c_1 \neq 0$. We can construct at least one nonzero determinant of the second order from the coefficients of the variables excluded from (1), that is, from the coefficients 1 and c_1, if $c_1 \neq 0$. Similarly we can construct such a determinant from the coefficients 1 and c_0 if $c_0 \neq 0$. Therefore, we conclude that this model is identified if the coefficients of the exogenous variables are not zero.

4. Generalization of the Counting Rules

Having traced through a few examples, we are now in a position to generalize the rules for establishing identification. Consider a model consisting of n equations in n endogenous variables and m exogenous variables. The ith equation is written

$$(i) \qquad a_i + \sum_{j=1}^{n} b_{ij} \cdot x_j + \sum_{k=1}^{m} c_{ik} \cdot y_k = u_i \qquad (i = 1, 2, \cdots, n),$$

where

$a_i =$ the constant term of the ith equation,

$x_j =$ endogenous variables (of which there are n),

$y_k =$ exogenous variables (of which there are m),

$u_i =$ random variables (of which there are n),

$b_{ij} =$ coefficient of the endogenous variable x_j in the ith equation (first subscript refers to the equation in which it appears and second to the variable of which it is the coefficient),

$c_{ik} =$ coefficient of the exogenous variable y_k in the ith equation.

Notice that all definitions have been solved out of the system, so the number of endogenous variables equals the total number of equations. For example, in the previous Model 3 equations (3), (4), and (5) would not appear. Instead, (3) and (4) would have been substituted in (1) and (2), and the variable on the left of the equality sign in (1) and (2) is x rather than x_d or x_s. In terms of this notation the constant terms and coefficients may be positive or negative, and some may be zero.

The necessary condition for identification of the ith equation is:

The number of variables excluded from (i) must be *at least* $(n - 1)$. To be exactly identified, the number excluded must equal $(n - 1)$. To be overidentified, the number excluded must be greater than $(n - 1)$.

The necessary and sufficient condition for identification of the ith equation is

It must be possible to construct *at least* one nonzero determinant of order $(n - 1)$ from the coefficients of the variables excluded from (i). If one and only one such nonzero determinant can be formed, the model is exactly identified. If more than one such nonzero determinant can be formed, the model is overidentified.

To illustrate, let Model 3 be written

(1) $x = a_0 + b_0p + c_0y_0 + u,$

(2) $x = a_1 + b_1p + c_1w_0 + v,$

where $n = 2$ and $m = 2$. The exogenous variable w_0 is the only variable not appearing in (1). From the number c_1 it is possible to form one and only one first-order determinant. Hence, if $c_1 \neq 0$, then (1) is exactly identified. An identical argument applies to equation (2) if $c_0 \neq 0$. Assuming $c_1 \neq 0$ and $c_0 \neq 0$, then the entire model is just identified.

Suppose instead that equation (1) were

(1) $$x = a_0 + b_0p + c_0y_0 + d_0q_0 + u,$$

where q_0 is another exogenous variable. The demand equation (1) is still just identified if $c_1 \neq 0$. However, the supply equation (2) is overidentified if both $c_0 \neq 0$ and $d_0 \neq 0$. Why? Because it is possible to form *two* nonzero first-order determinants (determinants of order $n - 1$) from c_0 and d_0 in this case.

D. THE STATISTICAL EFFECT OF IDENTIFICATION

If any equation of a model is underidentified, no change in the sample observations and no alteration of statistical techniques will generate estimates of the structural parameters. As a consequence, the only recourse open to the econometrician is a respecification of the model itself whereby it becomes identified. This does not mean, however, that the effects of exact and overidentification are no different. Overidentification, though very common and often inescapable, is not a desirable property. In this section the effects of underidentification will first be demonstrated. Then attention will be directed to the contrast between exactly identified and overidentified models.

1. Effects of Underidentification

In models that are not identified, it is impossible to estimate the parameters of the behavioral equations from knowledge of the sample data! This can be illustrated in a way similar to that described by Professor T. C. Koopmans.[1] Let the true demand and

---

[1] C. Hood and T. C. Koopmans, eds., *Studies in Econometric Method* (New York: John Wiley & Sons, Inc., 1953), pp. 29–31.

supply equations for a commodity X be given by the following model:

(1) $x_d = 18 - 6p + u$ (demand equation)

(2) $x_s = 3 + 9p + v$ (supply equation)

(3) $x_d = x_s$

where the variables have the same meanings attributed to them in Model 1 above. Suppose that some omniscient individual knows the actual or true values of the parameters and that these are known by no other person. Let us assume this individual is a prankster; he chooses two numbers by which he multiplies the two behavioral equations (1) and (2). Moreover, he chooses numbers such that when the equations are multiplied by these numbers, the signs of the coefficients are not changed. Let us suppose he multiplies (1) by $\frac{2}{3}$ and (2) by $\frac{1}{3}$. The false or deceptive model that results is

(1′) $\frac{2}{3}x_d = \frac{2}{3}(18) - \frac{2}{3}(6)p + \frac{2}{3}u = 12 - 4p + \frac{2}{3}u$

(2′) $\frac{1}{3}x_s = \frac{1}{3}(3) + \frac{1}{3}(9)p + \frac{1}{3}v = 1 + 3p + \frac{1}{3}v$

(3′) $x_d = x_s$

Next the prankster adds (1′) and (2′) and deceptively calls the resulting equation the demand function. Thus he obtains

(A) $x_d = 13 - 1p + (\frac{2}{3}u + \frac{1}{3}v)$

Finally the prankster multiplies equations (1) and (2) by $\frac{1}{4}$ and $\frac{3}{4}$ respectively:

(1″) $\frac{1}{4}x_d = \frac{1}{4}(18) - \frac{1}{4}(6)p + \frac{1}{4}u = 4.50 - 1.50p + \frac{1}{4}u$

(2″) $\frac{3}{4}x_s = \frac{3}{4}(3) + \frac{3}{4}(9)p + \frac{3}{4}v = 2.25 + 6.75 + \frac{3}{4}v$

He adds (1″) and (2″) to obtain

(B) $x_s = 6.75 + 5.25p + (\frac{1}{4}u + \frac{3}{4}v)$

He deceptively calls the equation (B) the supply equation. Now statistical analysis on any number of sample observations on the variables x and p will not tell us whether the true model has been "tampered with," for the data consists of observations on the values of the systematic variables only. Since u and v are random variables, so are $(\frac{2}{3}u + \frac{1}{3}v)$ and $(\frac{1}{4}u + \frac{3}{4}v)$ random variables; we cannot distinguish these variables from u and v by means of the data. From a sample, we may compute the regression of x on p. But even if the price coefficient turns out to be negative, there is no way to tell if the resulting regression equation is the true demand equation (1) or the false demand equation (A). Likewise, if the regression coefficient turns out positive, we cannot tell whether we have estimated (2) or (B). The fact that this model is not identified means that we cannot uniquely establish the population parameters. The estimates may or may not be estimates of the true population parameters.

This same situation exists with Model 2 of Section C. Suppose we multiply the demand equation (1) of that model by an arbitrary constant k_0:

$$(1') \qquad k_0 x_d = k_0 a_0 + k_0 b_0 p + k_0 c_0 y + k_0 u$$

We then multiply the supply equation (2) by a constant k_1:

$$(2') \qquad k_1 x_s = k_1 a_1 + k_1 b_1 p + k_1 v$$

The sample data give observations on x and p. Hence, we add $(1')$ and $(2')$ and get

$$(k_0 + k_1)x = (k_0 a_0 + k_1 a_1) + (k_0 b_0 + k_1 b_1)p + (k_0 c_0)y + (k_0 u + k_1 v)$$

or

$$(A) \qquad x = \frac{(k_0 a_0 + k_1 a_1)}{(k_0 + k_1)} + \frac{(k_0 b_0 + k_1 b_1)}{(k_0 + k_1)} p + \frac{(k_0 c_0)}{(k_0 + k_1)} y + \frac{(k_0 u + k_1 v)}{(k_0 + k_1)}$$

On the basis of the sample evidence and computed coefficients, there is no way to determine whether the computations yield (1) or (A). This follows from the fact that equation (1) is not identified.

Assuming that $c_0 \neq 0$ and $c_1 \neq 0$, Model 3 has satisfied both the necessary and sufficient conditions for identification. Consequently, no problem of ambiguity will arise in the empirical estimates of the population parameters. Consider the demand equation and multiply it by the constant k_0. This will be identical with equation $(1')$ in the preceding case. Then multiply the supply equation of Model 3 by the constant k_1. Addition of the resulting equations gives the "false" demand equation

$$(A) \qquad x = \frac{(k_0 a_0 + k_1 a_1)}{(k_0 + k_1)} + \frac{(k_0 b_0 + k_1 b_1)}{(k_0 + k_1)} p + \frac{(k_0 c_0)}{(k_0 + k_1)} y$$
$$+ \frac{(k_1 c_1)}{(k_0 + k_1)} w + \frac{(k_0 u + k_1 v)}{(k_0 + k_1)}$$

Purely on the basis of the sample observations alone, we can distinguish this equation (A) from the true demand equation (1) in Model 3. This is possible if, as we assumed, c_1 is not zero. The true demand equation does not include the systematic variable w, but (A) does include w if $c_1 \neq 0$.

We perform a similar operation to obtain a "false" supply equation. Multiply the demand equation (1) by the constant r_0 and the supply equation (2) by r_1. Call these resulting equations (1') and (2'). Addition of (1') and (2') yields the "false" supply equation

$$
\text{(B)} \quad x = \frac{(r_0 a_0 + r_1 a_1)}{(r_0 + r_1)} + \frac{(r_0 b_0 + r_1 b_1)}{(r_0 + r_1)} \, p + \frac{(r_0 c_0)}{(r_0 + r_1)} \, y
$$
$$
+ \frac{(r_1 c_1)}{(r_0 + r_1)} \, w + \frac{(r_0 u + r_1 v)}{(r_0 + r_1)}
$$

We can again distinguish (B) from the true supply equation if $c_0 \neq 0$, which was seen to be the necessary and sufficient condition for the identification of the supply equation. For if $c_0 \neq 0$, then (B) contains the systematic variable y whereas the supply equation (2) does not.

Consequently, if the necessary and sufficient conditions for identification of a model are satisfied, no ambiguity arises as to the interpretation of the empirical estimates. In the case of Model 3 if $c_0 \neq 0$ and $c_1 \neq 0$, then statistical inference will yield estimates that we know are estimates of the true population parameters.

2. Effects of Overidentification

In order to show the effects of overidentification—and especially to contrast them with those arising from exact and underidentification—it will be necessary to introduce the notion of a *reduced form*. The reduced form of a model is the expression of the endogenous variables in terms of the exogenous variables and the random variables.

Least squares estimation or regression analysis, as presented in Chapters 19 and 20, is a method designed basically to predict the behavior of one variable from an assumed known behavior of other variables. In other words, changes in the dependent variable are to be explained by changes in the independent variables. But this is precisely what is meant by the systematic variables of an economic model: exogenous variables determine endogenous variables and are not determined by the endogenous variables. Therefore, the desirable statistical features of least squares estimates hold true strictly only for reduced form equations, as we shall see in the following chapter.

Normally, statistical regression equations are interpreted, in the language of econometrics, as reduced form equations.

Let us first consider an exactly identified model, e.g., Model 3. We may reduce the size of this model by substituting equations (3) and (4) into equations (1) and (2) respectively. The model then appears as follows:

$$(1') \qquad x_d = a_0 + b_0 p + c_0 y_0 + u$$
$$(2') \qquad x_s = a_1 + b_1 p + c_1 w_0 + v$$
$$(3') \qquad x_d = x_s$$

The sample data to be used for estimation consist of observations on p, x, y_0, and w_0. Since each observation on the quantity of X traded is such that $x = x_d = x_s$, we may write x for x_d in $(1')$ and x for x_s in $(2')$. Then we can solve for x and p in terms of the exogenous variables y_0 and w_0 and the random variables u and v. Thus, substitution of $(1')$ and $(2')$ into $(3')$ yields

$$(4') \quad p = \frac{(a_1 - a_0)}{(b_0 - b_1)} + \frac{c_1}{(b_0 - b_1)} w_0 - \frac{c_0}{(b_0 - b_1)} y_0 + \frac{(v - u)}{(b_0 - b_1)}$$

Then setting $x_d = x$ and $x_s = x$, and solving for x, we obtain

$$(5') \quad x = \frac{(a_0 b_1 - a_1 b_0)}{(b_1 - b_0)} + \frac{(c_0 b_1)}{(b_1 - b_0)} y_0 - \frac{(c_1 b_0)}{(b_1 - b_0)} w_0 + \frac{(u b_1 - v b_0)}{(b_1 - b_0)}$$

These are the reduced-form equations of Model 3. The constants and coefficients of these equations are obtained by the usual multiple linear regression methods. When the least-squares estimates have been obtained, the constant terms and coefficients of these equations are known numbers. Let us suppose the two empirical regression equations are computed as

$$(6') \qquad p = \hat{\alpha} + \hat{\beta} w_0 + \hat{\gamma} y_0,$$
$$(7') \qquad x = \hat{\lambda} + \hat{\theta} y_0 + \hat{\phi} w_0,$$

From $(4')$ and $(5')$ it follows that

$$\hat{\alpha} = \frac{(a_1 - a_0)}{(b_0 - b_1)} \qquad\qquad \hat{\lambda} = \frac{(a_0 b_1 - a_1 b_0)}{(b_1 - b_0)}$$

$$\hat{\beta} = \frac{c_1}{(b_0 - b_1)} \qquad\qquad \hat{\theta} = \frac{c_0 b_1}{(b_1 - b_0)}$$

$$\hat{\gamma} = -\frac{c_0}{(b_0 - b_1)} \qquad\qquad \hat{\phi} = -\frac{c_1 b_0}{(b_1 - b_0)}$$

Since $\hat{\alpha}$, $\hat{\beta}$, $\hat{\gamma}$, $\hat{\lambda}$, $\hat{\theta}$, and $\hat{\phi}$ are known numbers, this system is comprised of six linear equations in six unknowns, namely a_0, b_0, c_0, a_1, b_1, and c_1. The system can be solved for unique values of all the structural parameters. The number of relationships between the reduced form coefficients and the structural coefficients is just sufficient to determine estimates of the structural parameters from estimates of the reduced form parameters.

Let us next examine the effects of underidentification. Model 2 was seen to be underidentified. By writing Model 2 as

$$(1')\qquad x = a_0 + b_0 p + c_0 y_0 + u,$$
$$(2')\qquad x = a_1 + b_1 p + v,$$

the reduced form (ignoring the residual terms for simplicity) is

$$(3')\qquad p = \frac{(a_1 - a_0)}{(b_0 - b_1)} - \frac{c_0}{(b_0 - b_1)} y_0,$$

$$(4')\qquad x = \frac{(b_1 a_0 - b_0 a_1)}{(b_1 - b_0)} + \frac{b_1 c_0}{(b_1 - b_0)} y_0.$$

Assume the regression equations are computed as

$$(5')\qquad p = \hat{\alpha} + \hat{\beta} y_0,$$
$$(6')\qquad x = \hat{\lambda} + \hat{\theta} y_0.$$

Then the system

$$\hat{\alpha} = \frac{(a_1 - a_0)}{(b_0 - b_1)} \qquad\qquad \hat{\lambda} = \frac{(b_1 a_0 - b_0 a_1)}{(b_1 - b_0)}$$

$$\hat{\beta} = -\frac{c_0}{(b_0 - b_1)} \qquad\qquad \hat{\theta} = \frac{b_1 c_0}{(b_1 - b_0)}$$

consists of four linear equations in five unknowns: a_0, b_0, c_0, a_1, and b_1. As a consequence, the equations cannot be solved to obtain the values of these structural parameters. Incidentally, this result is not something different from the explanation of underidentification already presented in terms of "false" equations. It is an alternative way of expressing the same effect.

Finally, an overidentified model was presented in Section C:

$$(1')\qquad x = a_0 + b_0 p + c_0 y_0 + d_0 q_0 + u,$$
$$(2')\qquad x = a_1 + b_1 p + c_1 w_0 + v.$$

The reduced form is as follows:

$$(3')\qquad p = \frac{(a_1 - a_0)}{(b_0 - b_1)} - \frac{c_0}{(b_0 - b_1)} y_0 - \frac{d_0}{(b_0 - b_1)} q_0 + \frac{c_1}{(b_0 - b_1)} w_0,$$

$$(4')\qquad x = \frac{(b_1 a_0 - b_0 a_1)}{(b_1 - b_0)} + \frac{c_0}{(b_1 - b_0)} y_0 + \frac{d_0}{(b_1 - b_0)} q_0 - \frac{b_0 c_1}{(b_1 - b_0)} w_0.$$

The computed regression equations are assumed to be

$$(5')\qquad\qquad\qquad p = \hat{\alpha} + \hat{\beta} y_0 + \hat{\gamma} q_0 + \hat{\delta} w_0,$$

$$(6')\qquad\qquad\qquad x = \hat{\lambda} + \hat{\theta} y_0 + \hat{\phi} q_0 + \hat{\pi} w_0.$$

We shall not bother to write out the system of equations. The computed constant terms and coefficients of $(5')$ and $(6')$ are set equal to the corresponding constant terms and coefficients in $(3')$ and $(4')$ as before. It is obvious at once that the resulting system is comprised of eight equations in only seven unknowns: $a_0, b_0, c_0, d_0, a_1, b_1,$ and c_1. The system is overdetermined. There are too many relations between the reduced form and structural parameters, so the structural parameters cannot be determined *uniquely* from knowledge of the reduced form parameters. Depending upon the procedure of solution (which unknowns are solved for first), more than one estimate is obtained for at least one of the structural parameters. If, say, two values are obtained for the parameter b_0, neither may be an estimate of the true population parameter.

Underidentified models permit no estimation of the entire model by any statistical methods. Whereas just identified models are estimated by least squares estimates of the reduced form, overidentified models can be estimated only by means of other statistical methods. In the following chapter we shall sketch briefly alternative methods of estimation and their statistical properties.

PROBLEMS

Tell whether the following models are identified. If a model is not identified, make appropriate adjustments to identify it.

1. (1) $x_d = a_0 + b_0 p + c_0 y + u$ $a_0 > 0, b_0 < 0, c_0 > 0$
   (2) $x_s = a_1 + b_1 p + v$ $a_1 < 0, b_1 > 0$
   (3) $x_d = x_s$

where x_d and x_s denote the quantities demanded and supplied respectively, p denotes the price of the commodity, y denotes consumer income, and u and v are random variables.

2. (1) $C = a_0 + b_0 Y + u$　　　　　　　　$a_0 > 0, b_0 > 0$
　 (2) $I = a_1 + b_1 Y + v$　　　　　　　　$a_1 < 0, b_1 > 0$
　 (3) $Y = C + I$
　 where C denotes aggregate consumption, Y denotes national income, and I denotes aggregate net investment.
3. The second demand-supply model in Section D.1, Chapter 14, page 217.
4. The second national income model in Section D.3, Chapter 14, page 220.

CHAPTER 24

A Survey of Parameter Estimation

In Chapter 18 a description of statistical inference was presented. In general, statistical estimation takes the form of upper and lower boundaries yielding a confidence interval, within which it is asserted the unknown population parameter lies. Point estimation is a special case of interval estimation, such that a single figure rather than an interval is obtained as an estimate. The present chapter is devoted to a brief sketch of point estimation applied to multiequation econometric models that are exactly identified or overidentified.

A. CRITERIA FOR DESIRABLE ESTIMATES

The inference from a given sample to a statistical population in a sense passes through the distribution of many samples or a larger sample even though one observes only a single sample of a fixed size. In other words, the virtue of an estimator computed from a sample is judged partly in terms of what would be expected to happen if many such samples were available or the sample size could be increased without limit. There are four common characteristics of a good estimator or sample statistic.

1. *Unbiased.* One desirable property of an estimator is that it be unbiased. An unbiased estimator is one which, on the basis of the theory of sampling, can be shown to converge to the population parameter as the *number of samples* of a given size increases.
2. *Consistent.* A second desirable property of an estimator is that it be consistent. A consistent statistic is one that converges to the population parameter as the *size of the sample* increases.
3. *Efficient.* An efficient statistic is one that has the minimum variance among all possible estimates. In terms of degree, the more efficient is a statistic the smaller is the variance of its distribution.

4. *Sufficient.* A sufficient statistic or estimator is one that contains all the information available from the sample about the population parameter. For example, the statistic gives the same information about the parameter as would knowledge of more details of the sample.

In actual empirical research in economics one must often be content with estimators that possess one or more of these properties, but not all of them. Assuming there is more than one way to estimate a parameter, a given estimator is said to be superior to others if it possesses more of these characteristics than do the others. Of primary importance are unbiasedness and consistency. Consequently, our discussion will be carried out with special reference to these two criteria.

B. EXACTLY IDENTIFIED MODELS

As indicated earlier, the structural equations of an exactly identified model are estimated by expressing the model in reduced form, estimating the reduced form parameters by least squares one equation at a time, and then solving back to the structural parameters. The justification for this procedure can be explained by contrasting the properties of structural estimates so obtained with the properties of estimates that result from direct application of least squares to the structural equations themselves.

1. Estimation of the Reduced Form

Referring once more to Chapter 18, the method of maximum likelihood was cited as a method of point estimation. The estimate is that value which, if it were correct, would maximize the probability of obtaining the sample actually observed. Let us suppose for simplicity that one reduced form equation is [1]

$$p = \alpha + \beta z + r,$$

where p denotes an endogenous variable, z an exogenous variable, and r a random variable. The constants α and β are linear combinations of the unknown structural parameters and are thus unknown. Likewise, r is a linear combination of the random variables of the structural equations.

---

[1] The principles of estimation to be developed apply also to any number of exogenous variables that might be included.

Now suppose the sample consists of observations on the pair

$$[p(s), z(s)], \qquad s = 1, 2, \ldots, S,$$

where $p(s)$ is one observation, the sth observation on p, and $z(s)$ is the corresponding observation on z. There are a total of S observations in the sample.

The following assumptions are introduced about the random variable r:

(1) The mathematical expectation of r is zero,
(2) The variance of r is constant,
(3) The variable r is normally distributed,
(4) The variable r is not autocorrelated,
(5) The variable r is not correlated with z.

Employing the concept of maximum likelihood, the probability of obtaining the observed sample is nothing other than the probability that the random variable r shall have assumed the values $r(s)$ for $s = 1, 2, \ldots, S$.[2] The likelihood function is therefore the probability that $r(1), r(2), \ldots, r(s)$ will occur together. By assumption (4) above the probability that one value of r will occur is independent of the probability that any other value will occur. And the multiplication Rule 2 under Section C of Chapter 17 states that the probability of two or more independent events occurring together is the product of their separate probabilities. Letting $\rho\,[r(s)]$ denote the probability that r will assume the value $r(s)$ and letting L denote the likelihood function, then

$$L = \rho\,[r(1)] \cdot \rho\,[r(2)] \cdot \ldots \cdot \rho\,[r(S)].$$

One more step remains. By assumption (3) above r is normally distributed. Hence, the formula for the normal distribution can be substituted in the expression for L, giving

$$L = \frac{1}{(2\pi)^{S/2}\,\sigma_r^{\,S/2}\,e^{\frac{1}{2\sigma_r^2}D}}$$

where σ_r^2 denotes the constant variance of r and

$$D = \sum_{s=1}^{S} [r(s)]^2 = \sum_{s=1}^{S} [p(s) - \alpha - \beta z(s)]^2.$$

[2] Each observation can be written $p(s) = \alpha + \beta z(s) + r(s)$. Given α and β as true constants, the occurrence of $p(s)$ and $z(s)$ yields a given $r(s)$. And the probability of $p(s)$ and $z(s)$ is the probability that $r(s)$ will occur.

Note first that D is the sum of squares of the random errors, and secondly that maximization of L is tantamount to minimization of D. The necessary conditions for maximization of L are

$$\frac{\partial L}{\partial \alpha} = 0, \quad \frac{\partial L}{\partial \beta} = 0, \quad \frac{\partial L}{\partial \sigma_r} = 0.$$

In maximizing, all partial derivatives of α, β and σ_r with respect to one another are zero because they are assumed constants. The above conditions yield the equations

$$\sum_{s=1}^{S} [p(s) - \alpha - \beta z(s)] = 0$$

$$\sum_{s=1}^{S} [p(s) - \alpha - \beta z(s)] z(s) = 0$$

$$\frac{1}{S} \sum_{s=1}^{S} [p(s) - \alpha - \beta z(s)]^2 = \sigma_r^2$$

Solution of these equations gives $\hat{\alpha}$, $\hat{\beta}$ and $\hat{\sigma}_r^2$ as maximum likelihood estimates of α, β and σ_r^2. But the first two equations above are nothing other than the normal equations of least squares, as shown in Chapter 19.[3] Thus least-squares estimates are maximum likelihood estimates of the reduced form population parameters.

2. Comparison with Direct Least Squares

If the model is exactly identified, such as Model 3 of the previous chapter, one might ask why multiple regressions are not applied directly to the structural equations. Since different exogenous variables appear in the two equations, it is to be expected that different regression coefficients will be obtained for the two equations. The answer is found in the estimating criteria described in Section A.

It can be shown that if all of the five assumptions about the random variable r are satisfied, then the least squares method applied to each reduced form equation one at a time yields maximum likelihood, unbiased, consistent, efficient, and sufficient estimates of the reduced form parameters. These desirable characteristics hinge upon the proposition that the independent or explanatory variables in each regression equation can be interpreted as exogenous variables in an economic model. If some of these independent regression varia-

[3] See especially footnote 1 in Chapter 19, where y plays the role of p here and x plays the role of z.

bles are instead endogenous variables—as in the case of least squares applied directly to the structural equations—then the estimates are both biased and inconsistent.

Once the reduced form parameters are estimated by least squares, estimates of the structural parameters are found by solving a system of equations as described in the previous chapter. Now it can also be shown that, although the reduced form estimators are unbiased and consistent, the structural estimators so obtained are biased except in special cases. Nevertheless, this procedure is superior to direct least squares for two reasons. First, the bias (underestimate or overestimate of the true structural parameters) is less than in the case of direct least squares. Secondly, the estimates of the structural parameters are consistent, whereas direct least squares estimates are not.

3. Violation of the Assumptions

The statistical desirability of reduced form, least squares estimators depends upon whether or not the five assumptions about the random variable are in fact satisfied. In practice it is not uncommon that some of these assumptions are violated. For example, assumption (2) states that the variance of the random error is constant. Instead its variance may change systematically with time or space.

In common-sense terms, violation of assumption (2) might follow from an improvement of data-collecting techniques over time so the error variance decreases. Or when figures are reported, say on tax returns, they are reported in even dollar figures, ignoring cents, whereas formerly both dollars and cents were reported. Then the variance increases. The statistical effect is to render the least squares estimates of reduced form parameters inefficient.

Violation of assumption (5) means the error term varies systematically with the size of an exogenous variable. For example, economic behavior is fairly exact (the value of r is small) for moderate values of z but very erratic for very large or very small values of z. Suppose z represents the government budget in an economy and p represents foreign holding of national debt securities. As long as the budget does not vary substantially, the holding of debt may be predictable with slight error. But if a large surplus or deficit is enacted, the fluctuations in foreign holding of government debt may exhibit substantial random behavior. The effect of such correlations is to produce a bias in the estimate of the reduced form parameters.

Probably more important in practical econometric research is the occurrence of autocorrelation in the error term: violation of assumption (4). The error term may actually include variables that act seasonally, or cyclically, or display a strong time trend. In addition, there may be errors of observation that vary systematically over time, so the variable r which absorbs these errors exhibits a correlation between its value in one time period and its value in another.

We have already discussed autocorrelation in Chapter 21. Once a reduced form equation is estimated, an empirical residual series can be computed by taking the difference between each observed value of the endogenous variable and the predicted value of the endogenous variable based upon the computed regression coefficients. This residual series can then be tested for the presence of autocorrelation and, if present, attempts can be made to eliminate or reduce it. One such test and a few of the methods for eliminating or reducing autocorrelation were discussed in Chapter 21. If significant autocorrelation persists, the reduced form estimators are inefficient. The sampling variances of the least-squares estimators are too large; one is very likely to obtain underestimates of the sampling variance of the regression coefficients. This means that the standard tests of statistical significance (such as the t test) are no longer valid.

Thus, even when a model is exactly identified, the problems encountered are numerous and thorny. The nature of the data and the true causal relationships actually operating in the economy often give rise to estimates of the structural parameters (if not also the reduced form parameters) which leave something to be desired.

C. OVERIDENTIFIED MODELS

If the structural model is overidentified, application of least squares to each reduced form equation of a model does not yield unique estimates of the structural parameters. Consequently, other estimation methods are used. Some of the methods available are: (1) least squares applied directly to the structural equations, (2) the method of instrumental variables, (3) two stage least squares, (4) limited information maximum likelihood, and (5) full information maximum likelihood. A complete discussion of these methods is beyond the scope of this book. A brief interpretation of each method will be presented and the computation procedure will be illustrated for only one, namely, two stage least squares because the computation design is simple.

The first method, as already noted, is biased and inconsistent. The others are all biased but consistent, varying in their degree of efficiency. They are listed in rough order of increasing efficiency.

A complete causal chain is inherent to every multiequation model. Every endogenous variable in the model, regardless of where it appears, exerts an effect upon the behavior of all other endogenous variables. And each endogenous variable is affected by other endogenous variables. Every exogenous variable, regardless of the equation in which it appears, affects all the endogenous variables of the model—both those in the same equation and indirectly those appearing elsewhere.

The method of instrumental variables estimates one structural equation at a time, recognizing that all other exogenous variables of the system affect the behavior of variables within the equation and thereby influence the true population parameters of the equation. But the method selects from among these other exogenous variables and ignores the remainder. Generally speaking, the variables selected as instrumental for the equation in question should be those least correlated with one another and which also affect strongly as many as possible of the variables present in the equation being estimated. However, there is no a priori information that assures the variables being selected as instrumental do indeed satisfy these requirements. As a consequence, the choice is basically arbitrary.

Limited information maximum likelihood estimation, in contrast to the method of instrumental variables, makes use of all the exogenous variables of the model rather than an arbitrary selection. But it does ignore part of the causal chain operating to determine the true structural parameters. Consider the following over-identified model:

(1) $$x = a_0 + b_0 p + c_0 y_0 + u$$
(2) $$x = a_1 + b_1 p + c_1 w_0 + d_1 q_0 + v,$$

where q_0 is exogenous. To estimate equation (1), limited information recognizes that w_0 and q_0 affect p and x in (2) and thus indirectly affect the behavior of p and x in (1) as well. The combined impact of w_0 and q_0 on (1) is not ignored, but their separate impacts are not known. Also, limited information would ignore the indirect effect of any endogenous variable not appearing in (1). For example, if there were a third equation in the model relating a third endogenous variable h to the endogenous variable p, then the effect of h on equation (1), operating through p, would be ignored.

The computation of limited information is quite cumbersome, but not as cumbersome as the computation of full information maximum likelihood estimation. Therefore, we shall disregard full information and discuss instead the computation procedure for two stage least squares.

Two stage least squares is also applied directly to one structural equation at a time. In doing so, the method attempts to take account of the effects exerted upon the equation in question by exogenous variables appearing elsewhere in the model. Consider equation (1) in the overidentified model just presented. Direct least squares applied to (1) is biased and inconsistent since p is not truly an exogenous variable. Two stage least squares first estimates the equation

$$\hat{p} = \hat{\alpha} + \hat{\beta}y_0 + \hat{\gamma}w_0 + \hat{\delta}q_0,$$

where $\hat{\alpha}$, $\hat{\beta}$, $\hat{\gamma}$, and $\hat{\delta}$ are the least squares computations of the constant term and coefficients of this equation, and $\hat{p}$ is the value of p predicted from all exogenous variables regardless of where they appear in the model. Then instead of estimating equation (1), the equation

$$(1') \qquad x = a_0 + b_0\hat{p} + c_0y_0 + u$$

is estimated by least squares. The endogenous variable p is replaced by the exogenously determined portion of p, namely $\hat{p}$.

The relative merits of these various estimating techniques have been debated in the literature of econometrics. Aside from ease of computation or elegance of design, no obvious grounds have been established that would lead to an unambiguous preference for one over all others. Indeed, the inconsistency of direct least squares may not be serious in many cases, and the difference between estimates of structural parameters obtained in this way may not differ significantly from estimates obtained by, say, limited information or two stage least squares. For this reason direct least squares is sometimes used in practice.

CHAPTER 25

Illustrations of Econometric Research

The most direct way to appreciate the practical value of econometric research is to review some of the results achieved in the field. Continuous developments have occurred in this area of economics over the past three decades. New theoretical models have been devised and their implications explored by means of mathematical analysis. Refinements in the theory of statistics have cast new light on problems of economic measurement. More and more empirical studies are being carried out, and these empirical findings have often led to revisions in the theoretical models. A completely representative review of the literature is, of course, impossible here. We may, however, examine the results of some actual studies conducted in various areas of economics. Since we have already discussed methods of statistical estimation, we shall concentrate attention on the results themselves. The models will be presented with the estimated values of the parameters contained in the structural equations.

A. MARKET DEMAND

One of the earliest statistical studies of market demand was done by the late Professor Henry Schultz of the University of Chicago.[1] His pioneering studies on demand have set the stage for much subsequent research. He estimated statistically the demand functions for wheat, sugar, corn, cotton, meats, and several other agricultural commodities. Using multiple regression analysis, he obtained the following least-squares estimate for the demand for wheat in the United States:

$$\log x = 1.0802 - .2143 \log p - .00358t - .00163t^2$$

[1] H. Schultz, *The Theory and Measurement of Demand* (Chicago: University of Chicago Press, 1938).

In the demand equation, x denotes the quantity of wheat purchased per year (less seed) in bushels per capita, that is, per person. The total quantity is divided by population, so the influence of changes in population on the quantity demanded is taken into account.[2] The symbol p represents the annual average price per bushel received by farmers, deflated by an index of wholesale prices (1913 = 100). Finally, t denotes time (the influence of a nonlinear trend) with its origin ($t = 0$) at 1928. The regression coefficient of log p is statistically significant, whereas the coefficients of t and t^2 are not. Therefore, the demand curve did not shift significantly during the period covered by the study: 1921 to 1934, inclusive. The first two terms on the right side of the equation give a statistically significant estimate of the stable logarithmic demand function for wheat in the United States for the period 1921 to 1934.

Schultz was not as aware of problems of identification, multicollinearity, and autocorrelation as were later writers. R. Stone has measured the demand functions for several commodities in the United States and the United Kingdom.[3] He employs the following symbols:

q = the quantity of the commodity demanded per year
Q = real disposable income per year
p = the annual average price of the commodity
π = the annual average price of all other commodities
t = time in years
e = the base of natural logarithms

From time series data covering the period 1929 to 1941, inclusive, he uses multiple regression analysis to obtain several demand functions. The equation used to estimate the demand for tobacco in the United States is

$$q = 9.436 \ Q^{.325} \ p^{-.266} \ \pi^{.590} \ e^{.0206t}$$

Similarly, the demand equation for automobiles is estimated as

$$q = 1.2103 \ Q^{4.164} \ p^{-2.704} \ e^{-.0674t}$$

The least-squares estimates of the population parameters were computed by logarithmic multiple regressions (see Chapter 20).

[2] Let X denote the total quantity demanded in the market, and let P denote population. Then $x = \dfrac{X}{P}$, and if P and X increase proportionately the variable x remains constant.

[3] R. Stone, "The Analysis of Market Demand," *Journal of the Royal Statistical Society*, Vol. 108, Parts III–IV (1945).

Another interesting demand study is that of James Tobin.[4] He estimated the quantity of all food demanded in the United States as a function of the relative price of food, real income, and lagged real income. Using annual time series data from 1912 to 1948, inclusive, he estimated the demand for food as

$$\log C_t = 1.54 + .45 \log Y_t + .11 \log Y_{t-1} - .53 \log P_t$$

In this equation, C_t is an index (1935–1939 = 100) of food consumed during the year t in the United States. Y_t designates real income in year t, and Y_{t-1} represents real income lagged one year. P_t is an index of food prices in the United States (1925–1939 = 100). Tobin performed multiple regressions on the reduced-form equations of the model and solved back to obtain the demand parameters.

B. MARKET SUPPLY

In comparison with the work done on demand functions, relatively little has been done on supply. One reason for this is the fact that empirical data corresponding to the theoretical concepts is more accessible for demand studies. R. M. Walsh has estimated the supply function for cotton in the United States from nine annual observations, 1925–1933.[5] Using a simple lagged regression he obtains the linear function

$$x_t = 32.926 + .918 p_{t-1}$$

where x_t signifies the acreage of cotton planted on July 1 of year t and p_{t-1} signifies the deflated price of cotton received by farmers in the preceding crop year. From this estimated supply equation, the price elasticity of supply at the mean values of price and quantity is computed as .22.

Subsequent research by M. Nerlove indicates that the price elasticity of supply is probably larger than .22.[6] Nerlove relates the acreage of cotton to the expected price of cotton, where the expected price of cotton is estimated empirically from a series of past prices. This formulation involves the so-called distributed lags discussed in Chapter 22. His estimation of the supply function leads to the conclusion that the elasticity of acreage with respect to the expected price is .67. There are some a priori reasons for choosing the Nerlove

[4] J. Tobin, "A Statistical Demand Function for Food in the United States," *Journal of the Royal Statistical Society*, Vol. 113, Part II (1950).

[5] R. M. Walsh, "Response to Price in the Production of Cotton and Cottonseed," *Journal of Farm Economics*, Vol. 26 (August, 1944).

[6] M. Nerlove, "Estimates of the Elasticities of Supply of Selected Agricultural Commodities," *Journal of Farm Economics*, Vol. 38 (May, 1956).

model over the Walsh model, but the final choice of an appropriate measure of the supply of cotton must await further investigations. Similar exploratory research is being carried out to measure the supply functions of other commodities—both farm and nonfarm commodities.

A supply function for all agricultural commodities as a whole has been estimated by G. Tintner.[7] He begins with an identified model that includes both the demand and supply equations. Using annual time series data (1920–1943), he employs weighted regression methods to estimate the supply parameters. His estimated linear supply equation is

$$x = 347.097 + 1.721p + .809t - 3.611c$$

where x is an index of agricultural production (1935–1939 = 100), p is an index of prices received by farmers (1910–1914 = 100), t denotes time with the origin between 1931 and 1932, and c is an index of prices paid by farmers for items they purchase (1910–1914 = 100). From this equation, the elasticity of total production with respect to prices received and with respect to prices paid can be computed.

C. PRODUCTION FUNCTIONS

The statistical measurement of production functions owes much to the work of Paul H. Douglas (formerly Professor of Economics at the University of Chicago and now a United States Senator). Together with C. W. Cobb,[8] he estimated the following production function for the United States as a whole:

$$P = 1.10\ L^{.75}\ C^{.25}$$

where P is an index of total production per year, L is an index of labor inputs, and C is an index of capital inputs. The sample indexes ran from 1900 through 1922 (1899 = 100). The estimated exponents are the elasticities of production with respect to labor and capital. The first tells by what percentage production will change for a given percentage change in labor input, that is, for a one per cent increase in labor input with the amount of capital held constant, the equation predicts that total production will increase by $\frac{3}{4}$ of one per cent. The second exponent states that for, say, a one per cent increase in

[7] G. Tintner, "Multiple Regression for Systems of Equations," *Econometrica*, Vol. 14 (January, 1946).

[8] P. H. Douglas and C. W. Cobb, "A Theory of Production," *American Economic Review*, Vol. 18 (1928) supplement.

capital input (labor held constant), total production will increase by $\frac{1}{4}$ of one per cent.

This formulation of the input-output relationship came to be known as the Cobb-Douglas production function. In the thirty years since its original presentation, many extensions and refinements have taken place. These numerous studies have appeared in books and journal articles covering production functions in the United States and other countries.

D. COST FUNCTIONS

It is of interest to business firms as well as to economists that cost functions have also been derived empirically. Professor Joel Dean has made statistical cost studies of a leather belt shop, a hosiery mill, and a department store.[9] For the hosiery knitting mill Dean computed the following cost functions:

(1) $$c = 2935.59 + 1.998x$$

(2) $$\frac{c}{x} = 1.998 + \frac{2935.59}{x}$$

(3) $$\frac{dc}{dx} = 1.998$$

where c denotes the total cost of production in dollars and x denotes the quantity of hosiery in dozens of pairs per month. Equation (1) shows the total cost function, (2) the average cost function, and (3) the marginal cost function. The estimate of total cost was computed by a simple regression from monthly data covering the five years, 1935 through 1939. The average and marginal cost functions were derived from the estimated total cost function. It is interesting to note that over the range of output observed the total cost function is linear, which implies decreasing average cost and constant marginal cost. This appears to be at variance with the usual theoretical assumptions of a U-shaped average cost curve and a rising marginal cost curve. One must realize, however, that the empirical data may not cover the entire range of output up to full plant capacity. Further extensions and analyses of the data might reveal increasing marginal cost.

[9] J. Dean, "The Relation of Cost to Output for a Leather Belt Shop," *Technical Paper 2* (New York: National Bureau of Economic Research, 1941); *Ibid.*, "Statistical Cost Functions of a Hosiery Mill," *Journal of Business of the University of Chicago*, Vol. 14 (1941); *Ibid.*, "Department Store Cost Functions," in O. Lange, *et al.*, eds., *Studies in Mathematical Economics and Econometrics, in Memory of Henry Schultz* (Chicago: University of Chicago Press, 1942).

The estimate of total cost computed for a leather belt shop is the following:

$$c = -60{,}178 + .770x_1 + 70{,}181.30x_2$$

Here, c signifies total cost in dollars, x_1 represents output in square feet of single-ply equivalent of belting, and x_2 designates the average weight in pounds per square foot. The statistical procedures used are similar to those used to estimate the cost of hosiery production; the parameters are computed from a multiple linear regression. The average and marginal costs appear similar to those derived for the hosiery mill.

E. NATIONAL INCOME AND RELATED AGGREGATES

The surge of interest in national income analysis which followed upon the depression of the 1930's led to econometric studies designed to measure the relationships among aggregate United States economic variables. Many theoretical models relating total consumption to national income, total net investment to interest rates, total money supply to prices and interest rates, etc. were formulated. Precise quantitative predictions and tests of hypotheses to permit choice among alternative models depended upon empirical research. We shall illustrate two such studies, one concerning a static econometric model and the other a dynamic one.

1. Static Models

T. Haavelmo has given an empirical estimate of the consumption function within the context of a static model.[10] His data for the United States as a whole consist of thirteen annual observations, 1929–1941. He defines the following variables:

C = total real consumption
Y = real disposable income (real income less taxes)
S = gross business savings
I = gross real investment

All variables are measured in dollars per capita, deflated by the Bureau of Labor Statistics cost of living index. Investment is assumed to be an exogenous variable, and the equations in the system are assumed to be linear. Finally, all errors are assumed to be errors of omission. The system of equations is shown to be complete

[10] T. Haavelmo, "Methods of Measuring the Marginal Propensity to Consume," *Journal of the American Statistical Association*, Vol. 42 (March, 1947).

and identified. The model, containing the estimated parameters, is as follows:

(1) $\qquad C = 95.05 + .712Y$
(2) $\qquad S = -34.03 + .158(C + I)$
(3) $\qquad Y = C + I - S$

The first equation is the estimated consumption function; the second is the estimated business savings function. Least-squares estimates were made of the parameters of the reduced-form equations. The parameters of the behavioral equations were obtained by solving backwards mathematically from the reduced-form equations.

Regarding the consumption function, we see that

$$\frac{dC}{dY} = .712$$

This is the empirical estimate of the marginal propensity to consume. When national disposable income increased by any given amount, total United States consumption increased by approximately seventy per cent of the increase in income.

2. Dynamic Models

Many dynamic national income models have been formulated by L. R. Klein.[11] Some of these were later extended and improved by other writers, and they have met with varying degrees of success. We shall discuss one dynamic model given by Klein. The following variables are expressed per capita:

C_t = total real consumption in year t
Y_t = disposable real income in year t
I_t = gross private investment in year t
G_t = total government expenditures in year t
T_t = total government receipts plus business reserves minus transfer payments minus inventory profits in year t
P_t = gross national product in year t

Each variable is expressed in money units, deflated by a cost of living index (1935–1939 = 100), and all errors are assumed to be errors of omission. The following quantified model results:

(1) $\qquad C_t = 84.74 + .58Y_t + .15Y_{t-1}$
(2) $\qquad P_t = C_t + I_t + G_t$
(3) $\qquad Y_t + T_t = P_t$

[11] L. R. Klein, "The Use of Econometric Models as a Guide to Economic Policy," *Econometrica*, Vol. 15 (April, 1947); *Ibid.*, *Economic Fluctuations in the United States, 1921–1941* (New York: John Wiley & Sons, Inc., 1950).

Equations (2) and (3) are definitions. The parameters of the behavioral equation (1)—the consumption function—are estimated by an adaptation of the method of least squares. They are obtained by solving back from the computed reduced-form parameters.

More complex dynamic models could be presented. For example, one of Klein's models contains twenty-nine variables. Whether simple or complex, one important advantage of dynamic models is that the time paths of the variables can be determined, and this is very useful for forecasting consumption, income or other aggregate economic magnitudes.

This chapter contains but a small sample of the econometric research that has been carried out over the past three decades. Additional references can be found in the Bibliography that appears at the end of the book. This survey should be sufficient, however, to convey the significance of empirical studies in economics. No economic theory can stand on its own merits without empirical verification. No significant quantitative predictions are possible without statistical measurement. Yet no empirical or statistical study can have meaning and direction without a logically correct framework provided by economic theory. In short, it takes both hydrogen and oxygen to make water!

CHAPTER 26

Econometrics and Economic Policy

The techniques and results of econometrics are of great interest to professional economists. Many recent studies have shown that business enterprise can also benefit from econometric research. The formulation of optimal production and inventory decision functions under conditions of uncertainty with respect to market demand, prices, or factor inputs has developed rapidly in recent years. Nevertheless, probably the greatest practical importance of econometrics lies in the contributions it can make to the formation of government economic policy. A sound economic policy depends more upon careful quantitative predictions than it does upon qualitative theoretical developments.

This fact is made obvious from a review of the quantitative results presented in Chapter 24. Consider first the demand studies. From Schultz's estimated demand for wheat one can compute the price elasticity of demand. For a logarithmic demand function it turns out to be the price coefficient: $-.2143$. Using the sample data, confidence limits for the elasticity of demand can be established. If these are chosen as 5 per cent, then one can say with 95 per cent confidence that the elasticity of demand for wheat lies within the specified limits. Since the price elasticity of demand is a measure of the percentage change in the quantity demanded in response to a given percentage change in price, the policy implications are clear. If a government storage policy for wheat is such that the administrators are planning to release a given quantity of wheat onto the market, then it is important to know what effect this action will have upon the market price. By approximately how much will it decrease? If the government follows some price-support program for wheat, it may decide to raise the support price by a given amount. Some important questions present themselves. By how much will consumption be reduced? If production is already given, by how much must the government be prepared to increase its stocks when consumption decreases?

An empirical estimate of the price elasticity of demand can help to answer these questions within definite probability limits. Assume the 5 per cent confidence limits for the elasticity of demand for wheat are $-.30$ and $-.12$. Then one can conclude that an increase of 1 per cent in the price of wheat will (with 95 per cent probability) result in a decrease in the quantity demanded of not less than $\frac{1}{8}$ of 1 per cent and not more than $\frac{3}{10}$ of 1 per cent. Information such as this is superior to the mere qualitative conclusion that an increase in price will reduce the quantity demanded.

Consider another example. Stone's study reveals that the income elasticity of the demand for automobiles in the United States is 4.164 for the period 1929 to 1941. Confidence limits can also be established for this estimate of a demand parameter. One can then say that a 1 per cent increase in income will result in a percentage increase in the quantity of automobiles demanded of not less than x per cent and not more than y per cent, other things being equal. Now if the government is contemplating an increase in income tax rates (a reduction of disposable income) at the time such a study is executed, this statistical study will permit an estimate of the quantitative effect this tax increase will have upon the demand for automobiles. If similar studies for other industries are utilized, the distributional effects among industries can be predicted.

Similarly, econometric studies of supply can be used to measure the effects of alternative economic policies. Knowledge of demand and supply elasticities permits an estimate of the incidence of sales taxes. Will the consumer or the producer bear most of the tax? How much more? The answers to these questions require econometric research. Knowledge of production functions can be used as evidence in settling labor-management disputes, for such knowledge can be used to estimate the marginal productivities of labor and capital in various industries.

One very important contribution of econometrics to economic policy grows out of national income analysis. The maintenance of economic stability and a high level of employment have become primary responsibilities of the federal government. The dominant tools employed by the government are monetary and fiscal policies. In the area of fiscal policy, it is recognized that the variation of government expenditures and tax receipts can be used as a counter-cyclical device. Suppose the government wishes to counteract inflation by increasing taxes while holding expenditures constant. Considerations of economic theory tell us that an increase of taxes will reduce disposable income, and this in turn will reduce consumption expenditures by operating through the consumption function. A reduction of consumption expenditures will, other things being equal, reduce the inflationary pressure. But, by *how much* will a given increase in taxes reduce consumption expenditures?

Let us turn to the Haavelmo model presented in the previous chapter. We saw that his estimate of the marginal propensity to consume out of disposable income is about .71. This means that for every $100 increase in taxes (reduction in disposable income), consumption will decrease by about $70. Alternatively, if the government contemplates a decrease in income taxes to fight a recession, the quantitative effect of the tax cut upon consumption is estimated from this measure of the marginal propensity to consume.

From the estimate of the marginal propensity to consume, the investment multiplier can be computed:

$$k = \frac{1}{1 - MPC} = \frac{1}{1 - .71} = \frac{1}{.29} = 3.5$$

We interpret this to mean that for every dollar of increase in investment, national income will eventually increase by about $3.5, given that other things do not change. A similar multiplier can be computed for government expenditures; for a given increase in government expenditures, the net eventual increase in national income, other things being equal, can be predicted within specified probability limits. Obviously this type of quantitative information is extremely useful to government officials in formulating long-range policy decisions. It can also be seen how dynamic models designed for forecasting national income, the general price level, aggregate savings, etc., aid in the construction of sound countercyclical monetary and fiscal policies.

When judging the usefulness of econometric models for economic policy, their limitations must be kept in mind. In a static model, some important dynamic factors may not have been taken into account. Even in a dynamic model errors of observation may have been neglected (as they were in the national income models of Chapter 24). In addition the time series data used for statistical estimation may be characterized strongly by autocorrelation, so the traditional interpretations of the estimates cannot validly be made.

In spite of these limitations, there is no doubt that present econometric research can greatly enrich the possibilities for sound economic policy. Through continued investigations, trials and errors, improvements and revisions, we may expect that this relatively new branch of the science of economics will lead to even greater potentialities in the very near future.

Bibliography

MATHEMATICS

Elementary

1. Cameron, E. A., and E. T. Browne. *College Algebra.* New York: Henry Holt & Co., Inc., 1956.
2. Richardson, M. *College Algebra.* New York: Prentice-Hall, Inc., 1947.
3. Steen, F. H., and D. H. Ballou. *Analytic Geometry.* Boston: Ginn & Company, 1946.
4. Sisam, C. S., and W. F. Atchison. *Analytic Geometry.* New York: Henry Holt & Co., Inc., 1955.
5. Randolph, J. F. *Calculus.* New York: The Macmillan Co., 1952.
6. Wylie, C. R., Jr., *Calculus.* New York: McGraw-Hill Book Company, Inc., 1953.
7. Paul Horst, *Matrix Algebra for Social Scientists.* New York: Holt, Rinehart, and Winston, Inc., 1963.

Advanced

1. Bôcher, M. *Introduction to Higher Algebra.* New York: The Macmillan Co., 1907.
2. Birkhoff, G., and S. MacLane. *A Survey of Modern Algebra.* New York: The Macmillan Co., 1941.
3. Aitken, A. C. *Determinants and Matrices.* Edinburgh: Oliver & Boyd, Ltd., 1942.
4. Courant, R. *Differential and Integral Calculus.* London: Interscience Publishers, Ltd., 1937.
5. Ford, L. R. *Differential Equations.* New York: McGraw-Hill Book Company, Inc., 1933.
6. Frazer, R. A., W. J. Duncan, and A. R. Collar. *Elementary Matrices.* Cambridge: Cambridge University Press, 1946.

PROBABILITY AND STATISTICS

Elementary

1. Wallis, W. A., and H. V. Roberts. *Statistics: A New Approach.* Glencoe: The Free Press, 1956.
2. Wessell, R. H., and E. R. Willett. *Statistics as Applied to Economics and Business.* New York: Henry Holt & Co., Inc., 1959.

3. Stockton, J. R. *Business Statistics*. Cincinnati: South-Western Publishing Co., 1958.
4. Croxton, F. E., and D. J. Cowden. *Applied General Statistics*. New York: Prentice-Hall, Inc., 1955.
5. Tippett, L. H. C. *The Methods of Statistics*. New York: John Wiley & Sons, Inc., 1952.
6. Ezekiel, M. *Methods of Correlation Analysis*. New York: John Wiley & Sons, Inc., 1945.
7. Hoel, P. G. *Introduction to Mathematical Statistics*. New York: John Wiley & Sons, Inc., 1950.

Advanced:

1. Feller, W. *An Introduction to Probability Theory and Its Applications*. New York: John Wiley & Sons, Inc., 1950.
2. Cramér, H. *The Elements of Probability Theory and Some of Its Applications*. New York: John Wiley & Sons, Inc., 1955.
3. Neyman, J. *First Course in Probability and Statistics*. New York: Henry Holt & Co., Inc., 1950.
4. Snedecor, G. H. *Statistical Methods*. Ames: Iowa State College Press, 1950.
5. Wilks, S. S. *Mathematical Statistics*. Princeton: Princeton University Press, 1943.
6. Kendall, M. G. *The Advanced Theory of Statistics*. London: Charles Griffin and Co., 1946.

MATHEMATICAL ECONOMICS

Elementary:

1. Crum, W. L., and J. A. Schumpeter. *Rudimentary Mathematics for Economists and Statisticians*. New York: McGraw-Hill Book Company, Inc., 1946.
2. Evans, G. C. *Mathematical Introduction to Economics*. New York: McGraw-Hill Book Company, 1930.
3. Allen, R. G. D. *Mathematical Analysis for Economists*. London: The Macmillan Co., 1947.
4. Bushaw, D. W., and R. W. Clower. *Introduction to Mathematical Economics*. Homewood: Richard D. Irwin, Inc., 1957.
5. Henderson, J. M., and R. E. Quant. *Microeconomic Theory, a Mathematical Approach*. New York: McGraw-Hill Book Company, Inc., 1958.

Advanced:

1. Allen, R. G. D. *Mathematical Economics*. New York: St. Martin's Press, Inc., 1956.

2. Baumol, W. J. *Economic Dynamics*. New York: The Macmillan Co., 1951.
3. Samuelson, P. A. *Foundations of Economic Analysis*. Cambridge: Harvard University Press, 1947.

ECONOMETRICS

Elementary:

1. Tinbergen, J. *Econometrics*. New York: The Blakiston Co., 1951.
2. Tintner, G. *Mathematics and Statistics for Economists*. New York: Rinehart & Company, Inc., 1953.
3. Beach, E. F. *Economic Models*. New York: John Wiley & Sons, Inc., 1957.
4. Allen, R. G. D. *Statistics for Economists*. London: Hutchinson's University Library, 1949.
5. Tinbergen, J., and J. J. Polak. *The Dynamics of Business Cycles: A Study of Economic Fluctuations*. Chicago: University of Chicago Press, 1950.
6. Charnes, A., W. W. Cooper, and A. Henderson. *An Introduction to Linear Programming*. New York: John Wiley & Sons, Inc., 1953.

Advanced

1. Tintner, G. *Econometrics*. New York: John Wiley & Sons, Inc., 1952.
2. Klein, L. *A Textbook of Econometrics*. Evanston: Row, Peterson & Company, 1953.
3. Davis, H. T. *The Theory of Econometrics*. Bloomington: The Principia Press, 1941.
4. Goldberger, A. S. *Econometric Theory*. New York: John Wiley & Sons, Inc., 1964.
5. Hood, W. C., and T. C. Koopmans. *Studies in Econometric Method*. New York: John Wiley & Sons, Inc., 1953.
6. Johnston, J. *Econometric Methods*. New York: McGraw-Hill Book Co., Inc., 1963.
7. Koopmans, T. C. *Statistical Inference in Dynamic Economic Models*. New York: John Wiley & Sons, Inc., 1950.
8. Wold, H., and L. Juréen. *Demand Analysis*. New York: John Wiley & Sons, Inc., 1953.

ARTICLES AND MONOGRAPHS

Elementary:

1. Cooper, G. "The Role of Econometric Models in Economic Theory," *Journal of Farm Economics*, 30 (1948), 101–116.

2. Koopmans, T. C. "Measurement Without Theory," *Review of Economics and Statistics*, 29 (1947), 161–172.
3. Tinbergen, J. "Econometric Business Cycle Research," *Review of Economic Studies*, 7 (1939–1940), 73–90.
4. Bennion, E. G. "The Cowles Commission's Simultaneous Equations Approach: A Simplified Explanation," *Review of Economics and Statistics*, 34 (1952), 49–56.
5. Leontief, W. W. "Econometrics," Chapter II of *A Survey of Contemporary Economics*, H. S. Ellis (ed.) Philadelphia: The Blakiston Co., 1948.
6. Chipman, J. "Linear Programming," *Review of Economics and Statistics*, 35 (1953), 101–117.

Advanced:

1. Clark, C. "A System of Equations Explaining the United States Trade Cycle, 1921 to 1941," *Econometrica*, 17 (1949), 93–124.
2. Hargerger, A. C. "Pitfalls in Mathematical Model Building," *American Economic Review*, 42 (1952), 855–865.
3. Modigliani, F. "Liquidity Preference and the Theory of Interest and Money," *Econometrica*, 12 (1944), 45–88.
4. Tintner, G. "Static Macro-economic Models and Their Economic Verifications," *Metroeconomica*, 1 (1949), 48–52.
5. Meade, J. E. "A Simplified Model of Mr. Keynes' System," *Review of Economic Studies*, 4 (1936), 98–107.
6. Haavelmo, T. "The Probability Approach to Econometrics," *Econometrica*, supplement (1944).
7. Christ, C. "A Test of an Econometric Model for the United States, 1921–1947," *Conference on Business Cycles*. New York: National Bureau of Economic Research, 1951.
8. Arrow, K., T. Harris, and J. Marschak. "Optimal Inventory Policy," *Econometrica*, 19 (1951), 250–272.
9. Modigliani, F., and E. Hohn, "Production Planning Over Time and the Nature of the Expectation and Planning Horizon," *Econometrica*, 23 (1955), 46–66.

ANSWERS TO ODD-NUMBERED PROBLEMS

Chapter 1

1. 1; 4; 16; 64.

3. 8; 10; 28; 2; −4.

5. 1; 6; 57; 2; 9.

7. 1; 2; 4; 8; $\frac{1}{2}$; $\frac{1}{4}$.

9. ∞; $\frac{1}{3}$; $-\frac{23}{15}$; $\frac{1}{3}$.

11. 4; 37; −20; 90.

Chapter 3

1.

p	q	p	q
10	250	5	375
9	275	4	400
8	300	3	425
7	325	2	450
6	350	1	475

5.

p	s	p	s
1	0	5	30
2	2	6	62
3	6	7	126
4	14		

11. (a) 244; 368.928; 416.11392

(b) 700; 6,300; 204,700

Chapter 4

1. $x = 3, y = 0$.

3. $x = 14, y = 4$.

5. No solution exists.

7. $x = \dfrac{62}{33}, y = \dfrac{-113}{33}, z = \dfrac{125}{33}$.

9. $x = 1, y = -1$ and $x = -.6, y = -2.6$.

Chapter 5

1. (a) $p = 3, q = 40$.

(c) $p = 20, q = 600$.

(b) $p = 7.8, q = 322$.

(d) $p = 10, q = 10$.

3. (a) $Y = 275$.

5. (a) $Y = 250$.

(b) $Y = 275$.

7. $p_x = 2, D_x = S_x = 5; p_y = 1, D_y = S_y = 21; p_z = 3, D_z = S_z = 28$.

Chapter 6

1. $x = -\frac{2}{5}, y = \frac{9}{5}$.

3. $x = \frac{3}{10}, y = \frac{7}{5}$.

7. $- 25$

Chapter 7

1. (c) 219; 128; 67; 45.875; 32.791; 30.027.

3. (a) 0.

(b) 4.

(c) 2.

Chapter 8

1. 4.   3. 0.   5. $5x^4$.   7. $\dfrac{4}{3\sqrt[3]{x^2}}$.

9. $\dfrac{3}{x^2} + \dfrac{2}{\sqrt{4x}} - \dfrac{1}{3\sqrt[3]{x^2}}$.

11. $\dfrac{-x^2 + 2x + 3}{x^4 + 6x^2 + 9}$.

13. $\dfrac{1}{2\sqrt{x+1}}$.

15. $\dfrac{4}{x}$.   17. $\dfrac{8x - 6}{2x^2 - 3x + 4}$.

19. $\dfrac{2x - 2e^x}{2\sqrt{x^2 - 2e^x}}$.   21. $\dfrac{-\frac{1}{2}x + \frac{1}{8}}{(-\frac{1}{2}x^2 + \frac{1}{4}x - 4)^{\frac{1}{2}}}$.

23. $-\dfrac{2}{x^3} + \dfrac{3}{x^2}$.

25. $\dfrac{3x^4 - 90x^2}{x^4 - 20x^2 + 100}$.

27. $\dfrac{-10x^2 - 70}{(x^2 + 3x - 7)^2}$.

29. $\dfrac{8(x^2 + 3x)}{(3x + 1)} \cdot \dfrac{(2x + 3)(3x + 1) - 3(x^2 + 3x)}{(3x + 1)^2}$.

31. $-\dfrac{12}{x^2 - 2x - 3} + \dfrac{8x}{x^2 + 2}$.   33. $-3x + 4$.

35. $\dfrac{8(2x^2 + 4x - 1) - (4x + 4)(8x + 8)}{(2x^2 + 4x - 1)^2}$.

37. $6x + 54$.

39. $120x^3 - 240x^2 + 240x - 144$.

41. $-\dfrac{3}{32\sqrt{x^5}}$.

Chapter 9

1. (a) -4.   (b) -1.   (c) $-\frac{1}{4}$.
3. (a) -18.   (b) $-\frac{4}{3}$.   (c) $-\frac{2}{9}$.
5. (a) $\frac{4}{109}$.   (b) $\frac{3}{58}$.   (c) 0.
7. (b) $8 + .012x$.   9. (a) $100 - 2x + .0075x^2$.

Chapter 10

1. $\dfrac{\partial z}{\partial x} = 9x^2 + 4xy - 2y^3$.

$\dfrac{\partial z}{\partial y} = -2y + 2x^2 - 6xy^2 + 1$.

$$\frac{4+13}{52} = \frac{1}{52}$$

$$\frac{4}{52} \quad \frac{16}{52.13}$$

$$= \frac{9 \times 8 \times 7 \times 6}{4 \times 3 \times 2} \cdot \frac{1}{32} \cdot \frac{1}{16} = \frac{63}{32 \times 8} = \frac{63}{256}$$

$$256 \overline{\smash)63.0} \, (\, .246$$
$$\underline{51\ 2}$$
$$11\ 8\ 0$$
$$10\ 2\ 4$$

$$9. \quad P\ _5 9^4$$
$$5.41.$$

$$\frac{8}{5}7$$
$$\overline{26}$$

100 100
100 101
101 100

I E<1 Inelastic

3. $\dfrac{\partial z}{\partial x} = \dfrac{2}{2x + y^2}; \dfrac{\partial z}{\partial y} = \dfrac{2y}{2x + y^2}.$

5. 0, 0, 1, 1.

7. $f_{xx} = \dfrac{-4}{(2x + y^2)^2}, f_{yy} = \dfrac{4x - 2y^2}{(2x + y^2)^2},$

   $f_{xy} = \dfrac{-4y}{(2x + y^2)^2}, f_{yx} = \dfrac{-4y}{(2x + y^2)^2}.$

9. $-.60; .0008; .04.$

11. $\dfrac{\partial z}{\partial x} = \dfrac{3(x^4 + 6x^2y + 9y^2)(x^2 + 4xy - 3y)}{(x + 2y)^4}.$

   $\dfrac{\partial z}{\partial y} = \dfrac{3(x^4 + 6x^2y + 9y^2)(3x - 2x^2)}{(x + 2y)^4}.$

13. $\dfrac{\partial z}{\partial x} = \dfrac{4 - 6xz}{3x^2 - 3yz^2}, \dfrac{\partial z}{\partial y} = \dfrac{z^3}{3x^2 - 3yz^2}.$

Chapter 11

1. $y = 0$, min.
3. $y = 20$, min.
5. $y = .025$, max.
7. $z = 9.6$ rounded, min.
9. $z = 41$, neither.

Chapter 12

1. (b) $MR = 25, \quad MC = 10 - .06x + .00015x^2, \quad AR = 25,$

   $AC = \dfrac{3000}{x} + 10 - .03x + .00005x^2.$

   (d) $x = 574$, rounded.   (e) 6039, rounded.

3. $l = 20, k = 13.33, x = 63.71.$

Chapter 13

1. $4x + 1.5x^2 + k.$
3. $-x^{-1} + 3x^2 + 4x + k.$
5. $-\tfrac{1}{2}x^{-2} - \log_e x + \tfrac{1}{4}x + k.$
7. $\dfrac{2}{3b} (a + bx)^{\frac{3}{2}} + k.$
9. 50.   11. 186.67.   13. 100.
15. $C = 1000 + 10x - .06x^2 + .002x^3.$
17. 160.95.

Chapter 17

1. (a) $\tfrac{8}{45}, \tfrac{8}{45}, \tfrac{7}{45}.$ (b) $\tfrac{1}{6}.$
3. .2461.
5. $\tfrac{2}{13}.$
7. $\tfrac{4}{13}.$
11. (a) 4.325, (b) 4.7194.

Chapter 18

1. (a) 5.6.   (b) .59.   (c) 5.76, 5.44.
3. Reject 6.0, accept 5.5.

Chapter 19

1. (b) $q = 120.48 - 1.92p$,   (c) $r^2 = .81$.
    (d) Significant.   (e) $- .85$.
3. $r = .90$, significant.
5. (b) GNP $= 106.7523 + 1.8883t$.
    (c) 66 per cent.

Chapter 20

1. (a) $x = 89.54 + 1.0532p_x - 7.4702w$.
    (b) .45.
3. (a) $s_t = 4.70 + .1446y_{t-1} + 258.63i_t$,
    (b) $r^2 = .94$,
    (c) .1446.

Hint: Remember to lag the y variable by one year in the table. Your answer may differ slightly from the one given here due to rounding.

Table A
Four-Place Natural Logarithms
$\text{Log}_e\, n$

n	$\text{Log}_e\, n$	n	$\text{Log}_e\, n$	n	$\text{Log}_e\, n$
1.0	0.0000	4.0	1.3863	7.0	1.9459
1.1	0.0953	4.1	1.4110	7.1	1.9601
1.2	0.1823	4.2	1.4351	7.2	1.9741
1.3	0.2624	4.3	1.4586	7.3	1.9879
1.4	0.3365	4.4	1.4816	7.4	2.0015
1.5	0.4055	4.5	1.5041	7.5	2.0149
1.6	0.4700	4.6	1.5261	7.6	2.0281
1.7	0.5306	4.7	1.5476	7.7	2.0412
1.8	0.5878	4.8	1.5686	7.8	2.0541
1.9	0.6419	4.9	1.5892	7.9	2.0669
2.0	0.6931	5.0	1.6094	8.0	2.0794
2.1	0.7419	5.1	1.6292	8.1	2.0919
2.2	0.7885	5.2	1.6487	8.2	2.1041
2.3	0.8329	5.3	1.6677	8.3	2.1163
2.4	0.8755	5.4	1.6864	8.4	2.1282
2.5	0.9163	5.5	1.7047	8.5	2.1401
2.6	0.9555	5.6	1.7228	8.6	2.1518
2.7	0.9933	5.7	1.7405	8.7	2.1633
2.8	1.0296	5.8	1.7579	8.8	2.1748
2.9	1.0647	5.9	1.7750	8.9	2.1861
3.0	1.0986	6.0	1.7918	9.0	2.1972
3.1	1.1314	6.1	1.8083	9.1	2.2083
3.2	1.1632	6.2	1.8245	9.2	2.2192
3.3	1.1939	6.3	1.8405	9.3	2.2300
3.4	1.2238	6.4	1.8563	9.4	2.2407
3.5	1.2528	6.5	1.8718	9.5	2.2513
3.6	1.2809	6.6	1.8871	9.6	2.2618
3.7	1.3083	6.7	1.9021	9.7	2.2721
3.8	1.3350	6.8	1.9169	9.8	2.2824
3.9	1.3610	6.9	1.9315	9.9	2.2925
				10.0	2.3026

Table A is reproduced from *Mathematical Tables* by Herbert Bristol Dwight, page 12, reprinted through permission by Dover Publications, Inc., New York 10, New York. ($1.75).

Table B
Square Roots

n	$\sqrt{n}$	$\sqrt{10n}$	n	$\sqrt{n}$	$\sqrt{10n}$
1.00	1.00000	3.16228	5.00	2.23607	7.07107
1.10	1.04881	3.31662	5.10	2.25832	7.14143
1.20	1.09545	3.46410	5.20	2.28035	7.21110
1.30	1.14018	3.60555	5.30	2.30217	7.28011
1.40	1.18322	3.74166	5.40	2.32379	7.34847
1.50	1.22474	3.87298	5.50	2.34521	7.41620
1.60	1.26491	4.00000	5.60	2.36643	7.48331
1.70	1.30384	4.12311	5.70	2.38747	7.54983
1.80	1.34164	4.24264	5.80	2.40832	7.61577
1.90	1.37840	4.35890	5.90	2.42899	7.68115
2.00	1.41421	4.47214	6.00	2.44949	7.74597
2.10	1.44914	4.58258	6.10	2.46982	7.81025
2.20	1.48324	4.69042	6.20	2.48998	7.87401
2.30	1.51658	4.79583	6.30	2.50998	7.93725
2.40	1.54919	4.89898	6.40	2.52982	8.00000
2.50	1.58114	5.00000	6.50	2.54951	8.06226
2.60	1.61245	5.09902	6.60	2.56905	8.12404
2.70	1.64317	5.19615	6.70	2.58844	8.18535
2.80	1.67332	5.29150	6.80	2.60768	8.24621
2.90	1.70294	5.38516	6.90	2.62679	8.30662
3.00	1.73205	5.47723	7.00	2.64575	8.36660
3.10	1.76068	5.56776	7.10	2.66458	8.42615
3.20	1.78885	5.65685	7.20	2.68328	8.48528
3.30	1.81659	5.74456	7.30	2.70185	8.54400
3.40	1.84391	5.83095	7.40	2.72029	8.60233
3.50	1.87083	5.91608	7.50	2.73861	8.66025
3.60	1.89737	6.00000	7.60	2.75681	8.71780
3.70	1.92354	6.08276	7.70	2.77489	8.77496
3.80	1.94936	6.16441	7.80	2.79285	8.83176
3.90	1.97484	6.24500	7.90	2.81069	8.88819
4.00	2.00000	6.32456	8.00	2.82843	8.94427
4.10	2.02485	6.40312	8.10	2.84605	9.00000
4.20	2.04939	6.48074	8.20	2.86356	9.05539
4.30	2.07364	6.55744	8.30	2.88097	9.11043
4.40	2.09762	6.63325	8.40	2.89828	9.16515
4.50	2.12132	6.70820	8.50	2.91548	9.21954
4.60	2.14476	6.78233	8.60	2.93258	9.27362
4.70	2.16795	6.85565	8.70	2.94958	9.32738
4.80	2.19089	6.92820	8.80	2.96648	9.38083
4.90	2.21359	7.00000	8.90	2.98329	9.43398

Table B (Continued)

n	$\sqrt{n}$	$\sqrt{10n}$	n	$\sqrt{n}$	$\sqrt{10n}$
9.00	3.00000	9.48683	9.60	3.09839	9.79796
9.10	3.01662	9.53939	9.70	3.11448	9.84886
9.20	3.03315	9.59166	9.80	3.13050	9.89949
9.30	3.04959	9.64365	9.90	3.14643	9.94987
9.40	3.06594	9.69536	10.00	3.16228	10.0000
9.50	3.08221	9.74679			

Table C
Student's t = Distribution

Degrees of Freedom	5 Per Cent	1 Per Cent	Degrees of Freedom	5 Per Cent	1 Per Cent
1	12.706	63.657	16	2.120	2.921
2	4.303	9.925	17	2.110	2.898
3	3.182	5.841	18	2.101	2.878
4	2.776	4.604	19	2.093	2.861
5	2.571	4.032	20	2.086	2.845
6	2.447	3.707	21	2.080	2.831
7	2.365	3.499	22	2.074	2.819
8	2.306	3.355	23	2.069	2.807
9	2.262	3.250	24	2.064	2.797
10	2.228	3.169	25	2.060	2.787
11	2.201	3.106	26	2.056	2.779
12	2.179	3.055	27	2.052	2.771
13	2.160	3.012	28	2.048	2.763
14	2.145	2.977	29	2.045	2.756
15	2.131	2.947	30	2.042	2.750

Table C is reprinted abridged from Table IV of R. A. Fisher: *Statistical Methods for Research Workers*, published by Oliver & Boyd, Ltd., Edinburgh, by permission of the author and publishers.

Table D—Areas of Normal Probability Curve

z	0.00	0.01	0.02	0.03	0.04	0.05	0.06	0.07	0.08	0.09
0.0	.0000	.0040	.0080	.0120	.0160	.0199	.0239	.0279	.0319	.0359
0.1	.0398	.0438	.0478	.0517	.0557	.0596	.0636	.0675	.0714	.0753
0.2	.0793	.0832	.0871	.0910	.0948	.0987	.1026	.1064	.1103	.1141
0.3	.1179	.1217	.1255	.1293	.1331	.1368	.1406	.1443	.1480	.1517
0.4	.1554	.1591	.1628	.1664	.1700	.1736	.1772	.1808	.1844	.1879
0.5	.1915	.1950	.1985	.2019	.2054	.2088	.2123	.2157	.2190	.2224
0.6	.2257	.2291	.2324	.2357	.2389	.2422	.2454	.2486	.2517	.2549
0.7	.2580	.2611	.2642	.2673	.2704	.2734	.2764	.2794	.2823	.2852
0.8	.2881	.2910	.2939	.2967	.2995	.3023	.3051	.3078	.3106	.3133
0.9	.3159	.3186	.3212	.3238	.3264	.3289	.3315	.3340	.3365	.3389
1.0	.3413	.3438	.3461	.3485	.3508	.3531	.3554	.3577	.3599	.3621
1.1	.3643	.3665	.3686	.3708	.3729	.3749	.3770	.3790	.3810	.3830
1.2	.3849	.3869	.3888	.3907	.3925	.3944	.3962	.3980	.3997	.4015
1.3	.4032	.4049	.4066	.4082	.4099	.4115	.4131	.4147	.4162	.4177
1.4	.4192	.4207	.4222	.4236	.4251	.4265	.4279	.4292	.4306	.4319
1.5	.4332	.4345	.4357	.4370	.4382	.4394	.4406	.4418	.4429	.4441
1.6	.4452	.4463	.4474	.4484	.4495	.4505	.4515	.4525	.4535	.4545
1.7	.4554	.4564	.4573	.4582	.4591	.4599	.4608	.4616	.4625	.4633
1.8	.4641	.4649	.4656	.4664	.4671	.4678	.4686	.4693	.4699	.4706
1.9	.4713	.4719	.4726	.4732	.4738	.4744	.4750	.4756	.4761	.4767
2.0	.4773	.4778	.4783	.4788	.4793	.4798	.4803	.4808	.4812	.4817
2.1	.4821	.4826	.4830	.4834	.4838	.4842	.4846	.4850	.4854	.4857
2.2	.4861	.4864	.4868	.4871	.4875	.4878	.4881	.4884	.4887	.4890
2.3	.4893	.4896	.4898	.4901	.4904	.4906	.4909	.4911	.4913	.4916
2.4	.4918	.4920	.4922	.4925	.4927	.4929	.4931	.4932	.4934	.4936
2.5	.4938	.4940	.4941	.4943	.4945	.4946	.4948	.4949	.4951	.4952
2.6	.4953	.4955	.4956	.4957	.4959	.4960	.4961	.4962	.4963	.4964
2.7	.4965	.4966	.4967	.4968	.4969	.4970	.4971	.4972	.4973	.4974
2.8	.4974	.4975	.4976	.4977	.4977	.4978	.4979	.4979	.4980	.4981
2.9	.4981	.4982	.4983	.4983	.4984	.4984	.4985	.4985	.4986	.4986
3.0	.4987	.4987	.4987	.4988	.4988	.4989	.4989	.4989	.4989	.4990
3.1	.4990	.4991	.4991	.4991	.4992	.4992	.4992	.4992	.4993	.4993
3.2	.4993	.4993	.4994	.4994	.4994	.4994	.4994	.4995	.4995	.4995
3.3	.4995	.4995	.4996	.4996	.4996	.4996	.4996	.4996	.4996	.4997
3.4	.4997	.4997	.4997	.4997	.4997	.4997	.4997	.4997	.4997	.4998
3.5	.4998	.4998	.4998	.4998	.4998	.4998	.4998	.4998	.4998	.4998
3.6	.4998	.4998	.4999	.4999	.4999	.4999	.4999	.4999	.4999	.4999
3.7	.4999	.4999	.4999	.4999	.4999	.4999	.4999	.4999	.4999	.4999
3.8	.4999	.4999	.4999	.4999	.4999	.4999	.4999	.4999	.4999	.5000

Table D is adapted from *Mathematical Tables* by Herbert Bristol Dwight, pp. 134–139, reprinted through permission by Dover Publications, Inc., New York 10, New York.

Index